The Original
U.S. CONGRESS
HANDBOOK

118th Congress First Session 2023
Published Annually Since 1974

The Sunwater Institute
North Bethesda, MD

THE ORIGINAL U.S. CONGRESS HANDBOOK™
PUBLISHED BY The Sunwater Institute
North Bethesda, MD

Acknowledgements the U.S. Congress, the U.S. Supreme Court, the White House staff, the Offices of the Governors, the U.S. Census Bureau and the Library of Congress.

Maps Map Resources

Pronunciations provided and copyrighted by inogolo.com

For information on obtaining photographs or data contact

The Sunwater Institute
12358 Parklawn Dr, Suite 220
North Bethesda, MD 20852
240.715.9507
www.sunwater.org and
www.uscongresshandbook.com
ISBN-10: 1-952374-21-9
ISBN-13: 978-1-952374-21-0

Managing Editor: Max Kratcoski
Editorial Director: Matthew Barnes

Printed in United States.

**Supreme Court photographs courtesy
of the Supreme Court Historical Society**

Data on members and staff, including room numbers and committee assignments, are subject to change. The following presented information reflects data available at the time of printing.

Publisher's cataloging in publication data
The Original U.S. Congress Handbook. - 118th Congress, First Session (2023).

March 2023: State Version

TABLE OF CONTENTS

GUIDE TO STATE/LEGISLATOR PROFILES

Governor Title First name Surname (pronunciation)		Phone

Photo	Address1	Capital
	Address2	Population (Rank)
	Website	Area (Rank)
	Fax	
	Term Ends	State Map
	Lt. Governor	

U.S. Senators

U.S. Representatives

Title First name Surname (pronunciation)	Party-State-District	Phone

🏛 - Democrat and 🐘 - Republican

Names are displayed in red for Republican, blue for Democrat and green for Independent.

Photo	Rm.	Web.	Fax
	Bio. Birth Date • Birth City/State/Country • Professional Information • Military Service • Educational Institutions, Degrees and Years • Religion • Marital Status and Number of Children		
	Cmte. Committees		
	CoS.		LD.
	Sched.		PS.
	Dist Off. listing of state offices and phone numbers		

R: T: Percentage of the vote. Elected Year Next election year (Senators only)

Legend: **Rm** - Room; **Web** - Website; **CoS** - Chief of Staff; **LD** - Legis. Dir.; **Sched** - Scheduler; **PS** - Press Sec.; **R** - Rank; **T** - Term; **M** - Married; **Se** - Separated; **D** - Divorced; **W** - Widowed; **DP** - Domestic Partner; **S** - Single; **E** - Engaged; **ch** - child/ren; **gr-ch** - grandchild/ren; **(CD)** - district office staff member

Above positions are a description of the staffer's role and function. Actual job titles may vary.

Ethics Guidelines for Lobbyists and Non-Lobbyists

The US House and US Senate prohibit a registered lobbyist from giving 'anything of value' to Members, officers or employees of the House or Senate. . This prohibition applies as well to reimbursing a non-lobbyist employee of a registered lobbying entity for 'anything of value' given to a covered legislative branch person. Further, the gift rules restrict to $100 per calendar year (and $49.99 maximum per occurrence) the value of any gift received by a Member, officer or employee of the Congress from a non-lobbyist, citizen advocate.

There are exceptions to the gift restrictions (citizen advocates) and gift ban (lobbyists).

Notwithstanding the rules and the exceptions, both the House and Senate Ethics Committees instruct Members and staff:

- NOT to accept any gifts that are linked to an official action (referred to as a "quid pro quo")
- Not to solicit a gift from anyone with business before Congress
- Not to allow third parties to pay for gifts, travel or entertainment for a Member or staffer, unless it is clearly permitted as an exception to the ban on gifts from lobbyists and lobbying entities
- Some Members have established stricter rules for their office staff in order to ensure that impermissible gifts are not accepted by those employed in that office

As indicated above, there are exceptions to the gift rules. Some of the more common exceptions are listed below. Note that this list is not exhaustive.[2]

Gifts of nominal value, including food and drink of nominal value, not as part of a meal. Generally, items valued at less than $10 are allowed, as are certain specific items: "greeting cards, baseball caps, or T-shirts" (which may cost more than $10). Food and drink, not as part of a meal, are allowed for attendance at receptions.

Home state/district items. Products that are made or produced in the state or district represented by a member of Congress, , and are displayed or available to members, staff and visitors, at no cost, at the Member's office are allowed.

Attendance and meals at widely attended events are exempt from the gift rules as long as the following conditions exist: the event must include at least 25 people who are not "from the Hill" (i.e. congressional members and staff) who may be from a specific industry or have a specific interest, the invitation to the event must be from the event sponsor, and the event must be related to a member or staffer's official duties. A sporting or recreational event does qualify under the exception for a "widely attended event" and free tickets / food at such an event would not be permissible.

Personal friendship allows a member or staffer to accept a gift from a lobbyist , provided there is a history of friendship, including the exchange of gifts between the congressional member/staffer and the person giving the gift, and provided that the gift is paid with personal funds and not reimbursed or deducted as a business expense by the one giving the gift. And, of course, the gift cannot be in exchange for or related to any official action.

Items given by federal, state or local government refer to gifts that are paid for directly by any of the three levels of government. These cannot be paid for by an outside source and then given by a federal, state or local government. In addition, the House and Senate rules are different insofar as defining certain entities as 'agencies of the federal government' under the gift rules.

[1] This information should not be relied on as complete legal advice. Please contact legal counsel if you need further guidance.

[2] A full listing of the exceptions under the gift rule is available in the Lobbying Compliance Handbook: A Practitioner's Guide to HLOGA, published by The Sunwater Institute.

Meals and transportation in the course of a site visit: the exception (specific to the House) allows a House member or staffer to accept a meal and local transportation to / from a site being visited by the House member/staffer, even if the source is a lobbying registrant.

Lobbyists and lobbying entities must certify compliance with the gift rules: Adhering to the gift rules is of prime importance. Registered organizations and individual lobbyists are required to file the LD-203 report semiannually, on which lobbyists and registrant organizations must certify under penalty of perjury that they did not knowingly violate the House and Senate gift rules by providing gifts and/ or travel to a Member, officer or employee of the House or Senate.

Congressional Demographics

Breakdown by Gender

- Male (71.67%)
- Female (28.33%)

Breakdown by Ethnic Group

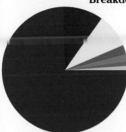

- White/Caucasian (74.49%)
- Black/African American (10.35%)
- Hispanic/Latino (8.69%)
- Asian/Pacific American (2.4%)
- Two or More Ethnicities (1.85%)
- Other (1.11%)
- Indian/Native American (0.74%)
- Not Specified (0.18%)
- Hawaiian/Pacific Islander (0.18%)

Breakdown by Marital Status

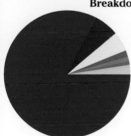

- Married (82.81%)
- Single (6.1%)
- Divorced (4.99%)
- Not Stated (1.66%)
- Widow (1.11%)
- Widower (0.92%)
- Not Specified (0.74%)
- Separated (0.74%)
- Engaged (0.74%)
- Life Partner (0.18%)

Breakdown by Religion

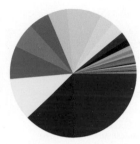

- Catholic (24.58%)
- Not Known (13.31%)
- Baptist (10.72%)
- Protestant - Unspecified Christian (8.32%)
- Methodist (6.28%)
- Jewish (5.18%)
- Christian - Non-Denominational (4.99%)
- Presbyterian (4.99%)
- Lutheran (3.88%)
- Episcopalian (3.7%)
- Unspecified/Other (3.14%)
- Evangelical (2.03%)
- Mormon (1.66%)
- Church of Christ (1.11%)
- Greek Orthodox (0.92%)
- African Methodist Episcopal (0.55%)
- Hinduism (0.55%)
- Islam (Muslim) (0.55%)
- Assembly of God (0.37%)
- Buddhism (0.37%)
- Christian Reformed Church (0.37%)
- Seventh-Day Adventist (0.37%)
- Unitarian (0.37%)
- Anglican (0.18%)
- Church of the United Brethren in Christ (0.18%)
- Congregationalist (0.18%)
- Disciples of Christ (0.18%)
- Eastern Orthodox (0.18%)
- None (0.18%)
- Quaker (0.18%)
- United Church of Christ (0.18%)
- Wesleyan (0.18%)

2023 Legislative Calendar

JANUARY 2023

S	M	T	W	T	F	S
1	2	3	4	5	6	7
8	9	10	11	12	13	14
15	16	17	18	19	20	21
22	23	24	25	26	27	28
29	30	31				

FEBRUARY 2023

S	M	T	W	T	F	S
			1	2	3	4
5	6	7	8	9	10	11
12	13	14	15	16	17	18
19	20	21	22	23	24	25
26	27	28				

MARCH 2023

S	M	T	W	T	F	S
			1	2	3	4
5	6	7	8	9	10	11
12	13	14	15	16	17	18
19	20	21	22	23	24	25
26	27	28	29	30	31	

APRIL 2023

S	M	T	W	T	F	S
						1
2	3	4	5	6	7	8
9	10	11	12	13	14	15
16	17	18	19	20	21	22
23	24	25	26	27	28	29
30						

MAY 2023

S	M	T	W	T	F	S
	1	2	3	4	5	6
7	8	9	10	11	12	13
14	15	16	17	18	19	20
21	22	23	24	25	26	27
28	29	30	31			

JUNE 2023

S	M	T	W	T	F	S
				1	2	3
4	5	6	7	8	9	10
11	12	13	14	15	16	17
18	19	20	21	22	23	24
25	26	27	28	29	30	

JULY 2023

S	M	T	W	T	F	S
						1
2	3	4	5	6	7	8
9	10	11	12	13	14	15
16	17	18	19	20	21	22
23	24	25	26	27	28	29
30	31					

AUGUST 2023

S	M	T	W	T	F	S
		1	2	3	4	5
6	7	8	9	10	11	12
13	14	15	16	17	18	19
20	21	22	23	24	25	26
27	28	29	30	30		

SEPTEMBER 2023

S	M	T	W	T	F	S
					1	2
3	4	5	6	7	8	9
10	11	12	13	14	15	16
17	18	19	20	21	22	23
24	25	26	27	28	29	30

OCTOBER 2023

S	M	T	W	T	F	S
1	2	3	4	5	6	7
8	9	10	11	12	13	14
15	16	17	18	19	20	21
22	23	24	25	26	27	28
29	30	31				

NOVEMBER 2023

S	M	T	W	T	F	S
			1	2	3	4
5	6	7	8	9	10	11
12	13	14	15	16	17	18
19	20	21	22	23	24	25
26	27	28	29	30		

DECEMBER 2023

S	M	T	W	T	F	S
					1	2
3	4	5	6	7	8	9
10	11	12	13	14	15	16
17	18	19	20	21	22	23
24	25	26	27	28	29	30
31						

Legend:
- ☐ Federal Holiday
- ☐ House in session
- ☐ Senate in session

<u>NOTES</u>

U.S. SENATE LEADERSHIP

Republican Party   49   Democratic Party   48   Independent   3

A senator must be at least 30 years old, a U.S. citizen for nine years, and a resident of the state in which he or she is elected. Each state sends two senators to serve six-year terms. They are elected on a rotating schedule, with one-third of the Senate being elected every two years.

THE LEADERSHIP

Senate Majority Leader
Chuck E. Schumer (D-NY)   HSOB 322   **202.224.6542**

Senate Majority Whip; Assistant Majority Leader
Dick Durbin (D-IL)   HSOB 711   **202.224.2152**

Senate Republican Conference Chairman
John A. Barrasso (R-WY)   DSOB 307   **202.224.6441**

Senate Democratic Conference Chairman
Chuck E. Schumer (D-NY)   The Capitol S-221   **202.224.6542**

Senate Minority Leader
Mitch McConnell (R-KY)   RSOB 317   **202.224.2541**

Senate Minority Whip
John Thune (R-SD)   DSOB 511   **202.224.2321**

Senate Democratic Conference Secretary
Tammy Baldwin (D-WI)   HSOB 709   **202.224.5653**

THE OFFICERS

President of the Senate
Kamala D. Harris   Eisenhower   **202.456.0373**
                                 Executive Office
                                 Bldg.

President Pro Tempore
Patty Murray   The Capitol 126   **202.224.3744**

Secretary of the Senate
Ann Berry   The Capitol S-312   **202.224.3622**

Sergeant at Arms and Doorkeeper of the Senate
Karen H. Gibson   The Capitol S-151   **202.224.2341**

Senate Majority Secretary
Gary Myrick   The Capitol S-337   **202.224.3835**

Senate Minority Secretary
Robert Duncan   The Capitol S-309   **202.224.3735**

Senate Parliamentarian
Elizabeth C. MacDonough   The Capitol S-133   **202.224.6128**

Chaplain of the Senate
Barry C. Black   The Capitol S-332   **202.224.2510**

THE SENATE OFFICE BUILDINGS

When addressing correspondence to Members of the Senate, use the following abbreviations for office buildings. No street address is required. The Senate ZIP code is 20510.

S	Senate-north side of Capitol Building
DSOB	Dirksen Senate Office Building
	Constitution Avenue and First Street NE
HSOB	Hart Senate Office Building
	Constitution Avenue and Second Street NE
RSOB	Russell Senate Office Building
	Constitution and Delaware Avenues NE

SENATE ELECTION INFORMATION

As set forth in Article I, Section 3 of the Constitution, Senators are divided into three classes so that one-third may be elected every second year:

Class I - Senators whose next election occurs in 2025:

Democrats (20)	Republicans (10)	Independents (3)
Baldwin, Tammy (D-WI)	Barrasso, John A. (R-WY)	King, Angus S. (I-ME)
Brown, Sherrod C. (D-OH)	Blackburn, Marsha (R-TN)	Sanders, Bernie (I-VT)
Cantwell, Maria (D-WA)	Braun, Mike (R-IN)	Sinema, Kyrsten (I-AZ)
Cardin, Ben L. (D-MD)	Cramer, Kevin J. (R-ND)	
Carper, Tom R. (D-DE)	Cruz, Ted (R-TX)	
Casey, Bob (D-PA)	Fischer, Deb (R-NE)	
Feinstein, Dianne (D-CA)	Hawley, Josh (R-MO)	
Gillibrand, Kirsten E. (D-NY)	Romney, Mitt (R-UT)	
Heinrich, Martin T. (D-NM)	Scott, Rick (R-FL)	
Hirono, Mazie K. (D-HI)	Wicker, Roger F. (R-MS)	
Kaine, Tim M. (D-VA)		
Klobuchar, Amy (D-MN)		
Manchin, Joe (D-WV)		
Menendez, Bob (D-NJ)		
Murphy, Chris S. (D-CT)		
Rosen, Jacky S. (D-NV)		
Stabenow, Debbie (D-MI)		
Tester, Jon (D-MT)		
Warren, Elizabeth (D-MA)		
Whitehouse, Sheldon (D-RI)		

Class II - Senators whose next election occurs in 2027:

Democrats (13)	Republicans (20)	Independents (0)
Booker, Cory (D-NJ)	Capito, Shelley Moore (R-WV)	
Coons, Chris A. (D-DE)	Cassidy, Bill (R-LA)	
Durbin, Dick (D-IL)	Collins, Susan M. (R-ME)	
Hickenlooper, John W. (D-CO)	Cornyn, John (R-TX)	
Luján, Ben Ray (D-NM)	Cotton, Tom B. (R-AR)	
Markey, Ed (D-MA)	Daines, Steve (R-MT)	
Merkley, Jeff A. (D-OR)	Ernst, Joni (R-IA)	
Ossoff, Jon (D-GA)	Graham, Lindsey (R-SC)	
Peters, Gary (D-MI)	Hagerty, Bill (R-TN)	
Reed, Jack F. (D-RI)	Hyde-Smith, Cindy (R-MS)	
Shaheen, Jeanne (D-NH)	Lummis, Cynthia M. (R-WY)	
Smith, Tina (D-MN)	Marshall, Roger W. (R-KS)	
Warner, Mark R. (D-VA)	McConnell, Mitch (R-KY)	
	Mullin, Markwayne (R-OK)	
	Ricketts, Pete (R-NE)	
	Risch, James E. (R-ID)	
	Rounds, Mike (R-SD)	
	Sullivan, Dan S. (R-AK)	
	Tillis, Thom R. (R-NC)	
	Tuberville, Tommy H. (R-AL)	

Class III - Senators whose next election occurs in 2023:

Democrats (15)	Republicans (19)	Independents (0)
Bennet, Michael F. (D-CO)	Boozman, John N. (R-AR)	
Blumenthal, Richard (D-CT)	Britt, Katie (R-AL)	
Cortez Masto, Catherine (D-NV)	Budd, Ted P. (R-NC)	
Duckworth, Tammy (D-IL)	Crapo, Mike D. (R-ID)	
Fetterman, John K. (D-PA)	Grassley, Chuck (R-IA)	
Hassan, Maggie (D-NH)	Hoeven, John H. (R-ND)	
Kelly, Mark (D-AZ)	Johnson, Ron H. (R-WI)	
Murray, Patty (D-WA)	Kennedy, John N. (R-LA)	
Padilla, Alex (D-CA)	Lankford, James P. (R-OK)	
Schatz, Brian E. (D-HI)	Lee, Mike (R-UT)	
Schumer, Chuck E. (D-NY)	Moran, Jerry (R-KS)	
Van Hollen, Chris J. (D-MD)	Murkowski, Lisa A. (R-AK)	
Warnock, Raphael (D-GA)	Paul, Rand (R-KY)	
Welch, Peter F. (D-VT)	Rubio, Marco (R-FL)	
Wyden, Ron (D-OR)	Schmitt, Eric S. (R-MO)	
	Scott, Tim E. (R-SC)	
	Thune, John (R-SD)	
	Vance, J.D. (R-OH)	
	Young, Todd C. (R-IN)	

U.S. HOUSE OF REPRESENTATIVES LEADERSHIP

Republican Party   225   Democratic Party   215

A representative must be at least 25 years old, a U.S. citizen for seven years, and a resident of the state in which he or she is elected. The U.S. Census determines each state's allocation of the 435 representative seats, and each state legislature determines congressional district boundaries in that state. Every state has at least one representative, and all representatives are elected every even-numbered year.

Delegates and commissioners represent the U.S. territories, commonwealths and the federal district. Although they may not vote on the House floor, they can vote on legislation in their committees.

THE LEADERSHIP

Speaker of the House
Kevin McCarthy (R-CA)   H-232   **202.225.4965**

House Majority Leader
Steve Scalise (R-LA)   H-328   **202.225.3015**

House Majority Whip
Tom Emmer (R-MN)   THUW   **202.225.2331**

House Republican Conference Chairman
Elise Stefanik (R-NY)   LHOB 2211   **202.225.4611**

House Republican Policy Committee Chairman
Gary Palmer (R-AL)   CHOB 170   **202.225.4921**

House Minority Leader
Hakeem Jeffries (D-NY)   2433   **202.225.4000**

House Minority Whip
Katherine Clark (D-MA)   The Capitol   **202.225.0197**

House Democratic Caucus Chairman
Pete Aguilar (D-CA)   LHOB B245   **202.225.1400**

THE OFFICERS

Clerk of the House
Cheryl Johnson   The Capitol H-154 **202.225.7000**

House Sergeant at Arms
Willie Walker   The Capitol H-124 **202.225.2456**

House Chief Administrative Officer
Catherine Szpindor   The Capitol HB-26 **202.225.5555**

House Parliamentarian
Jason A. Smith   The Capitol H-209 **202.225.7373**

Chaplain of the House
Margaret G. Kibben   The Capitol HB-25 **202.225.2509**

THE HOUSE OFFICE BUILDINGS

When addressing correspondence to Members of the House of Representatives, use the following abbreviations for office buildings. No street address is required. The ZIP code for the House is 20515.

CHOB	Cannon House Office Building	
	First Street and Independence Avenue SE	
FHOB	Ford House Office Building, 300 D St. SW	
H	House-south side of Capitol Building	
HB	House Basement-northwest side of Capitol Building	
LHOB	Longworth House Office Building	
	New Jersey and Independence Avenues SE	
RHOB	Rayburn House Office Building	
	South Capitol Street and Independence Avenue SW	

SENATORS - 118th Congress

REPRESENTATIVES - 118th Congress

INDEX OF LEGISLATORS BY RANK

HOUSE

STATE/LEGISLATOR PROFILES - 118th Congress

ALABAMA

⚑ Governor Kay Ivey ("EYE"-vee)   p 334.242.7100

600 Dexter Avenue
Montgomery, AL 36130
Website alabama.gov
Fax 334.353.0004
Term Ends 2027
Lt. Governor
Will Ainsworth, R

C: Montgomery
P: 4,887,871 (24)
A: 50,645.39 mi^2 (28th)

U.S. Senators
Tommy H. Tuberville, **R**
Katie Britt, **R**
U.S. Representatives
01 / Jerry L. Carl, **R**
02 / Barry Moore, **R**
03 / Mike D. Rogers, **R**
04 / Robert B. Aderholt, **R**
05 / Dale W. Strong, **R**
06 / Gary Palmer, **R**
07 / Terri A. Sewell, **D**

⚑ Sen. Katie Britt ()   R-AL-Jr.   p 202.224.5744

Rm. DSOB B40A **Web.**
katiebrittforsenate.com
Bio. 02/02/1982 • Enterprise • Univ. of Alabama, B.S., 2004;
Univ. of Alabama School of Law, J.D., 2013 • Methodist •
M. Wesley Britt, 2 ch   **Cmte.** Appropriations • Banking,
Housing & Urban Affairs • Rules & Administration
CoS. Clay Armentrout   **LD.** Daniel Hillenbrand
Sched. Amanda Peper   **PS.** Sean Ross
Dist. Off. Birmingham • Huntsville • Mobile •
Montgomery • Tuscaloosa

R: 99   **T:** 1st 67%
Elected Year: 2022
Next Election: 2028

⚑ Sen. Tommy H. Tuberville (TOO-bur-vil)   R-AL-Sr.   p 202.224.4124

Rm. RSOB 142 **Web.** tuberville.senate.gov   **f** 202.224.3149
Bio. 09/18/1954 • Camden • Southern Arkansas Univ.,
B.A.E., 1976 • Church of Christ • M. Suzanne Fette, 2 ch
Cmte. Agriculture, Nutrition & Forestry • Armed Services •
Health, Education, Labor & Pensions • Veterans' Affairs
Dist. Off. Birmingham 205.760.7307 • Dothan 334.547.7441
• Huntsville 256.692.7500 • Mobile 251.308.7233 •
Montgomery 334.523.7424

R: 89   **T:** 1st 60%
Elected Year: 2020
Next Election: 2026

ALABAMA

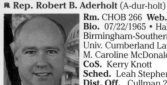

♞ Rep. Robert B. Aderholt (A-dur-holt)   R-AL-04   p 202.225.4876

Rm. CHOB 266 **Web.** aderholt.house.gov   **f** 202.225.5587
Bio. 07/22/1965 • Haleyville • Municipal Court Judge •
Birmingham-Southern College (AL), B.A., 1987; Samford
Univ. Cumberland Law School (AL), J.D., 1990 • Methodist •
M. Caroline McDonald Aderholt, 2 ch **Cmte.** Appropriations
CoS. Kerry Knott   **LD.** Megan Medley
Sched. Leah Stephenson   **PS.** Matthew Reed
Dist. Off. Cullman 256.734.6043 • Gadsden 256.546.0201
• Jasper 205.221.2310 • Tuscumbia 256.381.3450

R: 23   **T:** 14th 84%
Elected Year: 1996

♞ Rep. Jerry L. Carl Jr. (karl)   R-AL-01   p 202.225.4931

Rm. LHOB 1330 **Web.** carl.house.gov   **f** 202.225.0562
Bio. 06/17/1958 • Mobile • Southern Baptist • M. Tina Carl,
3 ch **Cmte.** Appropriations • Natural Resources
CoS. Chad Carlough
Sched. Brianna Nagle   **PS.** Zachary Weidlich
Dist. Off. Mobile 251.283.6280 • Summerdale 251.677.6630

R: 306   **T:** 2nd 84%
Elected Year: 2020

♞ Rep. Barry Moore (mor)   R-AL-02   p 202.225.2901

Rm. LHOB 1504 **Web.** barrymoore.house.gov
Bio. 09/26/1966 • Enterprise • Enterprise State Junior
College (AL), A.S., 1988; Auburn Univ., B.S., 1992 • Baptist •
M. Heather Moore, 4 ch **Cmte.** Agriculture • Judiciary
CoS. Shana Teehan   **LD.** Emma White
Sched. Maggie Thrailkill   **PS.** Bradley Jaye
Dist. Off. Andalusia 334.428.1129 • Dothan 334.547.6630 •
Troy 334.465.7244 • Wetumpka 334.478.6330

R: 333   **T:** 2nd 69%
Elected Year: 2020

♞ Rep. Gary Palmer (PALL-mur)   R-AL-06   p 202.225.4921

Rm. CHOB 170 **Web.** palmer.house.gov   **f** 202.225.2082
Bio. 05/14/1954 • Hackleburg • Univ. of Alabama, B.S.,
1977 • Presbyterian • M. Ann Cushing, 3 ch **Cmte.** Energy
& Commerce • Oversight & Accountability
CoS. William Smith   **LD.** Chris Bayles
Sched. Mary Morgan
Dist. Off. Birmingham 205.968.1290 • Oneonta
205.625.4160

R: 181   **T:** 5th 84%
Elected Year: 2014

♞ Rep. Mike D. Rogers (RAH-jurz)   R-AL-03   p 202.225.3261

Rm. RHOB 2469 **Web.** mikerogers.house.gov **f** 202.226.8485
Bio. 07/16/1958 • Hammond • Jacksonville State Univ.
(AL), B.A., 1981; Jacksonville State Univ. (AL), M.P.A., 1984;
Birmingham School of Law (AL), J.D., 1991 • Baptist • M.
Beth Rogers, 3 ch **Cmte.** Armed Services
CoS. Christopher Brinson   **LD.** Haley Wilson
Sched. Bronti Viskovich   **PS.** Carrie Cole
Dist. Off. Opelika 334.745.6221 • Oxford 256.236.5655

R: 50   **T:** 11th 72%
Elected Year: 2002

⚘ Rep. Terri A. Sewell (SOO-wull)   D-AL-07   p 202.225.2665

Rm. LHOB 1035 **Web.** sewell.house.gov   **f** 202.226.9567
Bio. 01/01/1965 • Huntsville • Selma High School (AL),
A.B., 1982; Princeton Univ. (NJ), A.B., 1986; Oxford Univ.
(England), M.A., 1988; Harvard Univ. Law School (MA), J.D.,
1992 • Protestant - Unspecified Christian • D. Theodore
Dixie **Cmte.** Administration • Armed Services • Ways &
Means
CoS. Hillary Beard   **LD.** Robert Nuttall
Sched. Jasmine Goodman   **PS.** Christopher Kosteva
Dist. Off. Birmingham 205.254.1960 • Montgomery
334.262.1919 • Selma 334.877.4414 • Tuscaloosa
205.752.5380

R: 114   **T:** 7th 64%
Elected Year: 2010

ALABAMA

🏛 Rep. Dale W. Strong () R-AL-05 p 202.225.4801

Rm. LHOB 1337 **Web.**
dalestrongforcongress.com
Bio. 05/08/1970 • Monrovia • Athens State Univ. (AL), B.S.
• Baptist • M. Laura Toney, 2 ch **Cmte.** Armed Services •
Homeland Security • Science, Space & Technology
CoS. Payne Griffin **LD.** Ella Sullins
 PS. Madison Neal
Dist. Off. Decatur 256.355.9400 • Huntsville 256.551.0190

R: 428 **T:** 1st 67%
Elected Year: 2022

ALASKA

🏛 Governor Mike Dunleavy (DUHN-lee-vee) p 907.465.3500

Office of the Governor, P.O. Box **C:** Juneau
110001 **P:** 737,438 (49)
Juneau, AK 99811 **A:** 570,640.61 mi^2 (1st)
Website alaska.gov
Fax 907.465.3532
Term Ends 2026
Lt. Governor
Nancy Dahlstrom, **R**

U.S. Senators
Lisa A. Murkowski, **R**
Dan S. Sullivan, **R**
U.S. Representatives
01 / Mary Sattler Peltola, **D**

🏛 Sen. Lisa A. Murkowski (mur-KOU-skee) R-AK-Sr. p 202.224.6665

Rm. HSOB 522 **Web.** murkowski.senate.gov **f** 202.224.5301
Bio. 05/22/1957 • Ketchikan • Attorney; State
Representative • Georgetown Univ. (DC), B.A., 1980;
Willamette Univ. College of Law (OR), J.D., 1985 • Roman
Catholic • M. Verne Martell, 2 ch **Cmte.** Appropriations •
Energy & Natural Resources • Health, Education, Labor &
Pensions • Indian Affairs
CoS. Kaleb D. Froehlich **LD.** Angela Ramponi
Sched. Kristen Daimler- **PS.** Karina Borger
 Nothdurft
Dist. Off. Anchorage 907.271.3735 • Fairbanks
907.456.0233 • Juneau 907.586.7277 • Ketchikan
907.225.6880 • Soldotna 907.262.4220 • Wasilla
907.376.7665

R: 15 **T:** 5th 54%
Elected Year: 2002
Next Election: 2028

🏛 Sen. Dan S. Sullivan (SULL-lih-vuhn) R-AK-Jr. p 202.224.3004

Rm. HSOB 302 **Web.** sullivan.senate.gov **f** 202.224.6501
Bio. 11/13/1964 • Fairview Park • Harvard Univ., B.A., 1987;
Georgetown Univ. Law Center (DC), J.D., 1993; Georgetown
Univ. Law Center (DC), M.S., 1993 • Roman Catholic •
M. Julie Fate, 3 ch **Cmte.** Armed Services • Commerce,
Science & Transportation • Environment & Public Works •
Veterans' Affairs
CoS. Larry Burton **LD.** Erik Elam
Sched. Avery Fogels **PS.** Mike Reynard
Dist. Off. Anchorage 907.271.5915 • Fairbanks
907.456.0261 • Juneau 907.586.7277 • Ketchikan
907.225.6880 • Soldotna 907.262.4040 • Wasilla
907.357.9956

R: 66 **T:** 2nd 54%
Elected Year: 2014
Next Election: 2026

ALASKA

❧ Rep. Mary Sattler Peltola ()   D-AK-01   p 202.225.5765

Rm. CHOB 153 **Web.** peltola.house.gov   **f** 202.225.0425
Bio. 08/31/1973 • Anchorage • M. Gene Peltola, 4 ch ;
3 stepch **Cmte.** Natural Resources • Transportation &
Infrastructure
CoS. Alex Ortiz   **LD.** Elizabeth Othmer
     PS. Sam Erickson

R: 358 **T:** 2nd 55%
Elected Year: 2022

ARIZONA

ARIZONA

❧ Governor Kathleen (Katie) Marie Hobbs ()   p 602.542.4331

1700 W. Washington St.   **C:** Phoenix
Phoenix, AZ 85007   **P:** 7,171,646 (14)
Website az.gov   **A:** 113,593.91 mi^2 (6th)
Fax 602.542.7601
Term Ends 2027

U.S. Senators
Mark Kelly, **D**
Kyrsten Sinema, I
U.S. Representatives
01 / David Schweikert, **R**
02 / Eli Crane, **R**
03 / Ruben Gallego, **D**
04 / Greg Stanton, **D**
05 / Andy Biggs, **R**
06 / Juan Ciscomani, **R**
07 / Raul M. Grijalva, **D**
08 / Debbie Lesko, **R**
09 / Paul A. Gosar, **R**

❧ Sen. Mark Kelly (KEH-lee)   D-AZ-Jr.   p 202.224.2235

Rm. HSOB 516 **Web.** kelly.senate.gov
Bio. 02/21/1964 • Orange • United States Merchant Marine
Academy, B.S., 1986; United States Naval Postgraduate
School, M.S., 1994; United States Naval Test Pilot School,
M.S., 1994 • Catholic • M. Hon. Gabrielle Giffords, 2 ch (2
from previous marriage); 1 gr-ch **Cmte.** Aging • Armed
Services • Energy & Natural Resources • Environment &
Public Works • Joint Economic
CoS. Jennifer Cox   **LD.** Katie Campbell
Sched. Tony McComiskey   **PS.** Jacob Peters
Dist. Off. Phoenix 602.671.7901 • Tucson 520.475.5177

R: 83 **T:** 2nd 51%
Elected Year: 2020
Next Election: 2028

❧ Sen. Kyrsten Sinema (SIH-nih-muh)   I-AZ-Sr.   p 202.224.4521

Caucuses with Democratic Party   **f** 202.228.0515
Rm. HSOB 317 **Web.** sinema.senate.gov
Bio. 07/12/1976 • Tucson • Brigham Young Univ. (UT),
Bach. Deg., 1995; Arizona State Univ., M.S., 1999; Arizona
State Univ. Law School, J.D., 2004; Arizona State Univ., Ph.D.,
2012 • None • S. **Cmte.** Banking, Housing & Urban Affairs •
Commerce, Science & Transportation • Homeland Security
& Government Affairs • Veterans' Affairs
CoS. Michael Brownlie   **LD.** Chris Leuchten
Sched. Laura Piccioli   **PS.** Hannah Hurley
Dist. Off. Phoenix 602.598.7327 • Tucson 520.639.7080

R: 76 **T:** 1st 50%
Elected Year: 2018
Next Election: 2024

Rep. Andy Biggs (bigz)   R-AZ-05   p 202.225.2635

Rm. CHOB 252 **Web.** biggs.house.gov
Bio. 11/07/1958 • Tucson • Brigham Young Univ. (UT), B.A., 1982; Univ. of Arizona College of Law, J.D., 1984; Arizona State Univ., M.A., 1999 • Mormon • M. Cindy Biggs, 6 ch
Cmte. Judiciary • Oversight & Accountability
CoS. Kate LaBorde   **LD.** Zachary C. Barnes
Sched. Amber Swinson   **PS.** Matthew Tragesser
Dist. Off. Mesa 480.699.8239

R: 199   T: 4th   57%
Elected Year: 2016

Rep. Juan Ciscomani ()   R-AZ-06   p 202.225.2542

Rm. LHOB 1429 **Web.** juanciscomani.com
Bio. • Pima Community College, Assc. Deg.; Univ. of Arizona, Bach. Deg., 2005 • M. Laura Ciscomani, 6 ch
Cmte. Appropriations • Veterans' Affairs
CoS. Becky Freeman   **LD.** Caroline Bender
                     PS. Dan Coulson
Dist. Off. Tucson

R: 371   T: 1st   51%
Elected Year: 2022

Rep. Eli Crane ()   R-AZ-02   p 202.225.3361

Rm. LHOB 1000 **Web.** eliforarizona.com
Bio. 01/03/1980 • Tucson • M. Jen Crane, 2 ch   **Cmte.** Homeland Security • Small Business • Veterans' Affairs
CoS. Gregory L. Smith
                     PS. Zach Kahler
Dist. Off. Cortaro 703.549.7705

R: 373   T: 1st   54%
Elected Year: 2022

Rep. Ruben Gallego (gah-YEH-go)   D-AZ-03   p 202.225.4065

Rm. LHOB 1114 **Web.** rubengallego.house.gov
Bio. 11/20/1979 • Chicago • Harvard Univ., A.B., 2004 • Catholic • M. Kate Gallego   **Cmte.** Armed Services • Natural Resources
CoS. Raphael Chavez-Fernandez   **LD.** Ryan McGuire
Sched. Jose Contreras   **PS.** Jacques Petit
Dist. Off. Phoenix 602.256.0551

R: 171   T: 5th   77%
Elected Year: 2014

Rep. Paul A. Gosar (go-SAR)   R-AZ-09   p 202.225.2315

Rm. RHOB 2057 **Web.** gosar.house.gov   **f** 202.226.9739
Bio. 11/27/1958 • Rock Springs • Creighton Univ., B.S., 1981, Creighton Boyne School of Dentistry (NE), D.D.S., 1985 • Roman Catholic • M. Maude Gosar, 3 ch   **Cmte.** Natural Resources • Oversight & Accountability
CoS. Thomas Van Flein   **LD.** Rory Burke
                     PS. Anthony Foti

R: 105   T: 7th   98%
Elected Year: 2010

Rep. Raul M. Grijalva (gree-HAHL-vah)   D-AZ-07   p 202.225.2435

Rm. LHOB 1203 **Web.** grijalva.house.gov   **f** 202.225.1541
Bio. 02/19/1948 • Tucson • Pima County Supervisor; Member, Tucson Unified School Board • Univ. of Arizona, B.A., 1986 • Roman Catholic • M. Ramona Grijalva, 3 ch
Cmte. Education & Workforce • Natural Resources
CoS. Amy Emerick Clerkin   **LD.** Sayanna Molina
Sched. Carlos Martinez   **PS.** Jason T. Johnson
Dist. Off. Avondale 623.536.3388 • Somerton 928.343.7933 • Tucson 520.622.6788

R: 48   T: 11th   65%
Elected Year: 2002

ARIZONA

♜ Rep. Debbie Lesko (LEH-skoh) R-AZ-08 p 202.225.4576

Rm. LHOB 1214 **Web.** lesko.house.gov **f** 202.225.6328
Bio. 11/14/1959 • Sheboygan • Univ. of Wisconsin - Madison, B.B.A. • Christian Church • M. Joe Lesko, 3 ch
Cmte. Energy & Commerce
CoS. Rachel Harris **LD.** Annie Clark
Sched. Brendon Gallo
Dist. Off. Surprise 623.776.7911

R: 227 **T:** 4th 97%
Elected Year: 2018

♜ Rep. David Schweikert (SHWY-kurt) R-AZ-01 p 202.225.2190

Rm. CHOB 460 **Web.** schweikert.house.gov **f** 202.225.3462
Bio. 03/03/1962 • Los Angeles • Scottsdale Community College (AZ), A.A., 1985; Arizona State Univ., B.S., 1988; Arizona State Univ., M.B.A., 2005 • Roman Catholic • M. Joyce Schweikert, 1 ch **Cmte.** Ways & Means
CoS. Kevin Knight (CD) **LD.** Chad Michaels
Sched. Breck Giltner **PS.** Hunter Lovell
Dist. Off. Scottsdale 480.946.2411

R: 112 **T:** 7th 50%
Elected Year: 2010

♜ Rep. Greg Stanton (STAN-tuhn) D-AZ-04 p 202.225.9888

Rm. CHOB 207 **Web.** stanton.house.gov
Bio. 03/08/1970 • Long Island • Marquette Univ. (WI), B.A., 1992; Univ. of Michigan Law School, J.D., 1995 • Catholic • M. Nicole Stanton, 2 ch **Cmte.** Foreign Affairs • Transportation & Infrastructure
CoS. Seth Scott **LD.** Tracee Gross Sutton
Sched. Mia Rubio **PS.** Allison Childress
Dist. Off. Phoenix 602.956.2463

R: 281 **T:** 3rd 56%
Elected Year: 2018

ARKANSAS

♜ Governor Sarah Huckabee Sanders () p 501.682.2345

State Capitol Room 250, 500 Woodlane Ave.
Little Rock, AR 72201
Website arkansas.gov
Fax 501.682.1382
Term Ends 2027
Lt. Governor
Leslie Carol Rutledge, **R**

C: Little Rock
P: 3,013,825 (34)
A: 52,035.35 mi^2 (27th)

U.S. Senators
John N. Boozman, **R**
Tom B. Cotton, **R**
U.S. Representatives
01 / Rick Crawford, **R**
02 / French Hill, **R**
03 / Steve Womack, **R**
04 / Bruce Westerman, **R**

♠ Sen. John N. Boozman (BOAZ-muhn)　　　R-AR-Sr.　　p 202.224.4843

Rm. HSOB 141 **Web.** boozman.senate.gov **f** 202.228.1371
Bio. 12/10/1950 • Shreveport • Optometrist • Univ. of Arkansas, O.D., 1972; Southern College of Optometry (TN), O.D., 1977 • Baptist • M. Cathy Marley Boozman, 3 ch ; 2 gr-ch **Cmte.** Agriculture, Nutrition & Forestry • Appropriations • Environment & Public Works • Veterans' Affairs
CoS. Toni-Marie Higgins　　**LD.** Dan Burgess
Sched. Lauren Holly　　**PS.** Sara Lasure
Dist. Off. El Dorado 870.863.4641 • Fort Smith 479.573.0189 • Jonesboro 870.268.6925 • Little Rock 501.372.7153 • Lowell 479.725.0400 • Mountain Home 870.424.0129 • Stuttgart 870.672.6941

R: 37 **T:** 3rd 66%
Elected Year: 2010
Next Election: 2028

♠ Sen. Tom B. Cotton (KAH-tuhn)　　　R-AR-Jr.　　p 202.224.2353

Rm. RSOB 326 **Web.** cotton.senate.gov
Bio. 05/13/1977 • Dardanelle • Harvard Univ., A.B., 1999; Harvard Law School (MA), J.D., 2002 • Methodist • M. Anna Cotton, 2 ch **Cmte.** Armed Services • Intelligence • Joint Economic • Judiciary
CoS. Doug Coutts
Sched. Joni Deoudes　　**PS.** Caroline M. Tabler
Dist. Off. El Dorado 870.864.8582 • Jonesboro 870.933.6223 • Little Rock 501.223.9081 • Rogers 479.751.0879

R: 61 **T:** 2nd 67%
Elected Year: 2014
Next Election: 2026

♠ Rep. Rick Crawford (KRAW-furd)　　　R-AR-01　　p 202.225.4076

Rm. RHOB 2422 **Web.** crawford.house.gov **f** 202.225.5602
Bio. 01/22/1966 • Homestead • Army 1985-89 • Arkansas State Univ., Jonesboro, B.S., 1996 • Baptist • M. Stacy Crawford, 2 ch **Cmte.** Agriculture • Permanent Select on Intelligence • Science, Space & Technology • Transportation & Infrastructure
CoS. Jonah Shumate　　**LD.** Ashley Shelton
Sched. Courtney Handey　　**PS.** Sara Robertson
Dist. Off. Cabot 501.843.3043 • Dumas 870.377.5571 • Jonesboro 870.203.0540 • Mountain Home 870.424.2075

R: 101 **T:** 7th 74%
Elected Year: 2010

♠ Rep. French Hill (hill)　　　R-AR-02　　p 202.225.2506

Rm. LHOB 1533 **Web.** hill.house.gov **f** 202.225.5903
Bio. 12/05/1956 • Little Rock • Vanderbilt Univ. (TN), B.S., 1979 • Roman Catholic • M. Martha Hill, 2 ch **Cmte.** Financial Services • Foreign Affairs • Permanent Select on Intelligence
CoS. A. Brooke Bennett　　**LD.** Dylan Frost
Sched. Kristen Sonderegger　**PS.** Brooke Nethercott
Dist. Off. Conway 501.358.3481 • Little Rock 501.324.5941

R: 174 **T:** 5th 60%
Elected Year: 2014

♠ Rep. Bruce Westerman (WES-tur-muhn)　　　R-AR-04　　p 202.225.3772

Rm. CHOB 202 **Web.** westerman.house.gov **f** 202.225.1314
Bio. 11/18/1967 • Hot Springs • Univ. of Arkansas, B.S., 1990; Yale Univ. (CT), M.S., 2001 • Southern Baptist • M. Sharon French, 4 ch **Cmte.** Natural Resources • Transportation & Infrastructure
CoS. Nancy Peele　　**LD.** Janet Rossi
Sched. Madeline Bryant　　**PS.** Sarah Henderson
Dist. Off. El Dorado 870.864.8946 • Hot Springs 501.609.9796 • Ozark 479.667.0075 • Pine Bluff 870.536.8178

R: 186 **T:** 5th 71%
Elected Year: 2014

ARKANSAS

⚑ Rep. Steve Womack (WOE-mak)　　　R-AR-03　　p 202.225.4301

Rm. RHOB 2412　**Web.** womack.house.gov　**f** 202.225.5713
Bio. 02/18/1957 • Russellville • Mayor of Rogers, AR •
Arkansas Army National Guard, 1979-2009 • Arkansas Tech
Univ., B.A., 1979 • Southern Baptist • M. Terri Williams
Womack, 3 ch ; 3 gr-ch　**Cmte.** Appropriations
CoS. Madison Nash　　　**LD.** Jessica Powell
　　　　　　　　　　　　　PS. Alexia Sikora
Dist. Off. Fort Smith 479.424.1146 • Rogers 479.464.0446

R: 117　**T:** 7th　64%
Elected Year: 2010

CALIFORNIA

CALIFORNIA

ꙭ Governor Gavin Newsom (NEW-sum)　　　p 916.445.2841

State Capitol Building, Suite 1173　**C:** Sacramento
Sacramento, CA 95814　　　　　　　**P:** 39,557,045 (1)
Website ca.gov　　　　　　　　　　**A:** 155,779.03 mi² (3rd)
Fax 916.558.3160
Term Ends 2027
Lt. Governor
Eleni Kounalakis, **D**

U.S. Senators
Dianne Feinstein, **D**
Alex Padilla, **D**
U.S. Representatives
01 / Doug LaMalfa, **R**
02 / Jared Huffman, **D**
03 / Kevin Kiley, **R**
04 / Mike C. Thompson, **D**
05 / Tom McClintock, **R**
06 / Ami Bera, **D**
07 / Doris Matsui, **D**
08 / John Garamendi, **D**
09 / Josh Harder, **D**
10 / Mark J. DeSaulnier, **D**
11 / Nancy Pelosi, **D**
12 / Barbara Lee, **D**
13 / John Duarte, **R**
14 / Eric Swalwell, **D**
15 / Kevin Mullin, **D**
16 / Anna G. Eshoo, **D**
17 / Ro Khanna, **D**
18 / Zoe Lofgren, **D**
19 / Jimmy Panetta, **D**
20 / Kevin McCarthy, **R**
21 / Jim Costa, **D**
22 / David Valadao, **R**
23 / Jay Obernolte, **R**
24 / Salud Carbajal, **D**
25 / Raul Ruiz, **D**
26 / Julia Brownley, **D**
27 / Mike Garcia, **R**
28 / Judy Chu, **D**
29 / Tony Cardenas, **D**
30 / Adam B. Schiff, **D**
31 / Grace F. Napolitano, **D**
32 / Brad J. Sherman, **D**
33 / Pete Aguilar, **D**
34 / Jimmy Gomez, **D**
35 / Norma J. Torres, **D**
36 / Ted Lieu, **D**
37 / Sydney K. Kamlager-Dove, **D**

38 / Linda T. Sanchez, **D**
39 / Mark A. Takano, **D**
40 / Young O. Kim, **R**
41 / Ken S. Calvert, **R**
42 / Robert Garcia, **D**
43 / Maxine Waters, **D**
44 / Nanette Diaz Barragan, **D**
45 / Michelle Park Steel, **R**
46 / Lou Correa, **D**
47 / Katie Porter, **D**
48 / Darrell E. Issa, **R**
49 / Mike Levin, **D**
50 / Scott H. Peters, **D**
51 / Sara Jacobs, **D**
52 / Juan C. Vargas, **D**

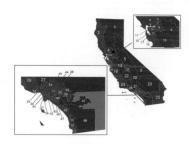

CALIFORNIA

Sen. Dianne Feinstein (FINE-stine)   D-CA-Sr.   p 202.224.3841

Rm. HSOB 331   **Web.** feinstein.senate.gov   **f** 202.228.3954
Bio. 06/22/1933 • San Francisco • Mayor (San Francisco, CA) • Stanford Univ. (CA), Bach. Deg., 1955 • Jewish • W. Richard C. Blum, 1 ch; 3 stepch   **Cmte.** Appropriations • Intelligence • Judiciary • Rules & Administration
CoS. David A. Grannis   **LD.** Ian Bryan
Sched. Megan Grosspietsch   **PS.** Tom Mentzer
Dist. Off. Fresno 559.485.7430 • Los Angeles 310.914.7300 • San Diego 619.231.9712 • San Francisco 415.393.0707

R: 3   **T:** 6th 54%
Elected Year: 1992
Next Election: 2024

Sen. Alex Padilla (pa-DEE-yah)   D-CA-Jr.   p 202.224.3553

Rm. HSOB 112   **Web.** padilla.senate.gov   **f** 202.224.2200
Bio. 03/22/1973 • Panorama City • Massachusetts Institute of Technology, B.S., 1994 • M. Angela Padilla, 3 ch   **Cmte.** Budget • Environment & Public Works • Homeland Security & Government Affairs • Judiciary • Rules & Administration
CoS. David Montes   **LD.** Joshua Esquivel
Sched. Symonne Smith   **PS.** Tess Whittlesey
Dist. Off. Fresno 559.497.5109 • Los Angeles 310.231.4494 • Sacramento 916.448.2787 • San Diego 619.239.3884 • San Francisco 415.981.9369

R: 90   **T:** 2nd 61%
Elected Year: 2021
Next Election: 2028

Rep. Pete Aguilar (ah-GEE-lar)   D-CA-33   p 202.225.3201

Rm. CHOB 108   **Web.** aguilar.house.gov   **f** 202.226.6962
Bio. 06/19/1979 • Fontana • Univ. of Redlands, B.R.E., 2001 • Roman Catholic • M. Alisha Aguilar, 2 ch   **Cmte.** Appropriations
CoS. Boris Medzhibovsky   **LD.** Victoria Rivas (CD)
Sched. Ivana Wright (CD)   **PS.** Owen Kilmer
Dist. Off. San Bernardino 909.890.4445

R: 160   **T:** 5th 58%
Elected Year: 2014

Rep. Nanette Diaz Barragan (BAIR-uh-guhn)   D-CA-44   p 202.225.8220

Rm. RHOB 2312   **Web.** barragan.house.gov   **f** 202.226.7290
Bio. 09/15/1976 • San Pedro • Univ. of California, Los Angeles, B.A., 2000; Univ. of Southern California, J.D., 2005 • Catholic • S.   **Cmte.** Energy & Commerce
CoS. Liam Forsythe   **LD.** Matt Dernoga
Sched. Nathalie Garcia   **PS.** Kevin McGuire
Dist. Off. Carson 310.831.1799 • Compton 310.831.1799 • San Pedro 310.831.1799 • South Gate 310.831.1799

R: 197   **T:** 4th 72%
Elected Year: 2016

Rep. Ami Bera (BAIR-uh)   D-CA-06   p 202.225.5716

Rm. CHOB 172   **Web.** bera.house.gov   **f** 202.226.1298
Bio. 03/02/1965 • Los Angeles • Univ. of California, Irvine, B.S., 1987; Univ. of California, Irvine, M.D., 1991 • Unitarian • M. Janine Bera, 1 ch   **Cmte.** Foreign Affairs • Permanent Select on Intelligence
CoS. Chad Obermiller   **LD.** Kelvin Lum
Sched. Aisha Mae Mughal   **PS.** Travis Horne
Dist. Off. Sacramento 916.635.0505

R: 126   **T:** 6th 56%
Elected Year: 2012

CALIFORNIA

Rep. Julia Brownley (BROWN-lee)   D-CA-26   p 202.225.5811

Rm. RHOB 2262 **Web.** f 202.225.1100
juliabrownley.house.gov
Bio. 08/28/1952 • Aiken • Mount Vernon College, B.A.,
1975; American Univ. (DC), M.B.A., 1979 • Episcopalian
• D., 2 ch **Cmte.** Natural Resources • Transportation &
Infrastructure • Veterans' Affairs
CoS. Lenny Young   **LD.** Sharon Wagener
Sched. Ryan Viessman   **PS.** Carina Armenta
Dist. Off. Oxnard 805.379.1779 • Thousand Oaks
805.379.1779

R: 127 **T:** 6th 55%
Elected Year: 2012

Rep. Ken S. Calvert (CAL-vurt)   R-CA-41   p 202.225.1986

Rm. RHOB 2205 **Web.** calvert.house.gov   f 202.225.2004
Bio. 06/08/1953 • Corona • Real Estate Agent; Restaurateur
• Chaffey Community College (CA), A.A., 1973; San Diego
State Univ., B.A., 1975 • Protestant - Unspecified Christian •
D. **Cmte.** Appropriations
CoS. Rebecca Keightley   **LD.** Jack Lincoln
Sched. Johannah Murphy   **PS.** Jason Gagnon (CD)
Dist. Off. Corona 951.277.0042

R: 12 **T:** 16th 52%
Elected Year: 1992

Rep. Salud Carbajal (KAR-bah-HAHL)   D-CA-24   p 202.225.3601

Rm. RHOB 2331 **Web.** carbajal.house.gov   f 202.225.5632
Bio. 11/18/1964 • Moroleon • Univ. of California, Santa
Barbara, B.A., 1990; Fielding Univ. (CA), Mast. Deg., 1994
• Catholic • M. Gina Carbajal, 2 ch **Cmte.** Agriculture •
Armed Services • Transportation & Infrastructure
CoS. Jeremy Tittle   **LD.** Johanna Montiel
Sched. Ruth Vazquez   **PS.** Ian Mariani
Dist. Off. San Luis Obispo 805.546.8348 • Santa Barbara
805.730.1710 • Santa Maria 805.730.1710

R: 201 **T:** 4th 61%
Elected Year: 2016

Rep. Tony Cardenas (KAR-deh-nahss)   D-CA-29   p 202.225.6131

Rm. RHOB 2181 **Web.** cardenas.house.gov   f 202.225.0819
Bio. 03/31/1963 • Pacoima • Univ. of California, Santa
Barbara, B.S., 1986 • Christian Church • M. Norma
Cárdenas, 4 ch **Cmte.** Energy & Commerce
CoS. Ahmed Elsayed   **LD.** Jaqueline Serrano
Dist. Off. Panorama City 818.221.3718

R: 128 **T:** 6th 59%
Elected Year: 2012

Rep. Judy Chu (choo)   D-CA-28   p 202.225.5464

Rm. RHOB 2423 **Web.** chu.house.gov   f 202.225.5467
Bio. 07/07/1953 • Los Angeles • Univ. of California,
Los Angeles, B.A., 1974; California School Professional
Psychology, Los Angeles, M.A., 1977; California School of
Professional Psychology, Ph.D., 1979 • Unspecified/Other •
M. Michael Eng **Cmte.** Small Business • Ways & Means
CoS. Ellen Hamilton   **LD.** David Silberberg
Sched. Jillian Smith   **PS.** Graeme Crews
Dist. Off. Claremont 909.625.5394 • Pasadena
626.304.0110

R: 94 **T:** 8th 66%
Elected Year: 2009

Rep. Lou Correa (ko-RAY-ah)   D-CA-46   p 202.225.2965

Rm. RHOB 2301 **Web.** correa.house.gov
Bio. 01/24/1958 • Los Angeles • California State Univ.
Fullerton, B.S., 1980; Univ. of California, Los Angeles,
J.D., 1985; Univ. of California, Los Angeles, M.B.A., 1985
• Catholic • M. Esther Reynoso Correa, 4 ch **Cmte.**
Agriculture • Homeland Security • Judiciary
CoS. Rene Munoz   **LD.** Ngoc Nguyen
Sched. Mariana Perera   **PS.** Adriano Pucci
Dist. Off. Santa Ana 714.559.6190

R: 202 **T:** 4th 62%
Elected Year: 2016

⟶ Rep. Jim Costa (KAHS-tuh)   D-CA-21   p 202.225.3341

Rm. RHOB 2081 **Web.** costa.house.gov   **f** 202.225.9308
Bio. 04/13/1952 • Fresno • State Legislator • California
State Univ., Fresno, B.S., 1974 • Roman Catholic • S. **Cmte.**
Agriculture • Foreign Affairs • Natural Resources
CoS. Juan E. Lopez   **LD.** John Lynch
Sched. Christy Bourbon   **PS.** Anthony Camacho
(CD)
Dist. Off. Fresno 559.495.1620

R: 57   **T:** 10th   54%
Elected Year: 2004

⟶ Rep. Mark J. DeSaulnier (deh-SOAN-yay)   D-CA-10   p 202.225.2095

Rm. CHOB 503 **Web.** desaulnier.house.gov   **f** 202.225.5609
Bio. 03/31/1952 • Lowell • College of The Holy Cross (MA),
B.A., 1974 • Roman Catholic • D., 2 ch **Cmte.** Education &
Workforce • Ethics • Transportation & Infrastructure
CoS. Betsy Arnold Marr   **LD.** Sarah Jackson
Sched. Brooklyn Alcott   **PS.** Mairead Glowacki
Dist. Off. Antioch 925.754.0716 • Walnut Creek
925.933.2660

R: 168   **T:** 5th   79%
Elected Year: 2014

⧆ Rep. John Duarte ()   R-CA-13   p 202.225.1947

Rm. LHOB 1535 **Web.**
johnduarteforcongress.com
Bio. 09/09/1966 • Modesto • Univ. of the Pacific, M.B.A.
• M. Alexandra Duarte, 4 ch **Cmte.** Natural Resources •
Transportation & Infrastructure
CoS. Alex Ross
Sched. Annie Martinez
Dist. Off. Modesto

R: 379   **T:** 1st   50%
Elected Year: 2022

⟶ Rep. Anna G. Eshoo (EH-shoo)   D-CA-16   p 202.225.8104

Rm. CHOB 272 **Web.** eshoo.house.gov   **f** 202.225.8890
Bio. 12/13/1942 • New Britain • San Mateo County Board of
Supervisors; Chief of Staff, CA Assembly Speaker • Canada
College (CA), A.A., 1975 • Roman Catholic • D., 2 ch **Cmte.**
Energy & Commerce
CoS. Aisling McDonough   **LD.** Eric Henshall
Sched. Caroline O'Connor
Dist. Off. Palo Alto 650.323.2984

R: 14   **T:** 16th   58%
Elected Year: 1992

⟶ Rep. John Garamendi (gair-uh-MEN-dee)   D-CA-08   p 202.225.1880

Rm. RHOB 2004 **Web.** garamendi.house.gov **f** 202.225.5914
Bio. 01/24/1945 • Camp Blanding • State Legislator; Lt
Governor (CA) • Univ. of California, Berkeley, B.A., 1966;
Harvard Univ., M.B.A., 1970 • Christian Church • M. Patricia
Wilkinson Garamendi, 6 ch ; 10 gr-ch **Cmte.** Armed
Services • Transportation & Infrastructure
CoS. Bradley Bottoms   **LD.** Iain Hart
Sched. Alyssa Dinh   **PS.** Eric Olsen
Dist. Off. Davis 530.753.5301 • Fairfield 707.438.1822

R: 95   **T:** 8th   76%
Elected Year: 2009

⧆ Rep. Mike Garcia (gar-SEE-uh)   R-CA-27   p 202.225.1956

Rm. CHOB 144 **Web.** mikegarcia.house.gov
Bio. 04/24/1976 • Santa Clarita • U.S. Naval Academy (MD),
B.S., 1998; Georgetown Univ. (DC), M.A., 1998 • M. Rebecca
Garcia, 2 ch **Cmte.** Appropriations • Permanent Select on
Intelligence • Science, Space & Technology
CoS. Will Turner   **LD.** Jacob Gattman
Sched. Marie Price   **PS.** Noah Sadlier
Dist. Off. Palmdale 661.839.0532 • Santa Clarita
661.568.4855 • Simi Valley 805.760.9090

R: 296   **T:** 3rd   53%
Elected Year: 2020

CALIFORNIA

⌖ Rep. Robert Garcia () D-CA-42 p 202.225.7924

Rm. LHOB 1305 **Web.** robertgarcia.com
Bio. 12/02/1977 • Lima • California State Univ. - Long
Beach, B.A.; Univ. of Southern California, M.A., 2005;
California State Univ. - Long Beach, Ed.D., 2010 • M.
Matthew Mendez Garcia **Cmte.** Homeland Security
• Oversight & Accountability • Permanent Select on
Intelligence

CoS. Robert Edmonson	**LD.** Andrew Bower
Sched. Patrick Swymer	**PS.** Sara Guerrero

Dist. Off. Long Beach

R: 385 **T:** 1st 68%
Elected Year: 2022

⌖ Rep. Jimmy Gomez (GO-mehz) D-CA-34 p 202.225.6235

Rm. CHOB 506 **Web.** gomez.house.gov f 202.225.2202
Bio. 11/25/1974 • Southern California • Univ. of California,
Los Angeles, B.A.; John F. Kennedy School of Government,
Harvard Univ., M.P.P. • M. Mary Hodge **Cmte.** Oversight &
Accountability • Permanent Select on Intelligence

CoS. Carlos Paz	**LD.** Ben Kane
Sched. Rosemarie Aceituno	**PS.** James Kwon

Dist. Off. Los Angeles 213.481.1425

R: 224 **T:** 4th 51%
Elected Year: 2017

⌖ Rep. Josh Harder (HAR-dur) D-CA-09 p 202.225.4540

Rm. CHOB 209 **Web.** harder.house.gov
Bio. 08/01/1986 • Turlock • Stanford Univ. (CA), Bach. Deg.,
2008; Harvard Business and Kennedy Schools (MA), M.P.P.,
2014 • Christian Church • M. Pamela Harder, 1 ch **Cmte.**
Appropriations
CoS. Rachael L. Goldenberg **LD.** Ata Khan
Sched. Ryan Feldman
Dist. Off. Modesto 209.579.5458

R: 255 **T:** 3rd 55%
Elected Year: 2018

⌖ Rep. Jared Huffman (HUF-muhn) D-CA-02 p 202.225.5161

Rm. RHOB 2445 **Web.** huffman.house.gov f 202.225.5163
Bio. 02/18/1964 • Independence • Univ. of California, Santa
Barbara, B.A., 1986; Boston College Law School (MA), J.S.D.,
1990 • Unspecified/Other • M. Susan Huffman, 2 ch **Cmte.**
Natural Resources • Transportation & Infrastructure
CoS. Jennifer Goedke **LD.** Shane Trimmer
Sched. Julia Diamond **PS.** Mary Hurrell
Dist. Off. Eureka 707.407.3585 • Fort Bragg 707.962.0933 •
Petaluma 707.981.8967 • San Rafael 415.258.9657 • Ukiah
707.671.7449

R: 133 **T:** 6th 74%
Elected Year: 2012

▣ Rep. Darrell E. Issa (EYE-suh) R-CA-48 p 202.225.5672

Rm. RHOB 2108 **Web.** issa.house.gov
Bio. 11/01/1953 • Cleveland • CEO, Auto Security Company
• Army 1970-72, 1976-80 • Kent State Univ. (OH), A.A.,
1976; Siena Heights Univ. (MI), B.A., 1976 • Christian - Non-
Denominational • D. Kathy Issa, 1 ch **Cmte.** Foreign Affairs
• Judiciary • Science, Space & Technology
CoS. Veronica Wong **LD.** Jennifer Haynes
Sched. Sally Lindsay **PS.** Jonathan Wilcox
Dist. Off. Escondido 760.304.7575 • Temecula
760.304.7575

R: 55 **T:** 2nd 60%
Elected Year: 2020

⌖ Rep. Sara Jacobs (JAY-kubz) D-CA-51 p 202.225.2040

Rm. LHOB 1314 **Web.** sarajacobs.house.gov f 202.225.2948
Bio. 02/01/1989 • Del Mar • Columbia Univ. (NY), B.A.,
2011; Columbia Univ. (NY), M.A., 2012 • Jewish • S. **Cmte.**
Armed Services • Foreign Affairs
CoS. Amy Kuhn **LD.** Brandon Mendoza
Sched. Katie Heller **PS.** Lauren McIlvaine
Dist. Off. San Diego 619.280.5353

R: 322 **T:** 2nd 62%
Elected Year: 2020

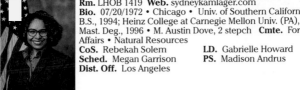

↬ Rep. Sydney K. Kamlager-Dove ()   D-CA-37   p 202.225.7084

Rm. LHOB 1419 **Web.** sydneykamlager.com
Bio. 07/20/1972 • Chicago • Univ. of Southern California, B.S., 1994; Heinz College at Carnegie Mellon Univ. (PA), Mast. Deg., 1996 • M. Austin Dove, 2 stepch **Cmte.** Foreign Affairs • Natural Resources
CoS. Rebekah Solem   **LD.** Gabrielle Howard
Sched. Megan Garrison   **PS.** Madison Andrus
Dist. Off. Los Angeles

R: 396   T: 1st 64%
Elected Year: 2022

↬ Rep. Ro Khanna (KAH-nuh)   D-CA-17   p 202.225.2631

Rm. CHOB 306
Bio. 09/13/1976 • Philadelphia • Univ. of Chicago (IL), A.B., 1998; Yale Univ. Law School (CT), J.D., 2001 • Hinduism • M. Ritu Ahuja, 2 ch **Cmte.** Agriculture • Armed Services • Oversight & Accountability • Select China Committee
CoS. Geo Saba   **LD.** Kevin D. Fox
Sched. Nicole Mata   **PS.** Marie Baldassarre
Dist. Off. Santa Clara 408.436.2720

R: 214   T: 4th 71%
Elected Year: 2016

☗ Rep. Kevin Kiley ()   R-CA-03   p 202.225.2523

Rm. LHOB 1032 **Web.** electkevinkiley.com
Bio. 01/30/1985 • Sacramento • Loyola Marymount Univ., M.A.; Harvard Univ., B.A., 2007; Yale Univ. Law School (CT), J.D., 2012 • Christian Church • S. **Cmte.** Education & Workforce • Judiciary
CoS. Bob Holste   **LD.** Jeannine M. Bender
Sched. Hollis LeMunyon   **PS.** Tyler Tate
Dist. Off. Rocklin 916.699.0377

R: 399   T: 1st 54%
Elected Year: 2022

☗ Rep. Young O. Kim (kim)   R-CA-40   p 202.225.4111

Rm. LHOB 1306 **Web.** youngkim.house.gov   f 202.225.1776
Bio. 10/18/1962 • Incheon • Univ. of Southern California, B.B.A., 1985 • Christian - Non-Denominational • M. Charles Kim, 4 ch **Cmte.** Financial Services • Foreign Affairs
CoS. Patrick Mocete   **LD.** Alex Cisneros
Sched. Alex Keledjian   **PS.** Callie Strock

R: 323   T: 2nd 57%
Elected Year: 2020

☗ Rep. Doug LaMalfa (luh-MAL-fuh)   R-CA-01   p 202.225.3076

Rm. CHOB 408 **Web.** lamalfa.house.gov
Bio. 07/02/1960 • Oroville • Butte College (CA), A.A., 1980; California Polytechnic State Univ., San Luis Obispo, B.S., 1982 • Evangelical • M. Jill LaMalfa, 4 ch **Cmte.** Agriculture • Natural Resources • Transportation & Infrastructure
CoS. Mark Spannagel   **LD.** John Veale
   PS. Alexandra Lavy
Dist. Off. Chico 530.343.1000 • Redding 530.223.5898

R: 139   T: 6th 62%
Elected Year: 2012

↬ Rep. Barbara Lee (lee)   D-CA-12   p 202.225.2661

Rm. RHOB 2470 **Web.** lee.house.gov   f 202.225.9817
Bio. 07/16/1946 • El Paso • Congressional Aide; Social Worker • Mills College (CA), B.A., 1973; Univ. of California, Berkeley, M.S.W., 1975 • Baptist • M. Clyde W. Oden, 2 ch ; 5 gr-ch **Cmte.** Appropriations • Budget
CoS. Joyce Kazadi   **LD.** Gregory Adams
Sched. Chris Keosian   **PS.** Sean Ryan
Dist. Off. Oakland 510.763.0370

R: 32   T: 14th 91%
Elected Year: 1998

CALIFORNIA

☆ Rep. Mike Levin (LEH-vin)   D-CA-49   p 202.225.3906

Rm. RHOB 2352 **Web.** mikelevin.house.gov
Bio. 10/20/1978 • Inglewood • Stanford Univ. (CA), B.A.,
2001; Duke Law School (NC), J.D., 2005 • Catholic • M.
Chrissy Levin, 2 ch **Cmte.** Natural Resources • Veterans'
Affairs
CoS. Jonathan Gilbert   **LD.** Faith Williams
Sched. Kelsey Gold   **PS.** Raymond Rodriguez
Dist. Off. Dana Point 949.281.2449 • Oceanside
760.599.5000

R: 262 **T:** 3rd 53%
Elected Year: 2018

☆ Rep. Ted Lieu (loo)   D-CA-36   p 202.225.3976

Rm. RHOB 2454 **Web.** lieu.house.gov   **f** 202.225.4099
Bio. 03/29/1969 • Taipei • St. Ignatius High School,
Cleveland, OH, J.D., 1987; Stanford Univ. (CA), B.A., 1991;
Stanford Univ. (CA), B.S., 1991; Georgetown Univ. Law
Center (DC), J.D., 1994 • Roman Catholic • M. Betty Lieu,
2 ch **Cmte.** Foreign Affairs • Judiciary • Science, Space &
Technology • Veterans' Affairs
CoS. Marc A. Cevasco   **LD.** Leah Uhrig
                                  PS. Jenna Bushnell
Dist. Off. Los Angeles 323.651.1040 • Manhattan Beach
310.321.7664

R: 175 **T:** 5th 70%
Elected Year: 2014

☆ Rep. Zoe Lofgren (LAHF-gruhn)   D-CA-18   p 202.225.3072

Rm. LHOB 1401 **Web.** lofgren.house.gov   **f** 202.225.3336
Bio. 12/21/1947 • San Mateo • Attorney; Immigration Law
Professor • Stanford Univ. (CA), B.A., 1970; Santa Clara
Univ. Law School (CA), J.D., 1975 • Lutheran • M. John
Marshall Collins, 2 ch **Cmte.** Judiciary • Science, Space &
Technology
CoS. Stacey E. Leavandosky
Sched. Andrew DeLuca   **PS.** Ally Kehoe
Dist. Off. San Jose 408.271.8700

R: 21 **T:** 15th 66%
Elected Year: 1994

☆ Rep. Doris Matsui (mat-SOO-ee)   D-CA-07   p 202.225.7163

Web. matsui.house.gov   **f** 202.225.0566
Bio. 09/25/1944 • Poston • Deputy Assistant, President
Clinton; Deputy Director, Public Liaison; Television
Executive; Civic Leader • Univ. of California, Berkeley, B.A.,
1966 • Methodist • M. Roger Sant, 1 ch ; 4 stepch ; 6 gr-ch
Cmte. Energy & Commerce
CoS. Jeremy Marcus (CD)
Sched. Nora Taktajian (CD)   **PS.** Maureen Elinzano (CD)
Dist. Off. Sacramento 916.498.5600

R: 67 **T:** 10th 68%
Elected Year: 2005

✿ Rep. Kevin McCarthy 1SG (muh-KAR-thee)   R-CA-20   p 202.225.2915

Rm. RHOB 2468 **Web.**   **f** 202.225.2908
kevinmccarthy.house.gov
Bio. 01/26/1965 • Bakersfield • Small Business Owner
• California State Univ., Bakersfield, B.A., 1989; Univ. of
California, Bakersfield, M.B.A., 1994 • Baptist • M. Judy
McCarthy, 2 ch
CoS. James Min   **LD.** Trevor Smith
Sched. Chris Duncan (CD)   **PS.** Matt Sparks
Dist. Off. Bakersfield 661.327.3611

R: 77 **T:** 9th 67%
Elected Year: 2006

✿ Rep. Tom McClintock (muh-KLIN-tahk)   R-CA-05   p 202.225.2511

Rm. RHOB 2256 **Web.** mcclintock.house.gov **f** 202.225.5444
Bio. 07/10/1956 • Bronxville • State Legislator • Univ.
of California, Los Angeles, B.S., 1978 • Baptist • W. Lori
McClintock, 2 ch **Cmte.** Budget • Judiciary • Natural
Resources
CoS. Chris Tudor   **LD.** Kyle Campbell
                                PS. Jennifer Cressy

R: 88 **T:** 8th 61%
Elected Year: 2008

⚓ Rep. Kevin Mullin () D-CA-15 p 202▲

Rm. LHOB 1404 **Web.** kevinmullinforcongress.com
Bio. 06/15/1970 • San Francisco • Univ. of San Francisc▲ (CA), B.A., 1992; San Francisco State Univ., M.P.A., 1998 • M. Jessica Mullin, 2 ch (twins) **Cmte.** Natural Resources ◄ Science, Space & Technology
CoS. Kate Adams
                                     PS. Luisa Gunn
Dist. Off. San Mateo 650.342.0300

R: 417 **T:** 1st 56%
Elected Year: 2022

⚓ Rep. Grace F. Napolitano (nah-poe-lee-TAH-no) D-CA-31 p 202.225.5256

Rm. LHOB 1610 **Web.** napolitano.house.gov **f** 202.225.0027
Bio. 12/04/1936 • Brownsville • Member, State Assembly; Mayor (Norwalk, TX) • Roman Catholic • M. Frank Napolitano, 5 ch (5 from previous marriage); 14 gr-ch ; 2 great-gr-ch **Cmte.** Natural Resources • Transportation & Infrastructure
CoS. Joe Sheehy **LD.** Joseph Ciccone
Sched. Melvin Sanchez
Dist. Off. El Monte 626.350.0150

R: 34 **T:** 13th 60%
Elected Year: 1998

⚑ Rep. Jay Obernolte (oh-bur-NOAL-tee) R-CA-23 p 202.225.5861

Rm. LHOB 1029 **Web.** obernolte.house.gov
Bio. 08/18/1970 • Chicago • California Institute of Technology, B.S., 1992; Univ. of California, Los Angeles, M.S., 1997 • Christian - Non-Denominational • M. Heather Obernolte, 2 ch **Cmte.** Energy & Commerce • Science, Space & Technology
CoS. Lorissa Bounds **LD.** Rob Hicks
Sched. Kalyn Schoreder **PS.** Emily Carlin
Dist. Off. Hesperia 760.247.1815

R: 337 **T:** 2nd 61%
Elected Year: 2020

⚓ Rep. Jimmy Panetta (puh-NEH-tuh) D-CA-19 p 202.225.2861

Rm. CHOB 304 **Web.** panetta.house.gov **f** 202.225.6791
Bio. 10/01/1969 • Washington • Monterey Peninsula College (CA), A.A., 1989; Univ. of California, Davis, B.A., 1991; Santa Clara Univ. (CA), J.D., 1996 • Catholic • M. Carrie Panetta, 2 ch **Cmte.** Agriculture • Armed Services • Budget • Ways & Means
CoS. Pete Spiro **LD.** Mark Dennin
Sched. Alexa Roth **PS.** Christian Unkenholz

R: 218 **T:** 4th 69%
Elected Year: 2016

⚓ Rep. Nancy Pelosi (puh-LO-see) D-CA-11 p 202.225.4965

Rm. LHOB 1236 **Web.** pelosi.house.gov **f** 202.225.8259
Bio. 03/26/1940 • Baltimore • Chairman, California State Democratic Party; Public Relations Consultant • Trinity College (DC), A.B., 1962 • Roman Catholic • M. Paul F. Pelosi, 5 ch ; 9 gr-ch
CoS. Terri McCullough **LD.** McKenzie Fields
Sched. Jacob Trauberman **PS.** Aaron Bennett
Dist. Off. San Francisco 415.556.4862

5 T: 19th 84%
ted Year: 1987

◗. Scott H. Peters (PEE-turz) D-CA-50 p 202.225.0508

Rm. LHOB 1201 **Web.** scottpeters.house.gov
Bio. 06/17/1958 • Springfield • Duke Univ. (NC), B.A., 1980; New York Univ. Law School, J.D., 1984 • Lutheran • M. Lynn Gorguze, 2 ch **Cmte.** Budget • Energy & Commerce
CoS. Daniel Zawitoski **LD.** Baillee Brown
Sched. Jackie Sobol **PS.** Daniela Contreras (CD)
Dist. Off. San Diego 858.455.5550

.atie Porter (POR-tur)   D-CA-47   p 202.225.5611

Rm. LHOB 1233 **Web.** porter.house.gov
Bio. 01/03/1974 • Des Moines • Yale Univ. (CT), B.A., 1996; Harvard Univ., J.D., 2001 • Episcopalian • D., 3 ch **Cmte.** Natural Resources • Oversight & Accountability
CoS. Nora Walsh-DeVries   **LD.** Max Ernst
Sched. Emily Silk   **PS.** Jordan Wong
Dist. Off. Irvine 949.668.6600

R: 272   **T:** 3rd 52%
Elected Year: 2018

⋔ Rep. Raul Ruiz (roo-EES)   D-CA-25   p 202.225.5330

Rm. RHOB 2342 **Web.** ruiz.house.gov   **f** 202.225.1238
Bio. 08/25/1972 • Zacatecas • Univ. of California, Los Angeles, B.S., 1994; Harvard Univ., M.P.P., 2001; Harvard Univ., M.D., 2001; Harvard Univ., M.PH, 2007 • Seventh-Day Adventist • M. Monica Ruiz, 2 ch (twins) **Cmte.** Energy & Commerce
CoS. Tom Nagle   **LD.** Erin Doty
Sched. Lauren Gedney   **PS.** Kelly O'Keeffe
Dist. Off. El Centro 760.312.9900

R: 144   **T:** 6th 57%
Elected Year: 2012

⋔ Rep. Linda T. Sanchez (SAN-chez)   D-CA-38   p 202.225.6676

Rm. RHOB 2428 **Web.**   **f** 202.226.1012
lindasanchez.house.gov
Bio. 01/28/1969 • Orange • Union Official; Attorney • Univ. of California, Berkeley, B.A., 1991; Univ. of California School of Law, Los Angeles (JD), J.D., 1995 • Roman Catholic • M. James M. Sullivan, 1 ch ; 3 stepch **Cmte.** Ways & Means
CoS. Ricky Xuan Le   **LD.** Cody Willming
Sched. Rachel Chasalow   **PS.** Michael Cummings
Dist. Off. Norwalk 562.860.5050

R: 52   **T:** 11th 58%
Elected Year: 2002

⋔ Rep. Adam B. Schiff (shihf)   D-CA-30   p 202.225.4176

Rm. RHOB 2309 **Web.** schiff.house.gov   **f** 202.225.5828
Bio. 06/22/1960 • Framingham • State Senator; U.S. Attorney, Los Angeles • Stanford Univ. (CA), B.A., 1982; Harvard Univ. Law School (MA), J.D., 1985 • Jewish • M. Eve Sanderson Schiff, 2 ch **Cmte.** Judiciary
CoS. Patrick Boland   **LD.** Danielle Fulfs
Sched. Kyle Abrams   **PS.** Lauren French
Dist. Off. Burbank 818.450.2900

R: 42   **T:** 12th 71%
Elected Year: 2000

⋔ Rep. Brad J. Sherman (SHUR-muhn)   D-CA-32   p 202.225.5911

Rm. RHOB 2365 **Web.** sherman.house.gov   **f** 202.225.5879
Bio. 10/24/1954 • Los Angeles • Harvard Law Instructor; CPA • Univ. of California, Los Angeles, B.A., 1974; Harvard Univ. Law School (MA), J.D., 1979 • Jewish • M. Lisa Kaplan Sherman, 3 ch **Cmte.** Financial Services • Foreign Affairs
CoS. Don MacDonald   **LD.** Johan Propst
Sched. Kathryn McCool   **PS.** Arya Ansari
Dist. Off. Sherman Oaks 818.501.9200

R: 29   **T:** 14th 69%
Elected Year: 1996

⋒ Rep. Michelle Park Steel (steel)   R-CA-45

Web. steel.house.gov
Bio. 06/21/1955 • Seoul • Pepperdine Univ., Bach. D 1997; Univ. of Southern California, M.B.A., 2010 • Ch - Non-Denominational • M. Shawn Steel, 2 ch **Cr** Education & Workforce • Select China Committe Means
CoS. Arie Dana (CD)   **LD.** Kenneth C
Sched. Shelby Kaplan (CD)   **PS.** Jack Pick
Dist. Off. Huntington Beach 714.960.6483

R: 344   **T:** 2nd 52%
Elected Year: 2020

⚓ Rep. Eric Swalwell (SWALL-well)   D-CA-14   p 202.225.5065

Rm. CHOB 174 **Web.** swalwell.house.gov   **f** 202.226.3805
Bio. 11/16/1980 • Sac City • Univ. of Maryland, B.A., 2003; Univ. of Maryland School of Law, J.D., 2006 • Christian - Non-Denominational • M. Brittany Ann Watts, 2 ch   **Cmte.** Homeland Security • Judiciary
CoS. Yardena Wolf   **LD.** Sarah Shapiro
Sched. Karina Gallardo   **PS.** Jessica Gail
Dist. Off. Castro Valley 510.370.3322

R: 146 **T:** 6th 69%
Elected Year: 2012

⚓ Rep. Mark A. Takano (tah-KAH-no)   D-CA-39   p 202.225.2305

Rm. RHOB 2078 **Web.** takano.house.gov   **f** 202.225.7018
Bio. 12/10/1960 • Riverside • La Sierra High School (CA), A.B., 1979; Harvard College (MA), A.B., 1983; School of Education, Univ. of California, Riverside, M.F.A., 2010 • Methodist • S.   **Cmte.** Education & Workforce • Veterans' Affairs
CoS. Richard McPike   **LD.** Justin Maturo
                         PS. Taylor Doggett
Dist. Off. Riverside 951.222.0203

R: 147 **T:** 6th 58%
Elected Year: 2012

⚓ Rep. Mike C. Thompson (TOMP-suhn)   D-CA-04   p 202.225.3311

Rm. CHOB 268 **Web.** mikethompson.house.gov   **f** 202.225.4335
Bio. 01/24/1951 • St. Helena • State Senator; CA State Assembly Fellow • Army 1969-73 • California State Univ., Chico, B.A., 1982; California State Univ., Chico, M.A., 1996 • Roman Catholic • M. Janet Thompson, 2 ch ; 3 gr-ch   **Cmte.** Ways & Means
CoS. Melanie Rhinehart Van Tassell
Sched. Emma Tomaszewski **PS.** Jack Stelzner
Dist. Off. Napa 707.226.9898 • Santa Rosa 707.542.7182 • Woodland 530.753.5301

R: 37 **T:** 13th 68%
Elected Year: 1998

⚓ Rep. Norma J. Torres (toe-ress)   D-CA-35   p 202.225.6161

Rm. RHOB 2227 **Web.** torres.house.gov   **f** 202.225.8671
Bio. 04/04/1965 • Escuintla • National Labor College (MD), B.A., 2012 • Roman Catholic • M. Louis Torres, 3 ch   **Cmte.** Administration • Appropriations
                         LD. Serena Gobbi
                         PS. Justin Krakoff
Dist. Off. Ontario 909.481.6474

R: 184 **T:** 5th 57%
Elected Year: 2014

⚓ Rep. David Valadao (va-luh-DAY-o)   R-CA-22   p 202.225.4695

Rm. RHOB 2465 **Web.** valadao.house.gov
Bio. 04/14/1977 • Hanford • Catholic • M. Terra Valadao, 3 ch   **Cmte.** Appropriations • Budget
CoS. Andrew Renteria   **LD.** Amanda Hall
Sched. Paola Arellano   **PS.** Faith Mabry
Dist. Off. Bakersfield 661.864.7736 • Hanford 559.460.6070

R: 193 **T:** 2nd 52%
Elected Year: 2020

⚓ Rep. Juan C. Vargas (VAR-guhs)   D-CA-52   p 202.225.8045

Rm. RHOB 2334 **Web.** vargas.house.gov   **f** 202.225.2772
Bio. 03/07/1961 • National City • Univ. of San Diego, B.A., 1983; Harvard Univ. Law School (MA), J.D., 1991 • Roman Catholic • M. Adrienne D'Ascoli, 2 ch   **Cmte.** Financial Services
CoS. Larry Cohen   **LD.** Scott Hinkle
Sched. Brittany Murray   **PS.** Brian Garcia
Dist. Off. Chula Vista 619.422.5963

R: 148 **T:** 6th 67%
Elected Year: 2012

CALIFORNIA

⚓ Rep. Maxine Waters (WAH-durs) D-CA-43 p 202.225.2201
Rm. RHOB 2221 **Web.** waters.house.gov f 202.225.7854
Bio. 08/15/1938 • St. Louis • Head Start Teacher; Delegate to Democratic National Convention • California State Univ., Los Angeles, B.A., 1970 • Christian Church • M. Amb. Sidney Williams, 2 ch ; 2 gr-ch **Cmte.** Financial Services
Sched. Darlene Murray
Dist. Off. Hawthrone 323.757.8900

R: 9 **T:** 17th 77%
Elected Year: 1990

COLORADO

COLORADO

⚓ Governor Jared S. Polis (POLL-lis) p 303.866.2471

136 State Capitol
Denver, CO 80203-1792
Website colorado.gov
Fax 303.866.2003
Term Ends 2027
Lt. Governor
Dianne Primavera, **D**

C: Denver
P: 5,695,564 (21)
A: 103,641.75 mi^2 (8th)

U.S. Senators
Michael F. Bennet, **D**
John W. Hickenlooper, **D**
U.S. Representatives
01 / Diana L. DeGette, **D**
02 / Joe Neguse, **D**
03 / Lauren Boebert, **R**
04 / Ken R. Buck, **R**
05 / Doug Lamborn, **R**
06 / Jason Crow, **D**
07 / Brittany Pettersen, **D**
08 / Yadira Caraveo, **D**

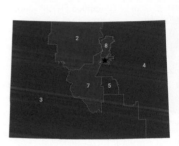

⚓ Sen. Michael F. Bennet (BEH-nuht) D-CO-Sr. p 202.224.5852
Rm. RSOB 261 **Web.** bennet.senate.gov f 202.228.5097
Bio. 11/28/1964 • New Delhi • Schools Superintendent; Political Aide • Wesleyan Univ. (CT), B.A., 1987; Yale Univ. Law School (CT), J.D., 1993 • Episcopalian • M. Susan Daggett Bennet, 3 ch **Cmte.** Agriculture, Nutrition & Forestry • Finance • Intelligence • Rules & Administration
CoS. Arian Herckis
Sched. Grace Bobertz **PS.** Olivia Bercow
Dist. Off. Alamosa 719.587.0096 • Colorado Springs 719.328.1100 • Denver 303.455.7600 • Durango 970.259.1710 • Fort Collins 970.224.2200 • Grand Junction 970.241.6631 • Pueblo 719.542.7550

R: 32 **T:** 4th 56%
Elected Year: 2009
Next Election: 2028

⚓ Sen. John W. Hickenlooper (HIH-kuhn-loo-pur) D-CO-Jr. p 202.224.5941
  f 202.224.3115
Bio. 02/07/1952 • Narberth • Wesleyan Univ. (CT), B.A., 1974; Wesleyan Univ. (CT), Mast. Deg., 1980 • Quaker • M. Robin Pringle, 2 ch (1 from previous marriage) **Cmte.** Commerce, Science & Transportation • Energy & Natural Resources • Health, Education, Labor & Pensions • Small Business & Entrepreneurship
CoS. Kirtan Mehta (CD) **LD.** Kate Cassling (CD)
Sched. Lea Davis (CD) **PS.** Anthony Rivera-Rodriguez (CD)
Dist. Off. Colorado Springs 719.632.6706 • Denver 303.244.1628 • Durango 970.880.7236 • Fort Collins 970.484.3502 • Grand Junction 970.822.4530 • Greeley 970.352.5546

R: 87 **T:** 1st 54%
Elected Year: 2020
Next Election: 2026

⚑ Rep. Lauren Boebert (BOE-burt)   R-CO-03   p 202.225.4761

Rm. LHOB 1713 **Web.** boebert.house.gov
Bio. 12/15/1986 • Orlando • Christian - Non-
Denominational • M. Jayson Boebert, 4 ch   **Cmte.** Natural
Resources • Oversight & Accountability
CoS. Jeff Small

                   PS. Jake S. Settle
Dist. Off. Durango 970.317.6130 • Grand Junction
970.208.0460 • Pueblo 719.696.6970

R: 302   **T:** 2nd   50%
Elected Year: 2020

⚑ Rep. Ken R. Buck (buck)   R-CO-04   p 202.225.4676

Rm. RHOB 2455 **Web.** buck.house.gov   **f** 202.225.5870
Bio. 02/16/1959 • Ossining • Princeton Univ. (NJ), A.B.,
1981; Univ. of Wyoming (WY), J.D., 1985 • Wesleyan • M.
Perry Lynn, 2 ch (2 from previous marriage) **Cmte.** Foreign
Affairs • Judiciary
CoS. Joe Jackson   **LD.** Keifer Wynn
Sched. Lucy Herrington
Dist. Off. Castle Rock 720.639.9165 • Windsor
970.702.2136

R: 166   **T:** 5th   61%
Elected Year: 2014

⚑ Rep. Yadira Caraveo ()   D-CO-08   p 202.225.5625

Rm. LHOB 1024 **Web.** caraveo.house.gov
Bio. 12/23/1980 • Denver • Regis Univ., B.S., 2003; Univ.
of Colorado School of Medicine, M.D., 2009 • NS. **Cmte.**
Science, Space & Technology
CoS. Brian Sowyrda   **LD.** Benjamin Harrison
Sched. Emma Salas   **PS.** Kaylin Dines

R: 368   **T:** 1st   48%
Elected Year: 2022

⚑ Rep. Jason Crow (kroe)   D-CO-06   p 202.225.7882

Rm. LHOB 1323 **Web.** crow.house.gov
Bio. 03/15/1979 • Beaver Dam • Univ. of Wisconsin -
Madison, B.A., 2002; Univ. of Denver (CO), J.D., 2009 •
Christian - Non-Denominational • M. Deserai Crow, 2 ch
Cmte. Armed Services • Foreign Affairs • Permanent Select
on Intelligence
CoS. Shira Siegel   **LD.** John R. Brodtke
Sched. Katie Solomon   **PS.** Kara Powell (CD)
Dist. Off. Aurora 720.748.7514

R: 243   **T:** 3rd   61%
Elected Year: 2018

⚑ Rep. Diana L. DeGette (deh-GET)   D-CO-01   p 202.225.4431

Rm. RHOB 2111 **Web.** degette.house.gov   **f** 202.225.5657
Bio. 07/29/1957 • Tachikawa • Attorney; State
Representative • Colorado College, B.A., 1979; New York
Univ. Law School, J.D., 1982 • Presbyterian • M. Lino
Lipinsky, 2 ch **Cmte.** Energy & Commerce • Natural
Resources

                 LD. Chris Schloesser
                 PS. Ryan Brown
Dist. Off. Denver 303.844.4988

R: 25   **T:** 14th   80%
Elected Year: 1996

⚑ Rep. Doug Lamborn (LAM-born)   R-CO-05   p 202.225.4422

Rm. RHOB 2371 **Web.** lamborn.house.gov   **f** 202.226.2638
Bio. 05/24/1954 • Leavenworth • Attorney • Univ. of
Kansas School of Journalism, B.S., 1978; Univ. of Kansas
School of Law, J.D., 1985 • Christian Church • M. Jeanie
Lamborn, 5 ch **Cmte.** Armed Services • Natural Resources
CoS. Dale Anderson   **LD.** Will Sacripanti
                 PS. Cassandra Sebastian
                   (CD)
Dist. Off. Colorado Springs 719.520.0055

R: 76   **T:** 9th   56%
Elected Year: 2006

COLORADO

Rep. Joe Neguse (neh-"GOOSE") D-CO-02 p 202.225.2161

Rm. RHOB 2400 **Web.** neguse.house.gov
Bio. 05/13/1984 • Bakersfield • Univ. of Colorado, Boulder,
Bach. Deg., 2005; Univ. of Colorado, Boulder, J.D., 2009
• Christian Church • M. Andrea Neguse, 1 ch **Cmte.**
Judiciary • Natural Resources • Rules
CoS. Bo Morris **LD.** Tia Bogeljic
Sched. Priya Robb **PS.** Hannah Rehm
Dist. Off. Boulder 303.335.1045 • Fort Collins 970.372.3971
• Frisco 303.335.1045

R: 266 **T:** 3rd 70%
Elected Year: 2018

Rep. Brittany Pettersen () D-CO-07 p 202.225.2645

Rm. LHOB 1230 **Web.** brittanypettersen.com
Bio. 12/06/1981 • Jefferson County • Metropolitan State
Univ. of Denver (CO), B.A. • M. Ian Silverii, 1 ch **Cmte.**
Financial Services
CoS. Macey Matthews **LD.** Adam Finkel
Sched. Victoria Houghtalen **PS.** MacKensie Kvalvik
Dist. Off. Lakewood

R: 421 **T:** 1st 56%
Elected Year: 2022

CONNECTICUT

CONNECTICUT

Governor Ned Lamont (LAH-mawnt) p 860.566.4840

State Capitol, 210 Capitol Ave. **C:** Hartford
Hartford, CT 06106 **P:** 3,572,665 (29)
Website ct.gov **A:** 4,842.49 mi^2 (48th)
Fax 860.524.7395
Term Ends 2027
Lt. Governor
Susan Bysiewicz, **D**

U.S. Senators
Richard Blumenthal, **D**
Chris S. Murphy, **D**
U.S. Representatives
01 / John B. Larson, **D**
02 / Joe Courtney, **D**
03 / Rosa L. DeLauro, **D**
04 / Jim A. Himes, **D**
05 / Jahana Hayes, **D**

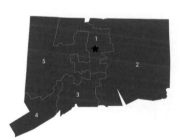

Sen. Richard Blumenthal (BLOOM-un-thawl) D-CT-Sr. p 202.224.2823

Rm. HSOB 706 **Web.** blumenthal.senate.gov **f** 202.224.9673
Bio. 02/13/1946 • Brooklyn • State Attorney General; State
Legislator • Marine Corps Reserve, 1970-75 • Harvard
College (MA), A.B., 1967; Yale Univ. Law School (CT),
J.D., 1973 • Jewish • M. Cynthia Allison Malkin, 4 ch
Cmte. Aging • Armed Services • Homeland Security &
Government Affairs • Judiciary • Veterans' Affairs
CoS. Joel Kelsey **LD.** Brian Steele
Sched. Michael Lawson **PS.** Maria McElwain
Dist. Off. Bridgeport 203.330.0598 • Hartford 860.258.6940

R: 42 **T:** 3rd 58%
Elected Year: 2010
Next Election: 2028

Sen. Chris S. Murphy (MUR-fee) D-CT-Jr. p 202.224.4041

Rm. HSOB 136 **Web.** murphy.senate.gov **f** 202.224.9750
Bio. 08/03/1973 • White Plains • State Legislator; Attorney • Williams College, B.A., 1996; Univ. of Connecticut School of Law, J.D., 2002 • Protestant - Unspecified Christian • M. Catherine Holahan Murphy, 2 ch **Cmte.** Appropriations • Foreign Relations • Health, Education, Labor & Pensions
CoS. Allison Herwitt **LD.** Chris Mewett
Sched. Farian Rabbani **PS.** Rebecca Drago
Dist. Off. Hartford 860.549.8463

R: 47 **T:** 2nd 60%
Elected Year: 2012
Next Election: 2024

Rep. Joe Courtney (KORT-nee) D-CT-02 p 202.225.2076

Rm. RHOB 2449 **Web.** courtney.house.gov **f** 202.225.4977
Bio. 04/06/1953 • West Hartford • Attorney • Tufts Univ. (MA), B.A., 1975; Univ. of Connecticut School of Law, J.D., 1978 • Roman Catholic • M. Audrey Courtney, 2 ch **Cmte.** Armed Services • Education & Workforce
CoS. Neil McKiernan **LD.** Maria Costigan
Sched. Rachel Newstadt **PS.** Patrick Cassidy
Dist. Off. Enfield 860.741.6011 • Norwich 860.886.0139

R: 73 **T:** 9th 58%
Elected Year: 2006

Rep. Rosa L. DeLauro (deh-LOOR-o) D-CT-03 n 202.225.3661

Rm. RHOB 2413 **Web.** delauro.house.gov **f** 202.225.4890
Bio. 03/02/1943 • New Haven • Executive Director, Emily's List, Congressional Aide • Marymount College (NY), B.A., 1964; Columbia Univ. (NY), M.A., 1966 • Roman Catholic • M. Stanley Greenberg, 3 ch ; 4 gr-ch **Cmte.** Appropriations
CoS. Rebecca Salay **LD.** John Rayburn
PS. King Green-Newton
Dist. Off. New Haven 203.562.3718

R: 8 **T:** 17th 57%
Elected Year: 1990

Rep. Jahana Hayes (hayz) D-CT-05 p 202.225.4476

Rm. RHOB 2458 **Web.** hayes.house.gov
Bio. 03/08/1973 • Waterbury • Naugatuck Valley Community College (CT), A.A., 2002; Southern Connecticut State Univ., B.S., 2005; Univ. of Saint Joseph (CT), M.A., 2012 • Methodist • M. Milford Hayes, 4 ch **Cmte.** Agriculture • Education & Workforce
CoS. Alex Ginis **LD.** Miranda Ganter
Sched. Brien Courchene **PS.** Annmarie Goyzueta
Dist. Off. Waterbury 860.223.8412

R: 256 **T:** 3rd 50%
Elected Year: 2018

Rep. Jim A. Himes (hymz) D-CT-04 p 202.225.5541

Rm. RHOB 2137 **Web.** himes.house.gov **f** 202.225.9629
Bio. 07/05/1966 • Lima • Financial Executive • Harvard Univ., B.A., 1988; Oxford Univ. (England), M.Phil, 1990 • Presbyterian • M. Mary Himes, 2 ch **Cmte.** Financial Services • Permanent Select on Intelligence
CoS. Mark Snyder **LD.** Hannah Aiken
Sched. Elizabeth Stanley **PS** Charlotte Hoffman
Dist. Off. Bridgeport 203.333.6600 • Stamford 203.353.9400

R: 86 **T:** 8th 59%
Elected Year: 2008

Rep. John B. Larson (LAR-suhn) D-CT-01 p 202.225.2265

Rm. LHOB 1501 **Web.** larson.house.gov **f** 202.225.1031
Bio. 07/22/1948 • Hartford • State Senator; Businessman • Central Connecticut State Univ. (CT), B.S., 1971 • Catholic • M. Leslie Best Larson, 3 ch **Cmte.** Ways & Means
CoS. Scott Stephanou **LD.** Mike Dunn
Sched. Sarah Gianni **PS.** Megan Perleoni
Dist. Off. East Hartford 860.278.8888

R: 33 **T:** 13th 61%
Elected Year: 1998

DELAWARE

DELAWARE

⚑ Governor John C. Carney Jr. (KAR-nee)   p 302.744.4101

150 Martin Luther King Jr. Blvd.,
2nd Floor
Dover, DE 19901
Website delaware.gov
Fax 302.739.2775
Term Ends 2025
Lt. Governor
Bethany Hall-Long, **D**

C: Dover
P: 967,171 (46)
A: 1,948.66 mi^2 (50th)

U.S. Senators
Tom R. Carper, **D**
Chris A. Coons, **D**
U.S. Representatives
01 / Lisa Blunt Rochester, **D**

⚑ Sen. Tom R. Carper (KAR-pur)   D-DE-Sr.   p 202.224.2441

Rm. HSOB 513 **Web.** carper.senate.gov   **f** 202.228.2190
Bio. 01/23/1947 • Beckley • Governor; U.S. Representative
• Navy 1968-73; Navy Reserve 1973-91 • Ohio State Univ.,
B.A., 1968; Univ. of Delaware, Newark, M.B.A., 1975 •
Presbyterian • M. Martha Ann Stacy Carper, 2 ch **Cmte.**
Environment & Public Works • Finance • Homeland
Security & Government Affairs
CoS. Jan Beukelman   **LD.** Lucy Xiao
Sched. Lydia Wehrley   **PS.** Katie Grasso (CD)
Dist. Off. Dover 302.674.3308 • Georgetown 302.856.7690
• Wilmington 302.573.6291

R: 11   **T:** 4th   60%
Elected Year: 2000
Next Election: 2024

⚑ Sen. Chris A. Coons (koonz)   D-DE-Jr.   p 202.224.5042

Rm. RSOB 218 **Web.** coons.senate.gov   **f** 202.228.3075
Bio. 09/09/1963 • Greenwich • Amherst College (MA),
B.A., 1985; Yale Univ. Law School (CT), J.D., 1992; Yale
Univ. Divinity School (CT), Mast. Deg., 1992 • Presbyterian
• M. Annie Lingenfelter, 3 ch **Cmte.** Appropriations •
Ethics • Foreign Relations • Judiciary • Small Business &
Entrepreneurship
CoS. Jonathan Stahler   **LD.** Brian Winseck
Sched. Chelsea Moser   **PS.** Will A. Baskin-Gerwitz
Dist. Off. Dover 302.736.5601 • Wilmington 302.573.6345

R: 35   **T:** 3rd   60%
Elected Year: 2010
Next Election: 2026

⚑ Rep. Lisa Blunt Rochester (RAH-chess-tur)   D-DE-01   p 202.225.4165

Rm. LHOB 1724 **Web.**
bluntrochester.house.gov
Bio. 02/10/1962 • Philadelphia • Fairleigh Dickinson Univ.,
Bach. Deg., 1985; The Univ. of Delaware, M.A., 2003 •
Christian Church • W., 2 ch **Cmte.** Energy & Commerce
CoS. Jacqueline Sanchez   **LD.** Kevin Diamond
Sched. Mika Alvarez   **PS.** Andrew Donnelly
Dist. Off. Georgetown 302.858.4773 • Wilmington
302.830.2330

R: 200   **T:** 4th   56%
Elected Year: 2016

FLORIDA

⚑ Governor Ron D. DeSantis (dee-SAN-tis)　　p 850.488.7146

The Capitol
400 S. Monroe St.
Tallahassee, FL 32399-0001
Website flgov.com
Fax 850.487.0801
Term Ends 2027
Lt. Governor
Jeanette Nunez, **R**

C: Tallahassee
P: 21,299,325 (3)
A: 53,624.55 mi² (26th)

U.S. Senators
Marco Rubio, **R**
Rick Scott, **R**

U.S. Representatives
01 / Matt Gaetz, **R**
02 / Neal P. Dunn, **R**
03 / Kat Cammack, **R**
04 / Aaron Bean, **R**
05 / John Rutherford, **R**
06 / Mike G. Waltz, **R**
07 / Cory Mills, **R**
08 / Bill Posey, **R**
09 / Darren M. Soto, **D**
10 / Maxwell Alejandro Frost, **D**
11 / Daniel A. Webster, **R**
12 / Gus M. Bilirakis, **R**
13 / Anna Paulina Luna, **R**
14 / Kathy A. Castor, **D**
15 / Laurel M. Lee, **R**
16 / Vern G. Buchanan, **R**
17 / Greg Steube, **R**
18 / Scott Franklin, **R**
19 / Byron Donalds, **R**
20 / Sheila Cherfilus-McCormick, **D**
21 / Brian Mast, **R**

22 / Lois J. Frankel, **D**
23 / Jared Evan Moskowitz, **D**
24 / Frederica S. Wilson, **D**
25 / Debbie Wasserman Schultz, **D**
26 / Mario Diaz-Balart, **R**
27 / Maria E. Salazar, **R**
28 / Carlos Gimenez, **R**

⚑ Sen. Marco Rubio (ROO-bee-o)　　R-FL-Sr.　　p 202.224.3041

Rm. RSOB 284 **Web.** rubio.senate.gov　　**f** 202.228.0285
Bio. 05/28/1971 • Miami • State Legislator; Spkr., Florida
House of Representatives • Univ. of Florida, B.S., 1993; Univ.
of Miami Law School (FL), J.D., 1996 • Roman Catholic •
M. Jeanette Dousdebes, 4 ch **Cmte.** Aging • Appropriations
• Foreign Relations • Intelligence • Small Business &
Entrepreneurship
CoS. Mike Needham　　**LD.** Lauren Reamy
Sched. Virginia Hinzman　　**PS.** Ansley Bradwell
Dist. Off. Fort Myers 239.318.6464 • Jacksonville
904.354.4300 • Miami 305.596.4224 • Orlando 407.254.2573
• Palm Beach Gardens 561.775.3360 • Pensacola
850.433.2603 • Tallahassee 850.599.9100 • Tampa
813.947.6288

R: 39　**T:** 3rd 58%
Elected Year: 2010
Next Election: 2028

⚑ Sen. Rick Scott (skaht)　　R-FL-Jr.　　p 202.224.5274

Rm. HSOB 502 **Web.** rickscott.senate.gov
Bio. 12/01/1952 • Bloomington • Univ. of Missouri, B.S.,
1975; Southern Methodist Univ. Law School (TX), J.D., 1978
• Christian Church • M. Ann Scott, 2 ch ; 6 gr-ch **Cmte.**
Aging • Armed Services • Budget • Homeland Security &
Government Affairs
CoS. Craig Carbone　　**LD.** Jon Foltz
Sched. Henia Mackenroth　　**PS.** McKinley Lewis
Dist. Off. Coral Gables 786.501.7141 • Jacksonville
904.479.7227 • Kissimmee 407.586.7879 • Naples
239.231.7890 • Orlando 407.872.7161 • Pensacola
850.760.5151 • Tallahassee 850.942.8415 • Tampa
813.225.7040 • West Palm Beach 561.514.0189

R: 82　**T:** 1st 50%
Elected Year: 2018
Next Election: 2024

⚑ Rep. Aaron Bean ()　　R-FL-04　　p 202.225.0123

Rm. LHOB 1239 **Web.** aaronbean.com
Bio. 01/25/1967 • Fernandina Beach • Jacksonville
Univ., B.S., 1989 • Methodist • M. Abigail 'Abby' Bradley,
3 ch **Cmte.** Education & Workforce • Small Business •
Transportation & Infrastructure
CoS. Jamie Robinette　　**LD.** James Thomas
Sched. Elizabeth Donahoo
Dist. Off. Fernandina Beach

R: 364　**T:** 1st 61%
Elected Year: 2022

FLORIDA

🏛 Rep. Gus M. Bilirakis (bih-lih-RAK-uhss) R-FL-12 p 202.225.5755

Rm. RHOB 2306 **Web.** bilirakis.house.gov **f** 202.225.4085
Bio. 02/08/1963 • Gainesville • Attorney; State Legislator • Univ. of Florida, B.S., 1986; Stetson Univ. College of Law (FL), J.D., 1989 • Greek Orthodox • M. Eva Lialios Bilirakis, 4 ch **Cmte.** Energy & Commerce
CoS. Liz Hittos **LD.** Jonathan Vecchi
Sched. Huntley Campbell **PS.** Summer Blevins (CD)
Dist. Off. Brooksville 352.691.1231 • Inverness 352.654.1004 • New Port Richey 727.232.2921

R: 68 **T:** 9th 70%
Elected Year: 2006

🏛 Rep. Vern G. Buchanan (byoo-KA-nuhn) R-FL-16 p 202.225.5015

Rm. RHOB 2110 **Web.** buchanan.house.gov **f** 202.226.0828
Bio. 05/08/1951 • Detroit • Automobile Dealer; Owner, Reinsurance Co. • Michigan Air National Guard 1969-1975 • Cleary Univ. (MI), B.B.A., 1975; Univ. of Detroit (MI), M.B.A., 1986 • Baptist • M. Sandy Harris Buchanan, 2 ch **Cmte.** Ways & Means
CoS. Sean Brady **LD.** Aaron Bill
Sched. Chase Babair **PS.** Savannah Glasgow
Dist. Off. Bradenton 941.747.9081 • Sarasota 941.951.6643

R: 69 **T:** 9th 62%
Elected Year: 2006

🏛 Rep. Kat Cammack (KAM-mek) R-FL-03 p 202.225.5744

Rm. RHOB 2421 **Web.** cammack.house.gov
Bio. 02/16/1988 • Denver • Univ. of Virginia, Mast. Deg., 2009; Metropolitan State Univ. of Denver (CO), Bach. Deg., 2011; Naval War College (RI), Mast. Deg., 2017 • Christian - Non-Denominational • M. Matt Harrison **Cmte.** Agriculture • Energy & Commerce
CoS. Larry Calhoun
Sched. Alexander Strizak **PS.** Adeline Sandridge
Dist. Off. Gainesville 352.505.0838

R: 305 **T:** 2nd 63%
Elected Year: 2020

🏛 Rep. Kathy A. Castor (KAS-tur) D-FL-14 p 202.225.3376

Rm. RHOB 2052 **Web.** castor.house.gov **f** 202.225.5652
Bio. 08/20/1966 • Miami • County Commissioner • Emory Univ. - Atlanta (GA), B.A., 1988; Florida State Univ. School of Law, J.D., 1991 • Presbyterian • M. Bill Lewis, 2 ch **Cmte.** Energy & Commerce • Select China Committee
CoS. Lara Hopkins **LD.** Nora Blalock
Sched. Mackenzie Brown **PS.** Rikki Miller
Dist. Off. Tampa 813.871.2817

R: 70 **T:** 9th 57%
Elected Year: 2006

🏛 Rep. Sheila Cherfilus-McCormick () D-FL-20 p 202.225.1313

Rm. CHOB 242 **Web.** cherfilus-mccormick.house.gov **f** 202.225.1171
Bio. 01/25/1979 • Brooklyn • Howard Univ., B.S., 2001; Saint Thomas Univ. College of Law (FL), J.D., 2010 • M. Corlie McCormick, 2 ch **Cmte.** Foreign Affairs • Veterans' Affairs
CoS. Naomie Pierre-Louis **LD.** LaTreshia Hamilton
Sched. Kaitlyn Kaufman **PS.** Shauna Pierre
Dist. Off. Tamarac 954.733.2800 • West Palm Beach 561.461.6767

R: 355 **T:** 2nd 72%
Elected Year: 2022

🏛 Rep. Mario Diaz-Balart (DEE-az-buh-LART) R-FL-26 p 202.225.4211

Rm. CHOB 374 **Web.** mariodiazbalart.house.gov **f** 202.225.8576
Bio. 09/25/1961 • Fort Lauderdale • State Legislator; President, Marketing and PR Firm • Roman Catholic • M. Tia Diaz-Balart, 1 ch **Cmte.** Appropriations
CoS. Cesar A. Gonzalez **LD.** Gisselle Reynolds
PS. Laura Hernandez
Dist. Off. Doral 305.470.8555 • Naples 239.348.1620

R: 48 **T:** 11th 71%
Elected Year: 2010

FLORIDA

Rep. Byron Donalds (DAH-nuld) R-FL-19 p 202.225.2536

Rm. LHOB 1719 **Web.** donalds.house.gov
Bio. 10/28/1978 • Brooklyn • Florida State Univ., B.S.,
2002 • Christian Church • M. Erika Donalds, 3 ch **Cmte.**
Financial Services • Oversight & Accountability
CoS. Mehgan Perez-Acosta **LD.** Alexandria Smith
Sched. Maddie Dawson **PS.** Daniel First
Dist. Off. Cape Coral 239.599.6033 • Naples 239.252.6225

R: 308 T: 2nd 68%
Elected Year: 2020

Rep. Neal P. Dunn (dun) R-FL-02 p 202.225.5235

Rm. CHOB 466 **Web.** dunn.house.gov **f** 202.225.5615
Bio. 02/16/1953 • New Haven • Washington and Lee Univ.
(VA), Bach. Deg.; George Washington Univ. Medical School
(DC), M.D. • Catholic • M. Leah Dunn, 3 ch ; 3 gr-ch **Cmte.**
Energy & Commerce • Select China Committee
CoS. Dirk J. Vande Beek **LD.** Sarah Gilbert
Sched. Meghan Myhill (CD) **PS.** Leah Courtney
Dist. Off. Panama City 850.785.0812 • Tallahassee
850.891.8610

R: 203 T: 4th 60%
Elected Year: 2016

Rep. Lois J. Frankel (FRANK-uhl) D-FL-22 p 202.225.9890

Rm. RHOB 2305 **Web.** frankel.house.gov **f** 202.225.1224
Bio. 05/16/1948 • New York • Boston Univ. (MA), B.A.,
1970; Georgetown Univ. Law Center (DC), J.D., 1973 •
Jewish • D., 1 ch **Cmte.** Appropriations
CoS. Brad Solyan **LD.** Becca Flikier
Sched. Kate Regan **PS.** Morgan Routman
Dist. Off. Delray Beach 561.998.9045

R: 131 T: 6th 55%
Elected Year: 2012

Rep. Scott Franklin (FRANK-luhn) R-FL-18 p 202.225.1252

Rm. CHOB 249 **Web.** franklin.house.gov **f** 202.226.0585
Bio. 08/23/1964 • Thomaston • U.S. Naval Academy (MD),
B.S., 1986; Embry-Riddle Aeronautical Univ., M.B.A., 1994;
Univ. of Pennsylvania Wharton School of Business (PA),
B.S., 2003 • Presbyterian • M. Amy Wood, 3 ch **Cmte.**
Appropriations • Science, Space & Technology • Veterans'
Affairs
CoS. Melissa Kelly **LD.** Andrew Korst
Sched. Katharine A. Tate **PS.** Russel Read

R: 313 T: 2nd 75%
Elected Year: 2020

Rep. Maxwell Alejandro Frost () D-FL-10 p 202.225.2176

Rm. LHOB 1224 **Web.** frostforcongress.com
Bio. 01/17/1997 • Orlando • **Cmte.** Oversight &
Accountability • Science, Space & Technology
CoS. Yuri Beckelman
Sched. Trinity Tresner **PS.** Samantha Ramirez
Dist. Off. Orlando

R: 383 T: 1st 59%
Elected Year: 2022

Rep. Matt Gaetz ("gates") R-FL-01 p 202.225.4136

Rm. RHOB 2021 **Web.** gaetz.house.gov **f** 202.225.3414
Bio. 05/07/1982 • Hollywood • Florida State Univ., B.S.,
2003; William & Mary Law School (VA), J.D., 2007 • Baptist
• M. Ginger Luckey, 1 adopted ch **Cmte.** Armed Services •
Judiciary
CoS. Jillian Lane Wyant **LD.** Mike Robertson
Sched. Jenna Hasz **PS.** Joel Valdez
Dist. Off. Pensacola 850.479.1183

R: 207 T: 4th 68%
Elected Year: 2016

FLORIDA

🏛 Rep. Carlos Gimenez (hym-MEHN-ez)   R-FL-28   p 202.225.2778

Rm. CHOB 448 **Web.** gimenez.house.gov
Bio. 01/17/1954 • Havana • Barry Univ., Bach. Deg., 1999 •
Catholic • M. Lourdes Portela, 3 ch ; 6 gr-ch **Cmte.** Armed
Services • Homeland Security • Select China Committee
CoS. Alex Ferro
                                                    PS. Brianna Dapuzzo
Dist. Off. Florida City 305.222.0160 • Key West
305.292.4485 • Miami 305.222.0160

R: 315   **T:** 1st 64%
Elected Year: 2022

🏛 Rep. Laurel M. Lee ()   R-FL-15   p 202.225.5626

Rm. LHOB 1118 **Web.** votelaurel.com
Bio. 03/26/1974 • • Univ. of Florida, Bach. Deg.; Univ.
of Florida Levin College of Law, J.D. • M. Tom Lee, 3 ch
Cmte. Administration • Homeland Security • Judiciary
CoS. Kevin F. Reilly   **LD.** Kevin O'Keefe
Sched. Megan Deusenberry   **PS.** Grace Bartlinski
Dist. Off. Branden

R: 404   **T:** 1st 59%
Elected Year: 2022

🏛 Rep. Anna Paulina Luna ()   R-FL-13   p 202.225.5961

Rm. LHOB 1017 **Web.** voteannapaulina.com
Bio. 05/06/1989 • Santa Ana • Univ. of West Florida, B.S.
• M. Andrew Gamberzky **Cmte.** Natural Resources •
Oversight & Accountability
CoS. Steve Koncar   **LD.** Alexandra Webb
Sched. Taylor Hawkins   **PS.** Edie Heipel
Dist. Off. Seminole 727.610.3980

R: 406   **T:** 1st 53%
Elected Year: 2022

🏛 Rep. Brian Mast ("mast")   R-FL-21   p 202.225.3026

Rm. RHOB 2182 **Web.** mast.house.gov   **f** 202.225.8398
Bio. 07/10/1980 • Grand Rapids • Harvard Univ., Bach.
Deg., 2016 • Christian Church • M. Brianna Mast, 3 ch
Cmte. Foreign Affairs • Transportation & Infrastructure
CoS. James Langenderfer   **LD.** Libby Tidwell
Sched. Madison Engelking **PS.** AnnMarie Graham
Dist. Off. Jupiter 561.530.7778 • Port St. Lucie
772.336.2877 • Stuart 772.403.0900

R: 217   **T:** 4th 64%
Elected Year: 2016

🏛 Rep. Cory Mills ()   R-FL-07   p 202.225.4035

Rm. LHOB 1237 **Web.** millsforflorida.com
Bio. 07/13/1980 • Winter Haven • Florida State College at
Jacksonville, A.A., 2005; American Military Univ., B.S., 2010 •
M. Rana Mills **Cmte.** Armed Services • Foreign Affairs
CoS. Catherine Treadwell   **LD.** Caleb Kostreva
Sched. Derrick Agustin   **PS.** Juan A. Ayala
Dist. Off. Lake Mary 301.654.3220 • Port Orange
386.238.9711

R: 413   **T:** 1st 59%
Elected Year: 2022

🏛 Rep. Jared Evan Moskowitz ()   D-FL-23   p 202.225.3001

Rm. LHOB 1130 **Web.** jaredforflorida.com
Bio. 12/18/1980 • Coral Springs • Nova Southeastern Univ.
Shepard Broad Law Center (FL), J.D.; George Washington
Univ. (DC), B.S., 2003 • Jewish • M. Leah Rifkin, 2 ch **Cmte.**
Foreign Affairs • Oversight & Accountability
CoS. Lale M. Morrison   **LD.** Clare Plassche
Sched. Catherine Magos   **PS.** Dylan Smith
Dist. Off. Boca Raton 954.651.5954

R: 416   **T:** 1st 52%
Elected Year: 2022

♞ Rep. Bill Posey (POE-zee)
R-FL-08   p 202.225.3671

Rm. RHOB 2150 **Web.** posey.house.gov **f** 202.225.3516
Bio. 12/18/1947 • Washington • State Legislator; Realtor •
Brevard Community College (FL), A.A., 1969 • Methodist
• M. Katie Ingram Posey, 2 ch; 3 gr-ch **Cmte.** Financial
Services • Science, Space & Technology
CoS. Stuart Burns   **LD.** Valentina J. Valenta
Sched. Corey Capman   **PS.** George Cecala
Dist. Off. Melbourne 321.632.1776

R: 90   **T:** 8th 65%
Elected Year: 2008

♞ Rep. John Rutherford (RUH-thur-furd)
R-FL-05   p 202.225.2501

Rm. LHOB 1711 **Web.** rutherford.house.gov **f** 202.225.2504
Bio. 09/02/1952 • Omaha • Florida Junior College, A.A.,
1972; Florida State Univ., B.S., 1974 • Catholic • M. Patricia
Rutherford, 2 ch ; 6 gr-ch **Cmte.** Appropriations • Ethics
CoS. Jenifer Bradley   **LD.** Hannah Morrow
Sched. Carole Anne
Dankler
Dist. Off. Jacksonville 904.831.5205

R: 220   **T:** 4th 100%
Elected Year: 2016

♞ Rep. Maria E. Salazar (SA-luh-zar)
R-FL-27   p 202.225.3931

Rm. RHOB 2162 **Web.** salazar.house.gov
Bio. 11/01/1961 • Miami • Univ. of Miami, B.A., 1983; John
F. Kennedy School of Government, Harvard Univ., M.P.A.,
1995 • Christian - Non-Denominational • M. Jaime Court, 2
ch **Cmte.** Foreign Affairs • Small Business
CoS. Tom Moran   **LD.** Josh Duncan
Sched. Paula Huff   **PS.** Daniel Bucheli
Dist. Off. Miami 305.668.2285

R: 342   **T:** 2nd 57%
Elected Year: 2020

♞ Rep. Darren M. Soto (so-toe)
D-FL-09   p 202.225.9889

Rm. RHOB 2353 **Web.** soto.house.gov **f** 202.225.9742
Bio. 02/25/1978 • Ringwood • Rutgers Univ. (NJ), B.A.,
2000; George Washington Univ. School of Law (DC),
J.D., 2004 • Catholic • M. Amanda Soto **Cmte.** Energy &
Commerce • Natural Resources
CoS. Liana Guerra   **LD.** Nicole McLaren
Sched. Dilenny Reyes   **PS.** Belen Sassone
Dist. Off. Kissimmee 407.452.1171 • Orlando 407.452.1171

R: 222   **T:** 4th 54%
Elected Year: 2016

♞ Rep. Greg Steube (STOO-bee)
R-FL-17   p 202.225.5792

Rm. RHOB 2457 **Web.** steube.house.gov **f** 202.225.3132
Bio. 05/19/1978 • Bradenton • Univ. of Florida, B.S., 2001;
Univ. of Florida Levin College of Law, J.D., 2003 • Methodist
• M. Jennifer Mary Retzer, 1 ch **Cmte.** Ways & Means
CoS. Alex Blair   **LD.** Twinkle Patel
                 PS. Sadie Thorman
Dist. Off. Punta Gorda 941.499.3214 • Sarasota
941.499.3214 • Venice 941.499.3214

R: 284   **T:** 3rd 64%
Elected Year: 2018

♞ Rep. Mike G. Waltz (walts)
R-FL-06   p 202.225.2706

Rm. CHOB 244 **Web.** waltz.house.gov
Bio. 01/31/1974 • Boynton Beach • Virginia Military
Institute, B.A., 1996 • Christian Church • D., 1 ch **Cmte.**
Armed Services • Foreign Affairs • Permanent Select on
Intelligence
CoS. Micah T. Ketchel   **LD.** Walker B. Barrett
                     PS. James Hewitt
Dist. Off. Deland 386.279.0707 • Palm Coast 386.302.0442
• Port Orange 386.238.9711

R: 292   **T:** 3rd 75%
Elected Year: 2018

FLORIDA

⚑ Rep. Debbie Wasserman Schultz (WAH-sur-muhn shullts)   D-FL-25   p 202.225.7931

Rm. CHOB 270 **Web.**   f 202.226.2052
wassermanschultz.house.gov
Bio. 09/27/1966 • Forest Hills • State Legislator; College Administrator • Univ. of Florida, B.A., 1988; Univ. of Florida, M.A., 1990 • Jewish • M. Steve Schultz, 3 ch **Cmte.** Appropriations
CoS. Tracie Pough
Sched. Lauren Mylott   **PS.** David Damron
Dist. Off. Sunrise 954.845.1179

R: 66   T: 10th 55%
Elected Year: 2004

⚏ Rep. Daniel A. Webster (WEB-stur)   R-FL-11   p 202.225.1002

Rm. RHOB 2184 **Web.** webster.house.gov
Bio. 04/27/1949 • Charleston • State Legislator; Spkr., House of Representatives • Georgia Institute of Technology, B.E.E., 1971 • Baptist • M. Sandy Jordan, 6 ch ; 14 gr-ch
Cmte. Natural Resources • Science, Space & Technology • Transportation & Infrastructure
CoS. Jaryn Emhof   **LD.** Scott Mackenzie
                PS. Adam Pakledinaz
Dist. Off. Brooksville 352.241.9230 • Inverness 352.241.9204 • Leesburg 352.241.9220 • The Villages 352.383.3552

R: 115   T: 7th 63%
Elected Year: 2010

⚑ Rep. Frederica S. Wilson (WILL-suhn)   D-FL-24   p 202.225.4506

Rm. RHOB 2080 **Web.** wilson.house.gov   f 202.226.0777
Bio. 11/05/1942 • Miami • State Legislator • Miami Northwestern Senior High School, B.S., 1959; Fisk Univ. (TN), B.S., 1963; Univ. of Miami, M.Ed., 1972 • Episcopalian • W., 3 ch ; 5 gr-ch **Cmte.** Education & Workforce • Transportation & Infrastructure
CoS. Jean Roseme   **LD.** Derron Bennett
                PS. Karol Molinares
Dist. Off. Miami Gardens 305.690.5905 • West Park 954.989.2688

R: 116   T: 7th 72%
Elected Year: 2010

GEORGIA

⚏ Governor Brian Kemp (kemp)   p 404.656.1776

206 Washington Street, 111 State Capitol
Atlanta, GA 30334
Website georgia.gov
Fax 404.657.7332
Term Ends 2027
Lt. Governor
Burt Jones, **R**

C: Atlanta
P: 10,519,475 (8)
A: 57,513.37 mi^2 (21st)

U.S. Senators
Raphael Warnock, **D**
Jon Ossoff, **D**
U.S. Representatives
01 / Buddy Carter, **R**
02 / Sanford D. Bishop, **D**
03 / Drew Ferguson, **R**
04 / Hank C. Johnson, **D**
05 / Nikema Williams, **D**
06 / Richard D. McCormick, **R**
07 / Lucy McBath, **D**
08 / Austin Scott, **R**
09 / Andrew Clyde, **R**
10 / Michael A. Collins, **R**
11 / Barry D. Loudermilk, **R**
12 / Rick W. Allen, **R**
13 / David A. Scott, **D**
14 / Marjorie Taylor Greene, **R**

Sen. Jon Ossoff (OSS-off) D-GA-Sr. p 202.224.3521

Rm. RSOB 455 **Web.** ossoff.senate.gov **f** 202.224.2575
Bio. 02/16/1987 • Atlanta • Georgetown Univ. Foreign
Service School (DC), B.S., 2009; London School of
Economics (England), M.S., 2013 • Jewish • M. Alisha
Kramer, 1 ch **Cmte.** Homeland Security & Government
Affairs • Intelligence • Judiciary • Rules & Administration
CoS. Reynaldo Benitez **LD.** Caitlin Frazer
Sched. Caroline Ehlich **PS.** Jake Best
Dist. Off. Atlanta 470.786.7800 • Columbus 706.780.7053

R: 91 **T:** 1st 50%
Elected Year: 2021
Next Election: 2026

Sen. Raphael Warnock (WAR-naak) D-GA-Jr. p 202.224.3643

Rm. RSOB 388 **Web.** warnock.senate.gov
Bio. 07/23/1969 • Savannah • Union Theological Seminary
(NY), M.Div.; Union Theological Seminary (NY), M.Phil;
Union Theological Seminary (NY), Ph.D.; Morehouse
College (GA), B.A., 1991 • Baptist • Se. Oulèye Ndoye,
2 ch **Cmte.** Aging • Agriculture, Nutrition & Forestry •
Banking, Housing & Urban Affairs • Commerce, Science &
Transportation
CoS. Mark Libell **LD.** Joshua Delaney
Sched. Stuart Guillory **PS.** Elena Radding
Dist. Off. Atlanta 770.694.7828

R: 92 **T:** 2nd 51%
Elected Year: 2021
Next Election: 2028

Rep. Rick W. Allen (A-luhn) R-GA-12 p 202.225.2823

Rm. CHOB 462 **Web.** allen.house.gov **f** 202.225.3377
Bio. 11/07/1951 • Augusta • Auburn Univ. School of
Architecture and Fine Arts (GA), B.S., 1973 • Methodist • M.
Robin Reeve, 4 ch ; 12 gr-ch **Cmte.** Education & Workforce
• Energy & Commerce
CoS. Lauren E. Hodge **LD.** Cam Shepherd
  PS. Michael Plummer
Dist. Off. Augusta 706.228.1980 • Dublin 478.272.4030 •
Statesboro 912.243.9452 • Vidalia 912.403.3311

R: 161 **T:** 5th 60%
Elected Year: 2014

Rep. Sanford D. Bishop Jr. (BIH-shuhp) D-GA-02 p 202.225.3631

Rm. RHOB 2407 **Web.** bishop.house.gov **f** 202.225.2203
Bio. 02/04/1947 • Mobile • Attorney; State Legislator •
Army ROTC 1969-71 • Morehouse College (GA), B.A., 1968;
Emory Univ. Law School (GA), J.D., 1971 • Baptist • M.
Vivian Creighton Bishop, 1 ch ; 1 gr-ch **Cmte.** Agriculture •
Appropriations
CoS. Kenneth Cutts **LD.** Julian Johnson
  PS. Haig Hovsepian
Dist. Off. Albany 229.439.8067 • Columbus 706.320.9477 •
Macon 478.803.2631

R: 11 **T:** 16th 55%
Elected Year: 1992

Rep. Buddy Carter (KAR-tur) R-GA-01 p 202.225.5831

Rm. RHOB 2432 **Web.** **f** 202.226.2269
buddycarter.house.gov
Bio. 09/06/1957 • Pooler • Young Harris College, A.S., 1977;
Univ. of Georgia School of Pharmacy (GA), B.S., 1980 •
Methodist • M. Amy Coppage, 3 ch ; 6 gr-ch **Cmte.** Budget
• Energy & Commerce
CoS. Chris Crawford
  PS. Harley Adsit
Dist. Off. Brunswick 912.265.9010 • Savannah
912.352.0101

R: 167 **T:** 5th 59%
Elected Year: 2014

GEORGIA

♣ Rep. Andrew Clyde (klyd)   R-GA-09   p 202.225.9893

Rm. CHOB 445 **Web.** clyde.house.gov   f 202.226.1224
Bio. 11/22/1963 • Ontario • Bethel College (KS),
B.B.A., 1985; Univ. of Georgia Terry College of Business,
M.B.A., 1999 • Baptist • M. Jennifer Clyde, 4 ch   **Cmte.**
Appropriations
CoS. Nicholas Brown   **LD.** Dawn-Marie Sullivan
Sched. Lindsay Roberts   **PS.** Madeline Corso
Dist. Off. Gainesville 470.768.6520

R: 307   T: 2nd   72%
Elected Year: 2020

♣ Rep. Michael A. Collins Jr. ()   R-GA-10   p 202.225.4101

Rm. LHOB 1223 **Web.** overhauldc.com
Bio. 07/02/1967 • Jackson • Georgia State Univ., B.B.A.,
1990 • Methodist • M. Leigh Ann, 3 ch ; 3 gr-ch   **Cmte.**
Natural Resources • Science, Space & Technology •
Transportation & Infrastructure
CoS. Brandon C. Phillips   **LD.** Kevin Petroccione
Sched. LeeAnn Perritt   **PS.** DJ Griffin
Dist. Off. Monroe 770.207.1776

R: 372   T: 1st   65%
Elected Year: 2022

♣ Rep. Drew Ferguson IV (FUR-guh-suhn)   R-GA-03   p 202.225.5901

Rm. RHOB 2239 **Web.** ferguson.house.gov   f 202.225.2515
Bio. 11/15/1967 • W. Point • Univ. of Georgia, Bach. Deg.,
1988; Medical College of Georgia, D.M.D., 1992 • Catholic •
M. Elizabeth Ferguson, 4 ch   **Cmte.** Budget • Ways & Means
CoS. David Sours   **LD.** Allie White
Sched. Jenna Lawler   **PS.** Brian Piper
Dist. Off. Newnan 770.683.2033

R: 205   T: 4th   69%
Elected Year: 2016

♣ Rep. Marjorie Taylor Greene (green)   R-GA-14   p 202.225.5211

Rm. CHOB 403 **Web.** greene.house.gov
Bio. 05/27/1974 • Univ. of Georgia, B.B.A.,
1996 • Christian - Non-Denominational • Se. Perry Greene, 3
ch   **Cmte.** Homeland Security • Oversight & Accountability
CoS. Ed Buckham   **LD.** Taylor LaJoie
                        PS. Nick Dyer
Dist. Off. Dalton 706.226.5320

R: 318   T: 2nd   66%
Elected Year: 2020

➤ Rep. Hank C. Johnson Jr. (JAHN-suhn)   D-GA-04   p 202.225.1605

Rm. RHOB 2240 **Web.**   f 202.226.0691
hankjohnson.house.gov
Bio. 10/02/1954 • Washington • Judge; Attorney • Clark
College (GA), B.A., 1976; Texas Southern Univ., Thurgood
Marshall School of Law, J.D., 1979 • Buddhism • M. Mereda
Davis Johnson, 2 ch   **Cmte.** Judiciary • Transportation &
Infrastructure
CoS. Scott R. Goldstein   **LD.** Khaula Kaiser
Sched. Sarah Penkava   **PS.** Andy Phelan (CD)
Dist. Off. Decatur 770.987.2291

R: 74   T: 9th   79%
Elected Year: 2006

♣ Rep. Barry D. Loudermilk (LOU-dur-milk)   R-GA-11   p 202.225.2931

Rm. RHOB 2133 **Web.** loudermilk.house.gov f 202.225.2944
Bio. 12/22/1963 • Riverdale • Community College of the
Air Force (AL), A.A.S., 1987; Wayland Baptist Univ. (TX),
B.S., 1992 • Baptist • M. Desiree Loudermilk, 3 ch ; 2 gr-ch
Cmte. Administration • Financial Services
CoS. Robert Adkerson   **LD.** Ashleigh Padgett
Sched. Ashley Adkerson   **PS.** Brandon Cockerham
Dist. Off. Atlanta 770.429.1776 • Cartersville 770.429.1776
• Woodstock 770.429.1776

R: 176   T: 5th   63%
Elected Year: 2014

🐦 Rep. Lucy McBath (mik-BATH)　　　D-GA-07　　p 202.225.4501

Rm. RHOB 2246 **Web.** mcbath.house.gov
Bio. 06/01/1960 • Joliet • Virginia State Univ., B.A., 1982
• Christian Church • M. Curtis McBath, 2 ch (2 deceased)
Cmte. Education & Workforce • Judiciary
CoS. Rebecca Walldorff
Sched. Sunny Chen　　　　**PS.** Tanner Palin
Dist. Off. Duluth 470.773.6330

R: 263　**T:** 3rd　61%
Elected Year: 2018

🐦 Rep. Richard D. McCormick ()　　　R-GA-06　　p 202.225.4272

Rm. LHOB 1213 **Web.** mccormick.house.gov
Bio. 10/07/1968 • Las Vegas • Morehouse School of
Medicine, M.D.; National Univ. (CA), M.B.A.; Oregon State
Univ., B.S. • M. Debra R. Miller, 7 ch **Cmte.** Armed Services
• Foreign Affairs • Science, Space & Technology
CoS. Philip Singleton　　　　**LD.** Nathan Barker
Sched. Dani Madda　　　　**PS.** Julie Singleton
Dist. Off. Cumming 770.232.3005

R: 409　**T:** 1st　62%
Elected Year: 2022

🐦 Rep. Austin Scott (skaht)　　　R-GA-08　　p 202.225 6531

Rm. RHOB 2185 **Web.** austinscott.house.gov　f 202.225.3013
Bio. 12/10/1969 • Augusta • State Legislator • Univ. of
Georgia Terry College of Business, B.B.A., 1993 • Baptist •
M. Vivien Scott, 2 ch **Cmte.** Agriculture • Armed Services •
Permanent Select on Intelligence
CoS. Alice Johnson
Sched. Alexis Littrell　　　　**PS.** Alex Enlow
Dist. Off. Tifton 229.396.5175 • Warner Robins
478.971.1776

R: 113　**T:** 7th　69%
Elected Year: 2010

🐦 Rep. David A. Scott (skaht)　　　D-GA-13　　p 202.225.2939

Rm. CHOB 468 **Web.** davidscott.house.gov　f 202.225.4628
Bio. 06/27/1945 • Aynor • State Legislator • Florida
Agricultural and Mechanical Univ., B.A., 1967; Univ. of
Pennsylvania Wharton School of Business Aresty Institute,
M.B.A., 1969 • Baptist • M. Alfredia Aaron Scott, 2 ch ; 2 gr-
ch **Cmte.** Agriculture • Financial Services
CoS. Catherine Kuerbitz　　　　**LD.** Christofer Horta
Sched. Kathleen Burke
Dist. Off. Jonesboro 770.210.5073 • Smyrna 770.432.5405

R: 53　**T:** 11th　82%
Elected Year: 2002

🐦 Rep. Nikema Williams (WILL-yuhmz)　　　D-GA-05　　p 202.225.3801

Rm. LHOB 1406 **Web.**
nikemawilliams.house.gov
Bio. 07/30/1978 • Smiths Station • Talladega College,
B.S., 2000 • Methodist • M. Leslie Williams, 1 ch **Cmte.**
Financial Services
CoS. Melanee Farrah
Sched. Maya Young　　　　**PS.** Amber English Coleman
Dist. Off. Atlanta 404.659.0110

R: 348　**T:** 2nd　83%
Elected Year: 2020

HAWAII

HAWAII

🔾 **Governor Joshua (Josh) Booth Green** ()   p 808.586.0034

Executive Chambers, State Capitol
Honolulu, HI 96813
Website hawaii.gov
Fax 808.586.0006
Term Ends 2026
Lt. Governor
Sylvia J. Luke, **D**

C: Honolulu
P: 1,420,491 (41)
A: 6,422.81 mi^2 (47th)

U.S. Senators
Brian E. Schatz, **D**
Mazie K. Hirono, **D**
U.S. Representatives
01 / Ed E. Case, **D**
02 / Jill N. Tokuda, **D**

🔾 **Sen. Mazie K. Hirono** (hee-RO-no)   D-HI-Jr.   p 202.224.6361

Rm. HSOB 109 **Web.** hirono.senate.gov   **f** 202.224.2126
Bio. 11/03/1947 • Fukushima • Lawyer • Univ. of Hawaii,
Manoa, B.A., 1970; Georgetown Univ. Law Center (DC),
J.D., 1978 • Buddhism • M. Leighton Kim Oshima, 1 stepch
Cmte. Armed Services • Energy & Natural Resources •
Judiciary • Small Business & Entrepreneurship • Veterans'
Affairs
CoS. Coti-Lynne Haia   **LD.** Jed Daniel D'Ercole
Sched. Blaine Nolan   **PS.** Madeleine Russak
Dist. Off. Honolulu 808.522.8970

R: 48 **T:** 2nd 69%
Elected Year: 2012
Next Election: 2024

🔾 **Sen. Brian E. Schatz** (shahts)   D-HI-Sr.   p 202.224.3934

Rm. HSOB 722 **Web.** schatz.senate.gov   **f** 202.228.1153
Bio. 10/20/1972 • Ann Arbor • Pomona College, B.A.,
1994 • Jewish • M. Linda Kwok Kai Yun, 2 ch   **Cmte.**
Appropriations • Commerce, Science & Transportation •
Ethics • Foreign Relations • Indian Affairs
CoS. Eric Einhorn   **LD.** Arun Revana
Sched. Diane Miyasato-
Vizmanos
Dist. Off. Honolulu 808.523.2061

R: 44 **T:** 4th 69%
Elected Year: 2012
Next Election: 2028

🔾 **Rep. Ed E. Case** (kayss)   D-HI-01   p 202.225.2726

Rm. RHOB 2210 **Web.** case.house.gov
Bio. 09/27/1952 • Hilo • Williams College, B.A., 1975; Univ.
of California Hastings College of Law, J.D., 1981 • Protestant
- Unspecified Christian • M. Audrey Nakamura, 4 ch **Cmte.**
Appropriations • Natural Resources
CoS. Timothy M. Nelson
Sched. Kristen Kimble   **PS.** Nestor R. Garcia (CD)
Dist. Off. Honolulu 808.650.6688

R: 159 **T:** 3rd 71%
Elected Year: 2018

HAWAII

➷ Rep. Jill N. Tokuda ()   D-HI-02   p 202.225.4906

Rm. LHOB 1005 **Web.** tokuda.house.gov   f 202.225.4987
Bio. 03/03/1976 • Kaneohe • George Washington Univ.
(DC), B.A., 1997 • Unspecified/Other • M. Kyle Michibata, 2
ch **Cmte.** Armed Services
CoS. Wendy Clerinx   **LD.** Ben Chao
                         PS. Carly Sylva-Gabrielson

R: 431 **T:** 1st 59%
Elected Year: 2022

IDAHO

➹ Governor Brad Little (LIH-tull)   p 208.334.2100

State Capitol, PO Box 83720   **C:** Boise
Boise, ID 83720   **P:** 1,754,208 (40)
Website idaho.gov   **A:** 82,643.20 mi^2 (11th)
Fax 208.334.3454
Term Ends 2027
Lt. Governor
Scott Conrad Bedke, **R**

U.S. Senators
Mike D. Crapo, **R**
James E. Risch, **R**
U.S. Representatives
01 / Russ M. Fulcher, **R**
02 / Mike K. Simpson, **R**

➹ Sen. Mike D. Crapo (KRAY-poe)   R-ID-Sr.   p 202.224.6142

Rm. DSOB 239 **Web.** crapo.senate.gov   f 202.228.1375
Bio. 05/20/1951 • Idaho Falls • U.S. Representative;
Attorney • Brigham Young Univ. (UT), B.A., 1973; Harvard
Univ. Law School (MA), J.D., 1977 • Mormon • M. Susan
Diane Hasleton Crapo, 5 ch ; 8 gr-ch **Cmte.** Banking,
Housing & Urban Affairs • Budget • Finance • Joint
Economic • Joint Taxation
CoS. Susan H. Wheeler   **LD.** Molly Carpenter
Sched. Kathleen Amacio   **PS.** Melanie Lawhorn
Dist. Off. Boise 208.334.1776 • Coeur D'Alene

R: 10 **T:** 5th 61%   208.664.5490 • Idaho Falls 208.522.9779 • Lewiston
Elected Year: 1998   208.743.1492 • Pocatello 208.236.6775 • Twin Falls
Next Election: 2028   208.734.2515

➹ Sen. James E. Risch (rish)   R-ID-Jr.   p 202.224.2752

Rm. RSOB 483 **Web.** risch.senate.gov   f 202.224.2573
Bio. 05/03/1943 • Milwaukee • Governor of Idaho; Lt.
Governor of Idaho; State Legislator • Univ. of Idaho, B.S ,
1965; Univ. of Idaho, Law School, J.D., 1968 • Roman
Catholic • M. Vicki L. Choborda, 3 ch ; 7 gr-ch **Cmte.**
Energy & Natural Resources • Ethics • Foreign Relations •
Intelligence • Small Business & Entrepreneurship
CoS. Ryan White   **LD.** Charles Adams
Sched. Kaitlyn Mahar   **PS.** Marty Boughton
Dist. Off. Boise 208.342.7985 • Coeur d'Alene 208.667.6130

R: 30 **T:** 3rd 63%   • Idaho Falls 208.523.5541 • Lewiston 208.743.0792 •
Elected Year: 2008   Pocatello 208.236.6817 • Twin Falls 208.734.6780
Next Election: 2026

IDAHO

⚑ Rep. Russ M. Fulcher (FUHL-chur)   R-ID-01   p 202.225.6611

Rm. LHOB 1514 **Web.** fulcher.house.gov
Bio. 03/09/1962 • Meridian • Boise State Univ., B.B.A., 1984; Boise State Univ., M.B.A., 1988; Micron Univ., E.E., 1993 • Protestant - Unspecified Christian • M. Kara Fulcher, 3 ch
Cmte. Energy & Commerce • Natural Resources
CoS. Cliff Bayer   **LD.** Steve Ackerman
Sched. Michele Jarvis (CD)   **PS.** Daniel Tellez
Dist. Off. Coeur d'Alene 208.667.0127 • Lewiston 208.743.1388 • Meridian 208.888.3188

R: 248 **T:** 3rd 71%
Elected Year: 2018

⚑ Rep. Mike K. Simpson (SIMP-suhn)   R-ID-02   p 202.225.5531

Rm. RHOB 2084 **Web.** simpson.house.gov   f 202.225.8216
Bio. 09/08/1950 • Burley • Dentist; State Representative; Speaker of State House • Washington Univ. School of Dental Medicine (MO), D.D.S., 1977; Utah State Univ., B.S., 2002 • Mormon • M. Kathy Johnson Simpson **Cmte.** Appropriations
CoS. Lindsay J. Slater   **LD.** Sarah Cannon
                                PS. Nicole Wallace (CD)
Dist. Off. Boise 208.334.1953 • Idaho Falls 208.523.6701 • Twin Falls 208.734.7219

R: 36 **T:** 13th 64%
Elected Year: 1998

ILLINOIS

🏛 Governor J.B. Pritzker (PRIT-skur)   p 217.782.0244

207 State House
Springfield, IL 62706
Website illinois.gov
Fax 217.524.4049
Term Ends 2027
Lt. Governor
Juliana Stratton, **D**

C: Springfield
P: 12,741,080 (6)
A: 55,518.76 mi^2 (24th)

U.S. Senators
Dick Durbin, **D**
Tammy Duckworth, **D**
U.S. Representatives
01 / Jonathan Jackson, **D**
02 / Robin L. Kelly, **D**
03 / Delia C. Ramirez, **D**
04 / Jesús G. Garcia, **D**
05 / Mike Quigley, **D**
06 / Sean Casten, **D**
07 / Danny K. Davis, **D**
08 / Raja Krishnamoorthi, **D**
09 / Jan D. Schakowsky, **D**
10 / Brad S. Schneider, **D**
11 / Bill Foster, **D**
12 / Mike Bost, **R**
13 / Nicole Jai Budzinski, **D**
14 / Lauren Underwood, **D**
15 / Mary Miller, **R**
16 / Darin M. LaHood, **R**
17 / Eric Sorensen, **D**

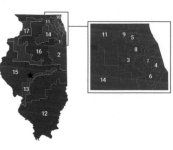

🏛 Sen. Tammy Duckworth (DUK-wurth)   D-IL-Jr.   p 202.224.2854

Rm. HSOB 524   f 202.228.0618
Bio. 03/12/1968 • Bangkok • Veterans Affairs • National Guard • Capella Univ., Ph.D.; Univ. of Hawaii, B.A., 1989; George Washington Univ. Elliot School of International Affairs (DC), M.A., 1992 • Unspecified/Other • M. Major Bryan Bowlsbey, 2 ch **Cmte.** Armed Services • Commerce, Science & Transportation • Small Business & Entrepreneurship
CoS. Kalina Bakalov-   **LD.** Benjamin Rhodeside
Thompson
Sched. Kelsey Becker   **PS.** Ben Garmisa
Dist. Off. Belleville 618.722.7070 • Carbondale 618.677.7000 • Chicago 312.886.3506 • Rock Island 309.606.7060 • Springfield 217.528.6124

R: 69 **T:** 2nd 57%
Elected Year: 2016
Next Election: 2028

⚘ Sen. Dick Durbin (DUR-bin)   D-IL-Sr.   p 202.224.2152

Rm. HSOB 711 **Web.** durbin.senate.gov   **f** 202.228.0400
Bio. 11/21/1944 • East St. Louis • U.S. Representative;
Attorney • Georgetown Univ. (DC), B.S., 1966; Georgetown
Univ. Law Center (DC), J.D., 1969 • Roman Catholic • M.
Loretta Schaefer Durbin, 3 ch (1 deceased); 3 gr-ch **Cmte.**
Agriculture, Nutrition & Forestry • Appropriations • Judiciary
CoS. Patrick J. Souders   **LD.** James Floyd
Sched. Claire A. Reuschel   **PS.** Emily Hampsten
Dist. Off. Carbondale 618.351.1122 • Chicago
312.353.4952 • Rock Island 309.786.5173 • Springfield
217.492.4062

R: 6   **T:** 5th 55%
Elected Year: 1996
Next Election: 2026

⚘ Rep. Mike Bost (bahst)   R-IL-12   p 202.225.5661

Rm. CHOB 352 **Web.** bost.house.gov   **f** 202.225.0285
Bio. 12/30/1960 • Murphysboro • Southern Baptist • M.
Tracy Stanton Bost, 3 ch ; 11 gr-ch **Cmte.** Transportation &
Infrastructure • Veterans' Affairs
CoS. Matt McCullough   **LD.** Noah Barger
           PS. Alexandra Naughton
Dist. Off. Carbondale 618.457.5787 • Effingham
217.240.3170 • O'Fallon 618.622.0766

R: 164   **T:** 5th 75%
Elected Year: 2014

⚘ Rep. Nicole Jai Budzinski ()   D-IL-13   p 202.225.2371

Rm. LHOB 1009 **Web.** nikkiforcongress.com
Bio. 03/11/1977 • Peoria • Univ. of Illinois at Urbana-
Champaign, B.A., 1999 • S. **Cmte.** Veterans' Affairs
CoS. Anne Sokolov   **LD.** John Lee
Sched. Michelle Young   **PS.** Philip Shelly
Dist. Off. Springfield

R: 366   **T:** 1st 57%
Elected Year: 2022

⚘ Rep. Sean Casten (KASS-tuhn)   D-IL-06   p 202.225.4561

Rm. RHOB 2440 **Web.** casten.house.gov
Bio. 11/23/1971 • Dublin • Middlebury College (VT), B.A.,
1993; Dartmouth College, M.S., 1998 • Unspecified/Other
• M. Kara Casten, 2 ch (1 deceased) **Cmte.** Financial
Services • Science, Space & Technology
CoS. Chloe Hunt   **LD.** Aaron Groce
Sched. Emma Arnesen   **PS.** Jacob Vurpillat
Dist. Off. Glen Ellyn 630.520.9450

R: 239   **T:** 3rd 54%
Elected Year: 2018

⚘ Rep. Danny K. Davis (DAY-vuhs)   D-IL-07   p 202.225.5006

Rm. RHOB 2159 **Web.** davis.house.gov   **f** 202.225.5641
Bio. 09/06/1941 • Parkdale • Cook County Commissioner;
Alderman, Chicago City Council • Arkansas Agricultural
and Mechanical College, B.A., 1961; Chicago State Univ. (IL),
M.A., 1968; Union Institute and Univ., Ph.D., 1977 • Baptist •
M. Vera G. Davis, 2 ch (1 deceased); 4 gr-ch (1 deceased)
Cmte. Ways & Means
CoS. Tumia Romero   **LD.** Jill Hunter-Williams
Sched. Joseph Peters
Dist. Off. Chicago 773.533.7520

R: 24   **T:** 14th 100%
Elected Year: 1996

⚘ Rep. Bill Foster (FAHSS-tur)   D-IL-11   p 202.225.3515

Rm. RHOB 2366 **Web.** foster.house.gov   **f** 202.225.9420
Bio. 10/07/1955 • Madison • Physicist • Univ. of Wisconsin,
B.A., 1976; Harvard Univ., Ph.D., 1983 • Unspecified/Other •
M. Aesook Byon, 2 ch **Cmte.** Financial Services
CoS. Samantha Warren   **LD.** Kim Soffen
Sched. Jenae Jackson
Dist. Off. Aurora 630.585.7672

R: 97   **T:** 6th 57%
Elected Year: 2012

ILLINOIS

🔊 Rep. Jesús G. Garcia (gar-SEE-uh)　　D-IL-04　　p 202.225.8203
Rm. LHOB 1519　**Web.** chuygarcia.house.gov
Bio. 04/12/1956 • Durango • Univ. of Illinois, Chicago,
B.A., 1999; Univ. of Illinois, Chicago, M.A., 2002 • Catholic
• M. Evelyn Garcia, 3 ch　**Cmte.** Natural Resources •
Transportation & Infrastructure
CoS. Patty Garcia (CD)
Sched. Julissa Santoy　　　　**PS.** Fabiola Rodriguez-
　　　　　　　　　　　　　　　　Ciampoli
Dist. Off. Chicago 773.475.0833

R: 249　**T:** 3rd 68%
Elected Year: 2018

🔊 Rep. Jonathan Jackson ()　　　　D-IL-01　　p 202.225.4372
Rm. LHOB 1641　**Web.** thejacksonfile.com
Bio. 01/07/1966 • Chicago • North Carolina Agricultural
and Technical State Univ., Bach. Deg., 1988; Northwestern
Univ. Kellogg School Management (IL), M.B.A., 1991 • M.
Marilyn Ann Richards, 3 ch　**Cmte.** Foreign Affairs
CoS. Edward Hamb
　　　　　　　　　　　　　PS. Alia Ammar
Dist. Off. Chicago 773.779.2400

R: 394　**T:** 1st 67%
Elected Year: 2022

🔊 Rep. Robin L. Kelly (KEH-lee)　　D-IL-02　　p 202.225.0773
Rm. RHOB 2329　**Web.** robinkelly.house.gov　**f** 202.225.4583
Bio. 04/30/1956 • New York • Bradley Univ., B.A., 1977;
Bradley Univ., M.A., 1982; Northern Illinois Univ., Ph.D., 2004
• Christian - Non-Denominational • M. Nathaniel Horn, 2 ch
Cmte. Energy & Commerce
CoS. Matt McMurray　　　　**LD.** Earl Flood
Sched. Alan Banks (CD)　　　**PS.** Eliana Locke
Dist. Off. Chicago 773.321.2001 • Matteson 708.679.0078

R: 154　**T:** 6th 67%
Elected Year: 2013

🔊 Rep. Raja Krishnamoorthi (krish-nuh-MOR-thee) D-IL-08　p 202.225.3711
Rm. RHOB 2367　　　　　　　　　　　**f** 202.225.7830
Bio. 07/19/1973 • New Delhi • Princeton Univ. (NJ),
B.A., 1995; Harvard Univ., J.D., 2000 • Hinduism • M. Priya
Krishnamoorthi, 2 ch　**Cmte.** Oversight & Accountability •
Permanent Select on Intelligence • Select China Committee
CoS. Brian Kaissi
Sched. Nicole Malec　　　　**PS.** Wilson Baldwin
Dist. Off. Schaumburg 847.413.1959

R: 215　**T:** 4th 57%
Elected Year: 2016

🔊 Rep. Darin M. LaHood (luh-"HOOD")　　R-IL-16　　p 202.225.6201
Rm. LHOB 1424　**Web.** lahood.house.gov　**f** 202.225.9249
Bio. 07/05/1968 • Peoria • Loras College, B.A., 1990; John
Marshall Law School, J.D., 1997 • Catholic • M. Kristen
LaHood, 3 ch　**Cmte.** Permanent Select on Intelligence •
Select China Committee • Ways & Means
CoS. Mary Ellen Richardson　**LD.** Greg Warren
　　　　　　　　　　　　　PS. John Rauber
Dist. Off. Bloomington 309.205.9556 • Peoria 309.671.7027

R: 188　**T:** 5th 66%
Elected Year: 2015

🔊 Rep. Mary Miller (MIH-lur)　　　R-IL-15　　p 202.225.5271
Rm. LHOB 1740　**Web.** marymiller.house.gov　**f** 202.225.5880
Bio. 08/27/1959 • Naperville • Univ. of Eastern Illinois, B.S.,
1981 • Christian - Non-Denominational • M. Chris Miller, 7
ch; 16 gr-ch　**Cmte.** Agriculture • Education & Workforce
CoS. Benjamin E. DeMarzo　**LD.** Christina Rabuse
Sched. William Wadsworth　**PS.** Erin O'Malley
Dist. Off. Danville 217.703.6100 • Effingham 217.240.3155
•Harrisburg

R: 331　**T:** 2nd 71%
Elected Year: 2020

⚘ Rep. Mike Quigley (KWIG-lee)　　　　D-IL-05　　p 202.225.4061

Rm. RHOB 2083　**Web.** quigley.house.gov
Bio. 10/17/1958 • Indianapolis • Member, Cook County
Board of Commissioners • Roosevelt Univ. (IL), B.A., 1981;
Univ. of Chicago (IL), M.P.P., 1985; Loyola Univ. Law School
(IL), J.D., 1989 • Christian - Non-Denominational • M.
Barbara Quigley, 2 ch　**Cmte.** Appropriations
CoS. Allison M. Jarus　　　　**LD.** Charlie Chamness
Sched. Isabella Lee (CD)　　**PS.** Victoria Oms
Dist. Off. Chicago 773.267.5926

R: 93　**T:** 8th　70%
Elected Year: 2009

⚘ Rep. Delia C. Ramirez ()　　　　　D-IL-03　　p 202.225.5701

Rm. LHOB 1523　**Web.** deliaramirez.com
Bio. 06/02/1983 • Chicago • Northeastern Illinois Univ.,
B.A. • Methodist • M. Boris Hernandez　**Cmte.** Homeland
Security • Veterans' Affairs
CoS. Fae Rabin
Dist. Off. Chicago

R: 422　**T:** 1st　69%
Elected Year: 2022

⚘ Rep. Jan D. Schakowsky (shuh-KOU-skee)　　D-IL-09　　p 202.225.2111

Rm. RHOB 2408　**Web.**　　　　　　　**f** 202.226.6890
schakowsky.house.gov
Bio. 05/26/1944 • Chicago • Nonprofit Coordinator; State
Legislator • Univ. of Illinois, B.A., 1965 • Jewish • M.
Robert Creamer, 3 ch ; 6 gr-ch　**Cmte.** Budget • Energy &
Commerce
CoS. Syd Terry　　　　　　**LD.** Kate Durkin
Sched. Kim Muzeroll　　　**PS.** Alex Moore
Dist. Off. Chicago 773.506.7100 • Glenview 847.328.3409

R: 35　**T:** 13th　72%
Elected Year: 1998

⚘ Rep. Brad S. Schneider (SHNY-dur)　　　D-IL-10　　p 202.225.4835

Rm. CHOB 300　**Web.** schneider.house.gov　**f** 202.225.0837
Bio. 08/20/1961 • Denver • Northwestern Univ., B.S., 1983;
Kellogg Graduate School of Management, Northwestern
Univ. (IL), M.B.A., 1988 • Jewish • M. Julie Dann, 2 ch
Cmte. Ways & Means
CoS. Casey O'Shea　　　　**LD.** Tommy Brown
Sched. Daniela Altamirano　**PS.** Matt Fried
　Crosby
Dist. Off. Lincolnshire 847.383.4870

R: 192　**T:** 4th　63%
Elected Year: 2016

⚘ Rep. Eric Sorensen ()　　　　　　D-IL-17　　p 202.225.5905

Rm. LHOB 1205　**Web.** ericforillinois.com
Bio. Rockford • Northern Illinois Univ., B.S., 1999 • LP.
Shawn Sorensen　**Cmte.** Science, Space & Technology
CoS. Joseph Goldberg　　　**LD.** Meryl Harold
Sched. Maggie Pillis　　　**PS.** Thomas Falcigno
Dist. Off. Rock Island 309.786.3406

R: 427　**T:** 1st　52%
Elected Year: 2022

⚘ Rep. Lauren Underwood (UN-dur-"wood")　　D-IL-14　　p 202.225.2976

Rm. LHOB 1410　**Web.** underwood.house.gov
Bio. 10/04/1986 • Mayfield Heights • Univ. of Michigan,
B.S., 2008; Johns Hopkins Univ., M.S.N., 2009; Johns
Hopkins Univ., M.PH, 2009 • Christian Church • S.　**Cmte.**
Appropriations
CoS. Caroline Paris-Behr
Sched. Kleya Dhenin　　**PS.** Justin Kidd
Dist. Off. West Chicago 630.549.2190

R: 290　**T:** 3rd　54%
Elected Year: 2018

INDIANA

🏛 **Governor Eric Holcomb** (HOL-kum) p 317.232.4567

State House, Room 206
Indianapolis, IN 46204
Website in.gov
Fax 317.232.3443
Term Ends 2025
Lt. Governor
Suzanne Crouch, **R**

C: Indianapolis
P: 6,691,878 (17)
A: 35,826.02 mi² (38th)

U.S. Senators
Todd C. Young, **R**
Mike Braun, **R**
U.S. Representatives
01 / Frank J. Mrvan, **D**
02 / Rudy Yakym, **R**
03 / Jim E. Banks, **R**
04 / Jim Baird, **R**
05 / Victoria Spartz, **R**
06 / Greg Pence, **R**
07 / Andre D. Carson, **D**
08 / Larry D. Bucshon, **R**
09 / Erin Houchin, **R**

🏛 **Sen. Mike Braun** ("brown") R-IN-Jr. p 202.224.4814

Rm. RSOB 404 **Web.** braun.senate.gov
Bio. 03/24/1954 • Jasper • Wabash College (IN), B.A., 1976;
Harvard Univ., M.B.A., 1978 • Catholic • M. Braun Braun,
4 ch **Cmte.** Aging • Agriculture, Nutrition & Forestry •
Budget • Health, Education, Labor & Pensions
CoS. Joshua Kelley **LD.** Katie Bailey
Sched. Jessica Wedgewood **PS.** Zach Riddle
Dist. Off. Fort Wayne 260.427.2164 • Hammond
219.937.9650 • Indianapolis 317.822.8240

R: 80 **T:** 1st 51%
Elected Year: 2018
Next Election: 2024

🏛 **Sen. Todd C. Young** (yung) R-IN-Sr. p 202.224.5623

Rm. DSOB 185 **Web.** young.senate.gov f 202.224.1845
Bio. 08/24/1972 • Lancaster • Attorney • Marine Corps,
1990-2000 • U.S. Naval Academy (MD), B.S., 1995; Univ.
of Chicago's Graduate School of Business, M.B.A., 2000;
Univ. of London's Institute of U.S. Studies, M.A., 2001;
Indiana Univ. Law School, J.D., 2006 • Christian Church
• M. Jennifer B. Young, 4 ch **Cmte.** Commerce, Science
& Transportation • Finance • Foreign Relations • Small
Business & Entrepreneurship
CoS. John Connell **LD.** Lauren O'Brien
Sched. Natalie Goodwin **PS.** Matt Lahr
(CD)
Dist. Off. Evansville 812.288.3999 • Fort Wayne
260.422.7397 • Indianapolis 317.226.6700 • New Albany
812.542.4820

R: 68 **T:** 2nd 59%
Elected Year: 2016
Next Election: 2028

🏛 **Rep. Jim Baird** (baird) R-IN-04 p 202.225.5037

Rm. RHOB 2303 **Web.** baird.house.gov f 202.226.0544
Bio. 06/04/1945 • Covington • Purdue Univ. (IN), B.S., 1967;
Purdue Univ. (IN), M.S., 1969; Univ. of Kentucky, Ph.D., 1975
• Methodist • M. Denise Baird, 3 ch **Cmte.** Agriculture •
Foreign Affairs • Science, Space & Technology
CoS. Phillip Pinegar **LD.** Robert Rische
Sched. Alyssa Jennings **PS.** Katie Milner
Dist. Off. Danville 317.563.5567

R: 237 **T:** 3rd 68%
Elected Year: 2018

🏛 Rep. Jim E. Banks (banks)   R-IN-03   p 202.225.4436

Rm. RHOB 2418 **Web.** banks.house.gov
Bio. 07/16/1979 • Columbia City • Indiana Univ.,
Bloomington, Bach. Deg., 2004; Grace College, M.B.A.,
2013 • Evangelical • M. Amanda Banks, 3 ch **Cmte.**
Armed Services • Education & Workforce • Select China
Committee
CoS. David Keller
                  PS. Tim Goeglein
Dist. Off. Fort Wayne 260.702.4750

R: 196   **T:** 4th   65%
Elected Year: 2016

🏛 Rep. Larry D. Bucshon (boo-SHAHN)   R-IN-08   p 202.225.4636

Rm. RHOB 2313 **Web.** bucshon.house.gov   **f** 202.225.3284
Bio. 05/31/1962 • Taylorsville • Heart Surgeon • Navy
Reserve, 1989-98 • Univ. of Illinois - Urbana, B.S., 1984; Univ.
of Illinois Medical School - Chicago, M.D., 1988 • Lutheran •
M. Kathryn Bucshon, 4 ch **Cmte.** Energy & Commerce
CoS. Kyle Jackson
                  PS. Charlotte Taylor
Dist. Off. Evansville 812.465.6484 • Terre Haute
812.232.0523

R: 99   **T:** 7th   66%
Elected Year: 2010

🕊 Rep. Andre D. Carson (KAR-suhn)   D-IN-07   p 202.225.4011

Rm. RHOB 2135 **Web.** carson.house.gov   **f** 202.225.5633
Bio. 10/16/1974 • Indianapolis • Marketing Executive •
Concordia Univ. of Wisconsin, B.S., 2003; Indiana Wesleyan
Univ., M.A., 2005 • Islam (Muslim) • M. Mariama Carson, 1
ch **Cmte.** Permanent Select on Intelligence • Select China
Committee • Transportation & Infrastructure
CoS. Kim Rudolph   **LD.** Andrea Martin
Sched. Holly Woytcke   **PS.** Caroline Ellert
Dist. Off. Indianapolis 317.283.6516

R: 82   **T:** 9th   67%
Elected Year: 2008

🏛 Rep. Erin Houchin ()   R-IN-09   p 202.225.5315

Rm. LHOB 1632 **Web.** erinhouchin.com
Bio. 09/24/1976 • Salem • Indiana Univ., Bloomington,
B.A.; George Washington Univ. (DC), Mast. Deg. • Christian
Church • M. Dustin Houchin, 3 ch **Cmte.** Education &
Workforce • Financial Services • Rules
CoS. Kyle Kizzier   **LD.** Jonathan Van Buren
                  PS. Heidi Reutebuch
Dist. Off. Jeffersonville 812.288.3999

R: 389   **T:** 1st   64%
Elected Year: 2022

🕊 Rep. Frank J. Mrvan (MER-van)   D-IN-01   p 202.225.2461

Rm. LHOB 1607 **Web.** mrvan.house.gov   **f** 202.225.2493
Bio. 04/16/1969 • Hammond • Ball State Univ., B.A., 1992
• M. Jane Mrvan, 2 ch **Cmte.** Education & Workforce •
Veterans' Affairs
CoS. Mark Lopez (CD)   **LD.** Jamie Spitz
Sched. Zachary Gossett   **PS.** Kevin Spicer
Dist. Off. Merrillville 219.795.1844

R: 335   **T:** 2nd   53%
Elected Year: 2020

🏛 Rep. Greg Pence (pence)   R-IN-06   p 202.225.3021

Rm. CHOB 404 **Web.** pence.house.gov
Bio. 11/14/1956 • Columbus • Loyola Univ. Chicago (IL),
Bach. Deg., 1981; Loyola Univ. Chicago (IL), M.B.A., 1986 •
Catholic • M. Denice Pence, 4 ch ; 5 gr-ch **Cmte.** Energy &
Commerce
CoS. Kyle Robertson   **LD.** Andrew Furman
                  PS. Hannah Osantowske
Dist. Off. Columbus 812.799.5230 • Greenfield
812.799.5233 • Richmond 765.660.1083

R: 270   **T:** 3rd   68%
Elected Year: 2018

INDIANA

Rep. Victoria Spartz (spartss)   R-IN-05   p 202.225.2276

Rm. LHOB 1609 **Web.** spartz.house.gov
Bio. 10/06/1978 • Nosivka • Kyiv National Univ. of
Economics (Ukraine), B.S., 2000; Kyiv National Univ. of
Economics (Ukraine), M.B.A., 2000; Indiana Univ. Kelley
School of Business, Mast. Deg., 2006 • Eastern Orthodox •
M. Jason Spartz, 2 ch **Cmte.** Judiciary
CoS. Liz Dessauer   **LD.** Sean Lerner
Dist. Off. Anderson 765.639.0671 • Carmel 317.848.0201

R: 343   **T:** 2nd   61%
Elected Year: 2020

Rep. Rudy Yakym III ()   R-IN-02   p 202.225.3915

Web. yakym.house.gov
Bio. 02/24/1984 • • Indiana Univ., South Bend, A.D.,
2009; Indiana Univ., South Bend - Judd Leighton School of
Business and Economics, B.S., 2011; Univ. of Notre Dame
(IN), M.B.A., 2019 • M. Sallyann Yakym, 3 ch **Cmte.** Budget
• Transportation & Infrastructure
CoS. Ben Falkowski (CD)

                       PS. Andrew T. Brennan (CD)
Dist. Off. Mishawaka 574.204.2645 • Rochester
574.223.4373

R: 360   **T:** 2nd   65%
Elected Year: 2022

IOWA

Governor Kim Reynolds (REH-nuhldz)   p 515.281.5211

State Capitol
1007 E. Grand Ave.
Des Moines, IA 50319
Website iowa.gov
Fax 515.725.3527
Term Ends 2027
Lt. Governor
Adam Gregg, **R**

C: Des Moines
P: 3,156,145 (32)
A: 55,856.99 mi^2 (23rd)

U.S. Senators
Chuck Grassley, **R**
Joni Ernst, **R**
U.S. Representatives
01 / Mariannette Miller-Meeks, **R**
02 / Ashley Hinson, **R**
03 / Zach Nunn, **R**
04 / Randy Feenstra, **R**

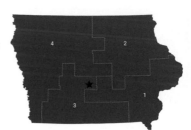

Sen. Joni Ernst (urnst)   R-IA-Jr.   p 202.224.3254

Rm. HSOB 730 **Web.** ernst.senate.gov   **f** 202.224.9369
Bio. 07/01/1970 • Red Oak • Iowa State Univ. (IA), B.S.,
1992; Columbus College (IA), M.P.A., 1995 • Lutheran
• D. Gail Ernst, 1 ch ; 2 stepch **Cmte.** Agriculture,
Nutrition & Forestry • Armed Services • Small Business &
Entrepreneurship
CoS. Lisa Goeas   **LD.** Kristina M. Sesek
Sched. Hannah Thomas   **PS.** Paige Lindgren
Dist. Off. Cedar Rapids 319.365.4504 • Council Bluffs
712.352.1167 • Davenport 563.322.0677 • Des Moines
515.284.4574 • Sioux City 712.252.1550

R: 65   **T:** 2nd   52%
Elected Year: 2014
Next Election: 2026

♠ Sen. Chuck Grassley (GRASS-lee) R-IA-Sr. p 202.224.3744

Rm. HSOB 135 **Web.** grassley.senate.gov **f** 202.224.6020
Bio. 09/17/1933 • New Hartford • U.S. Representative;
Farmer • Univ. of Northern Iowa, B.A., 1955; Univ. of
Northern Iowa, M.A., 1956 • Baptist • M. Barbara Ann
Speicher Grassley, 5 ch **Cmte.** Agriculture, Nutrition &
Forestry • Budget • Finance • Joint Economic • Joint
Taxation • Judiciary
CoS. Aaron Cummings   **LD.** James Rice
Sched. Jennifer Heins   **PS.** Taylor Foy
Dist. Off. Cedar Rapids 319.363.6832 • Council Bluffs
712.322.7103 • Davenport 563.322.4331 • Des Moines
515.288.1145 • Sioux City 712.233.1860 • Waterloo
319.232.6657

R: 1 **T:** 8th 56%
Elected Year: 1980
Next Election: 2028

♠ Rep. Randy Feenstra (FEEN-strah) R-IA-04 p 202.225.4426

Rm. LHOB 1440 **Web.** feenstra.house.gov **f** 202.225.3193
Bio. 01/14/1969 • Hull • Dordt College, B.A., 1991; Iowa
State Univ. (IA), M.P.A., 2008 • Protestant - Unspecified
Christian • M. Lynette Feenstra, 4 ch **Cmte.** Agriculture •
Ways & Means
CoS. Matthew Leopold   **LD.** Tim Medeiros
    PS. Billy Fuerst
Dist. Off. Council Bluffs 712.256.5653 • Fort Dodge
515.302.7060 • Sioux City 712.224.4692

R: 310 **T:** 2nd 67%
Elected Year: 2020

♠ Rep. Ashley Hinson (HIN-suhn) R-IA-02 p 202.225.2911

Rm. LHOB 1717 **Web.** hinson.house.gov
Bio. 06/27/1983 • Iowa • Univ. of Southern California,
B.A., 2004 • Christian Church • M. Matthew Arenholz, 2 ch
Cmte. Appropriations • Select China Committee
    LD. Brittany Madni
Sched. Jude Al-Hmoud   **PS.** Sophie Seid
Dist. Off. Cedar Rapids 319.364.2288 • Dubuque
563.557.7789 • Waterloo 319.266.6925

R: 320 **T:** 2nd 54%
Elected Year: 2020

♠ Rep. Mariannette Miller-Meeks (MIH-lur R-IA-01 p 202.225.6576
meeks)

Rm. LHOB 1034 **Web.**
millermeeks.house.gov
Bio. 09/06/1955 • Herlong • Texas Christian Univ., B.S.N.,
1976; Univ. of Southern California, M.S., 1980; Univ. of Texas
Health Science Center, San Antonio, M.D., 1986 • Roman
Catholic • M. Curt Meeks, 2 ch **Cmte.** Energy & Commerce
• Veterans' Affairs
CoS. Tyler Menzler   **LD.** Kyle Jacobs
Sched. Tara Pinette   **PS.** Mary Collins Atkinson

R: 332 **T:** 2nd 53%
Elected Year: 2020

♠ Rep. Zach Nunn () R-IA-03 p 202.225.5476

Rm. LHOB 1232 **Web.** zachnunn.com
Bio. 05/04/1979 • Altoona • Air Command and Staff
College (AL), Mast. Deg.; Drake Univ. (IA), B.A., 2002;
Cambridge Univ. (England), M.S., 2007 • Roman Catholic •
M. Kelly Nunn, 3 ch **Cmte.** Financial Services
CoS. Brad Stewart   **LD.** Ashley Gutwein
Sched. Emily Tuttle-Millard   **PS.** Lydia Hallock
Dist. Off. Creston • Des Moines 515.400.8180 • Ottumwa

R: 419 **T:** 1st 50%
Elected Year: 2022

KANSAS

Governor Laura Kelly (KEH-lee)   p 785.296.3232

Kansas State Capitol
300 S.W. Tenth Ave., Suite 241-S
Topeka, KS 66612
Website kansas.gov
Fax 785.296.7973
Term Ends 2027
Lt. Governor
David Toland, **D**

C: Topeka
P: 2,911,505 (36)
A: 81,758.64 mi^2 (13th)

U.S. Senators
Jerry Moran, **R**
Roger W. Marshall, **R**
U.S. Representatives
01 / Tracey R. Mann, **R**
02 / Jake A. LaTurner, **R**
03 / Sharice Davids, **D**
04 / Ron Estes, **R**

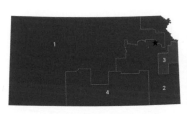

Sen. Roger W. Marshall (MAR-shull)   R-KS-Jr.   p 202.224.4774

Rm. RSOB 479A   **f** 202.224.3514
Bio. 08/09/1960 • El Dorado • Butler Community College,
A.S., 1980; Kansas State Univ., B.S., 1982; Univ. of Kansas,
M.D., 1987 • Christian Church • M. Laina Marshall, 4 ch ; 2
gr-ch   **Cmte.** Agriculture, Nutrition & Forestry • Budget •
Health, Education, Labor & Pensions • Homeland Security &
Government Affairs
CoS. Brent Robertson   **LD.** Pace McMullan
                     PS. William Bensur
Dist. Off. Garden City 620.765.7800 • Overland Park
913.879.7070 • Salina 785.829.9000 • Topeka 785.414.7501
• Wichita 316.803.6120

R: 86   **T:** 1st 53%
Elected Year: 2020
Next Election: 2026

Sen. Jerry Moran (moor-AHN)   R-KS-Sr.   p 202.224.6521

Rm. DSOB 521   **Web.** moran.senate.gov   **f** 202.228.6966
Bio. 05/29/1954 • Great Bend • State Senator; Attorney
• Univ. of Kansas, B.S., 1976; Univ. of Kansas, J.D., 1981
• Methodist • M. Robba Addison Moran, 2 ch   **Cmte.**
Appropriations • Commerce, Science & Transportation •
Intelligence • Veterans' Affairs
CoS. James Kelly (CD)   **LD.** Nathan Heiman
Sched. Emily Whitfield   **PS.** Tom Brandt
Dist. Off. Garden City 620.260.3025 • Hays 785.628.6401 •
Manhattan 785.539.8973 • Olathe 913.393.0711 • Pittsburg
620.232.2286 • Wichita 316.269.9257

R: 36   **T:** 3rd 60%
Elected Year: 2010
Next Election: 2028

Rep. Sharice Davids (DAY-vidz)   D-KS-03   p 202.225.2865

Rm. RHOB 2435   **Web.** davids.house.gov   **f** 202.225.2807
Bio. 05/22/1980 • Frankfurt • Johnson County Community
College (KS), A.A., 2003; Univ. of Missouri - Kansas City,
B.A., 2007; Cornell Univ. Law School (NY), J.D., 2010 •
Unspecified/Other • S.   **Cmte.** Agriculture • Small Business
• Transportation & Infrastructure
CoS. Allison Teixeira Sulier   **LD.** Brandon Naylor
Sched. Zac Donley   **PS.** Ellie Turner
Dist. Off. Overland Park 913.621.0832

R: 244   **T:** 3rd 55%
Elected Year: 2018

🏛 Rep. Ron Estes (ESS-tess) R-KS-04 p 202.225.6216

Rm. RHOB 2234 **Web.** estes.house.gov **f** 202.225.3489
Bio. 07/19/1956 • Topeka • Tennessee Technological Univ.,
B.S.; Tennessee Technological Univ., M.B.A. • Lutheran • M.
Susan Oliver, 3 ch **Cmte.** Budget • Education & Workforce
• Ways & Means
CoS. Joshua Bell **LD.** Nicholas O'Boyle
Sched. Brandon T. Smith **PS.** Kelsey Holt
Dist. Off. Wichita 316.262.8992

R: 223 **T:** 4th 63%
Elected Year: 2017

🏛 Rep. Jake A. LaTurner (lah-TUR-nur) R-KS-02 p 202.225.6601

Rm. RHOB 2441 **Web.** laturner.house.gov
Bio. 02/17/1988 • Galena • Pittsburg State Univ., B.A.,
2011 • Catholic • M. Suzanne LaTurner, 4 ch **Cmte.**
Appropriations • Oversight & Accountability
CoS. Braden Dreiling **LD.** Jake Middlebrooks
Sched. Marisa Burleson **PS.** Michael Howard
Dist. Off. Pittsburg 620.308.7450 • Topeka 785.205.5253

R: 324 **T:** 2nd 58%
Elected Year: 2020

🏛 Rep. Tracey R. Mann (man) R-KS-01 p 202.225.2715

Rm. CHOB 344 **Web.** mann.house.gov **f** 202.225.5124
Bio. 10/17/1976 • Quinter • Kansas State Univ., B.S., 2000 •
Evangelical • M. Audrey Haynes, 4 ch **Cmte.** Agriculture •
Small Business • Transportation & Infrastructure
CoS. Brandon Harder **LD.** Riley Pagett
Sched. Emily Woods **PS.** Brendan Welsh
Dist. Off. Dodge City 620.682.7340 • Manhattan
785.370.7277

R: 328 **T:** 2nd 68%
Elected Year: 2020

KENTUCKY

🎗 Governor Andy Beshear (Beh-SHEER) p 502.564.2611

State Capitol **C:** Frankfort
700 Capitol Ave., Suite 100 **P:** 4,468,402 (26)
Frankfort, KY 40601 **A:** 39,486.27 mi² (37th)
Website kentucky.gov
Fax 502.564.0437
Term Ends 2023
Lt. Governor
Jacqueline Coleman, **D**

U.S. Senators
Mitch McConnell, **R**
Rand Paul, **R**
U.S. Representatives
01 / James R. Comer, **R**
02 / Brett Guthrie, **R**
03 / Morgan McGarvey, **D**
04 / Thomas H. Massie, **R**
05 / Hal D. Rogers, **R**
06 / Andy Barr, **R**

KENTUCKY

✿ Sen. Mitch McConnell (mih-KAH-null) R-KY-Sr. p 202.224.2541

Rm. RSOB 317 **Web.** mcconnell.senate.gov **f** 202.224.2499
Bio. 02/20/1942 • Tuscumbia • Deputy Assistant Attorney
General (President Ford) • Univ. of Louisville (KY), B.A.,
1964; Univ. of Kentucky Law School, J.D., 1967 • Baptist
• M. Elaine Chao, 3 ch from previous marriage **Cmte.**
Agriculture, Nutrition & Forestry • Appropriations • Rules &
Administration
CoS. Terry Carmack   **LD.** Tiffany Ge
                          PS. Robert Steurer
Dist. Off. Bowling Green 270.781.1673 • Fort Wright
859.578.0188 • Lexington 859.224.8286 • London
606.864.2026 • Louisville 502.582.6304 • Paducah
270.442.4554

R: 2 **T:** 7th 58%
Elected Year: 1984
Next Election: 2026

✿ Sen. Rand Paul (pall) R-KY-Jr. p 202.224.4343

Rm. RSOB 167 **Web.** paul.senate.gov **f** 202.228.6917
Bio. 01/07/1963 • Pittsburgh • Duke Univ. (NC), M.D.,
1988 • Presbyterian • M. Kelley Paul, 3 ch **Cmte.** Foreign
Relations • Health, Education, Labor & Pensions •
Homeland Security & Government Affairs • Small Business
& Entrepreneurship
CoS. William Henderson   **LD.** John Maniscalco
Sched. John Sansone   **PS.** Madeline Meeker
Dist. Off. Bowling Green 270.782.8303

R: 41 **T:** 3rd 62%
Elected Year: 2010
Next Election: 2028

✿ Rep. Andy Barr IV (bar) R-KY-06 p 202.225.4706

Rm. RHOB 2430 **Web.** barr.house.gov **f** 202.225.2122
Bio. 07/24/1973 • Lexington • Univ. of Virginia, B.A., 1996;
Univ. of Kentucky College of Law, J.D., 2001 • Episcopalian
• W. Eleanor Carol Leavell, 2 ch **Cmte.** Financial Services
• Foreign Affairs • Select China Committee
CoS. Mary Rosado   **LD.** Hunt VanderToll
Sched. Meghan Selip   **PS.** Alexander Bellizzi
Dist. Off. Lexington 859.219.1366

R: 124 **T:** 6th 63%
Elected Year: 2012

✿ Rep. James R. Comer Jr. (KOAM-ur) R-KY-01 p 202.225.3115

Rm. RHOB 2410   **f** 202.225.3547
Bio. 08/19/1972 • Carthage • Western Kentucky Univ., B.S.,
1993 • Baptist • M. Tamera Jo, 3 ch **Cmte.** Education &
Workforce • Oversight & Accountability
                          PS. Austin Hacker
Dist. Off. Madisonville 270.487.9509 • Paducah
270.408.1865 • Tompkinsville 270.487.9509

R: 190 **T:** 5th 75%
Elected Year: 2016

✿ Rep. Brett Guthrie (GUH-three) R-KY-02 p 202.225.3501

Rm. RHOB 2434 **Web.** guthrie.house.gov **f** 202.226.2019
Bio. 02/18/1964 • Florence • State Legislator • Army • U.S.
Military Academy (NY), B.S., 1987; Yale Univ. (CT), M.P.A.,
1997 • Church of Christ • M. Elizabeth Clemons, 3 ch **Cmte.**
Energy & Commerce
CoS. Sophie Trainor   **LD.** Brian Fahey
   Khanahmadi
Sched. Jennifer Beil   **PS.** S.K. Bowen
Dist. Off. Bowling Green 270.842.9896 • Owensboro
270.842.9896 • Radcliff 270.842.9896

R: 85 **T:** 8th 72%
Elected Year: 2008

⚑ Rep. Thomas H. Massie (MASS-ee)   R-KY-04   p 202.225.3465

Rm. RHOB 2453 **Web.** massie.house.gov   **f** 202.225.0003
Bio. 01/13/1971 • Huntington • Massachusetts Institute of Technology, B.S., 1993; Massachusetts Institute of Technology, M.M.E., 1996 • Methodist • M. Rhonda Massie, 4 ch   **Cmte.** Judiciary • Rules • Transportation & Infrastructure
CoS. Matt Gurtler   **LD.** Seana Cranston
Sched. Mary Troutman (CD)   **PS.** John Kennedy
Dist. Off. Ashland 606.324.9898 • Crescent Springs 859.426.0080 • LaGrange 502.265.9119

R: 121   **T:** 7th 65%
Elected Year: 2012

⚑ Rep. Morgan McGarvey ()   D-KY-03   p 202.225.5401

Rm. LHOB 1527 **Web.** mcgarvey.house.gov
Bio. Louisville • Univ. of Missouri, B.J.; Univ. of Kentucky College of Law, J.D., 2007 • Presbyterian • M. Chris McGarvey, 3 ch (twins)   **Cmte.** Small Business • Veterans' Affairs
CoS. Amy Soenksen   **LD.** Michael Demakos
Sched. Madeline Roberts   **PS.** Gabriella Salazar
Dist. Off. Louisville 502.582.5129

R: 410   **T:** 1st 62%
Elected Year: 2022

⚑ Rep. Hal D. Rogers (RAH-jurz)   R-KY-05   p 202.225.4601

Rm. RHOB 2406 **Web.** halrogers.house.gov   **f** 202.225.0940
Bio. 12/31/1937 • Barrier • Commonwealth's Attorney • Kentucky and North Carolina National Guards 1956-63 • Univ. of Kentucky, Bach. Deg., 1962; Univ. of Kentucky Law School, J.D., 1964 • Baptist • M. Cynthia Doyle Rogers, 3 ch (from a previous marriage)   **Cmte.** Appropriations
CoS. Jakob Johnsen   **LD.** Austin Gage
Sched. Kelley Kurtz   **PS.** Danielle Smoot (CD)
Dist. Off. Hazard 606.439.0794 • Prestonsburg 606.886.0844 • Somerset 606.679.8346

R: 1   **T:** 22nd 82%
Elected Year: 1980

LOUISIANA

⚑ Governor John Bel Edwards (EHD-wurdz)   p 225.342.7015

PO Box 94004   **C:** Baton Rouge
Baton Rouge, LA 70804-9004   **P:** 4,659,978 (25)
Website louisiana.gov   **A:** 43,204.04 mi^2 (33rd)
Fax 225.342.7099
Term Ends 2024
Lt. Governor
Billy Nungesser, **R**

U.S. Senators
Bill Cassidy, **R**
John N. Kennedy, **R**
U.S. Representatives
01 / Steve Scalise, **R**
02 / Troy Carter, **D**
03 / Clay Higgins, **R**
04 / Mike Johnson, **R**
05 / Julia Letlow, **R**
06 / Garret N. Graves, **R**

LOUIS..

Sen. Bill Cassidy (KA-sih-dee) R-LA-Sr. p 202.224.5824

Rm. HSOB 520 **Web.** cassidy.senate.gov
Bio. 09/28/1957 • Highland Park • State Legislator
• Louisiana State Univ., B.S., 1979; Louisiana State
Univ. Medical School, M.D., 1983 • Christian - Non-
Denominational • M. Laura Layden Cassidy, 3 ch **Cmte.**
Energy & Natural Resources • Finance • Health, Education,
Labor & Pensions • Veterans' Affairs
CoS. James Quinn   **LD.** Katie Hadji
                              PS. Molly Block
Dist. Off. Alexandria 318.448.7176 • Baton Rouge
225.929.7711 • Lafayette 337.261.1400 • Metairie
504.838.0130 • Monroe 318.324.2111 • Shreveport
318.798.3215

R: 59 **T:** 2nd 59%
Elected Year: 2014
Next Election: 2026

Sen. John N. Kennedy (KEH-nuh-dee) R-LA-Jr. p 202.224.4623

Rm. RSOB 416 **Web.** kennedy.senate.gov **f** 202.228.0447
Bio. 11/21/1951 • Centreville • Vanderbilt Univ. (TN), B.A.,
1973; Univ. of Virginia School of Law, J.D., 1977; Oxford
Univ. (England), B.CL, 1979 • Methodist • M. Rebecca Stulb
Kennedy, 1 ch **Cmte.** Appropriations • Banking, Housing
& Urban Affairs • Budget • Judiciary • Small Business &
Entrepreneurship
CoS. David Stokes   **LD.** Nathan Flagg
Sched. Mary Kirchner   **PS.** Bernadette Breslin
Dist. Off. Alexandria 318.445.2892 • Baton Rouge
225.926.8033 • Houma 985.851.0956 • Lafayette
337.269.5980 • Mandeville 985.809.8153 • Monroe
318.361.1489 • New Orleans 504.581.6190 • Shreveport
318.670.5192

R: 71 **T:** 2nd 62%
Elected Year: 2016
Next Election: 2028

Rep. Troy Carter (KAR-tur) D-LA-02 p 202.225.6636

Rm. CHOB 442 **Web.** troycarter.house.gov **f** 202.225.1988
Bio. 10/26/1963 • New Orleans • Holy Cross Univ., M.B.A.;
Xavier Univ. of Louisiana, B.A., 1986; Univ. of Holy Cross
(LA), M.B.A., 2021 • Baptist • M. Andreé (Ana) Navarro, 2
ch (2 from previous marriage) **Cmte.** Homeland Security •
Transportation & Infrastructure
CoS. Chonya Johnson
                              PS. Sara Severens
Dist. Off. Baton Rouge 504.381.3970 • Gretna 504.381.3999
• New Orleans 504.288.3777 • New Orleans 504.381.3970 •
Reserve 504.381.3970

R: 350 **T:** 2nd 77%
Elected Year: 2021

Rep. Garret N. Graves (grayvz) R-LA-06 p 202.225.3901

Rm. RHOB 2402 **Web.**   **f** 202.225.7313
garretgraves.house.gov
Bio. 01/31/1972 • Baton Rouge • Roman Catholic •
M. Carissa Graves, 3 ch **Cmte.** Natural Resources •
Transportation & Infrastructure
CoS. Paul Sawyer   **LD.** Logan de La Barre-Hays
Sched. Alexandra Erwin   **PS.** Zach Barnett
Dist. Off. Baton Rouge 225.442.1731 • Gonzales
225.450.1672 • Livingston 225.686.4413 • Thibodaux
985.448.4103

R: 172 **T:** 5th 80%
Elected Year: 2014

Rep. Clay Higgins (HIH-guhnz) R-LA-03 p 202.225.2031

Rm. CHOB 572 **Web.** clayhiggins.house.gov **f** 202.225.5724
Bio. 08/24/1961 • New Orleans • Christian - Non-
Denominational • M. Becca Higgins, 4 ch (1 deceased)
Cmte. Homeland Security • Oversight & Accountability
CoS. Andrew David
                              PS. Mackenzie Martinez
Dist. Off. Lafayette 337.703.6105 • Lake Charles
337.656.2833

R: 211 **T:** 4th 64%
Elected Year: 2016

Rep. Mike Johnson (JAHN-suhn) R-LA-04 p 202.225.2777
f 202.225.8039

Rm. CHOB 568 **Web.** mikejohnson.house.gov
Bio. 01/30/1972 • Shreveport • Louisiana State Univ., B.S., 1995; Louisiana State Univ. Law School, J.D., 1998 • Southern Baptist • M. Kelly Lary Johnson, 4 ch **Cmte.** Armed Services • Judiciary
CoS. Hayden Haynes **LD.** Garrett Fultz
Sched. Krista Perkins **PS.** Taylor S. Haulsee
Dist. Off. Bossier City 318.840.0309 • Leesville 337.423.4232 • Natchitoches 318.951.4316

R: 213 **T:** 4th 100%
Elected Year: 2016

Rep. Julia Letlow () R-LA-05 p 202.225.8490

Rm. CHOB 142 **Web.** letlow.house.gov
Bio. 03/16/1981 • Monroe • Univ. of Louisiana Monroe, B.A., 2002; Univ. of Louisiana Monroe, M.A., 2005; Univ. of South Florida, Ph.D., 2011 • Presbyterian • W., 2 ch **Cmte.** Appropriations • Education & Workforce
CoS. Ted Verrill **LD.** Lindsay Linhares
Sched. Caroline Courville **PS.** Mitch Rabalais
Dist. Off. Alexandria 318.319.6465 • Amite 985.284.5200 • Monroe 318.570.6440

R: 349 **T:** 2nd 68%
Elected Year: 2021

Rep. Steve Scalise (skuh-LEESS) R-LA-01 p 202.225.3015

Rm. RHOB 2049 **Web.** scalise.house.gov **f** 202.226.0386
Bio. 10/06/1965 • New Orleans • State Legislator • Louisiana State Univ., B.S., 1989; Louisiana State Univ., B.S., 1989 • Catholic • M. Jennifer Letulle Scalise, 2 ch
CoS. Megan Bel Miller **LD.** Claire Trokey
Sched. Sara Brooks Adams **PS.** Rebecca Rybczyk
Dist. Off. Houma 985.879.2300 • Mandeville 985.893.9064 • Metairie 504.837.1259 • Ponchatoula 985.340.2185

R: 83 **T:** 9th 73%
Elected Year: 2008

MAINE

Governor Janet Mills (millz) p 207.287.3531

One State House Station
Augusta, ME 04333-0001
Website maine.gov
Fax 207.287.1034
Term Ends 2027

C: Augusta
P: 1,338,404 (43)
A: 30,842.99 mi^2 (39th)

U.S. Senators
Susan M. Collins, **R**
Angus S. King, **I**
U.S. Representatives
01 / Chellie M. Pingree, **D**
02 / Jared F. Golden, **D**

Sen. Susan M. Collins (KAH-luhnz)　　　　R-ME-Sr.　　p 202.224.2523

Rm. DSOB 413 **Web.** collins.senate.gov　**f** 202.224.2693
Bio. 12/07/1952 • Caribou • Association Director; Small
Business Administration Director • St. Lawrence Univ. (NY),
B.A., 1975 • Roman Catholic • M. Thomas Daffron **Cmte.**
Appropriations • Health, Education, Labor & Pensions •
Intelligence
CoS. Steve Abbott　　　　　**LD.** Katie Brown
Sched. Tess Haller　　　　　**PS.** Annie Clark
Dist. Off. Augusta 207.622.8414 • Bangor 207.945.0417 •
Biddeford 207.283.1101 • Caribou 207.493.7873 • Lewiston
207.784.6969 • Portland 207.780.3575

R: 8　**T:** 5th　51%
Elected Year: 1996
Next Election: 2026

Sen. Angus S. King Jr. (king)　　　　I-ME-Jr.　　p 202.224.5344

Caucuses with Democratic Party　　　　**f** 202.224.1946
Rm. HSOB 133 **Web.** king.senate.gov
Bio. 03/31/1944 • Alexandria • Governor • Dartmouth
College, A.B., 1966; Univ. of Virginia Law School, J.D., 1969
• Episcopalian • M. Mary J. Herman, 5 ch ; 5 gr-ch **Cmte.**
Armed Services • Energy & Natural Resources • Intelligence
• Veterans' Affairs
CoS. Kathleen Connery　　　**LD.** Morgan Cashwell
　Dawe
Sched. Claire Bridgeo　　　**PS.** Matthew Felling
Dist. Off. Augusta 207.622.8292 • Bangor 207.945.8000 •
Biddeford 207.352.5216 • Portland 207.245.1565 • Presque
Isle 207.764.5124

R: 50　**T:** 2nd　54%
Elected Year: 2012
Next Election: 2024

Rep. Jared F. Golden (GOAL-duhn)　　　　D-ME-02　　p 202.225.6306

Rm. LHOB 1710 **Web.** golden.house.gov　**f** 202.225.2943
Bio. 07/25/1982 • Leeds • Bates College (ME), B.A., 2011
• Unspecified/Other • M. Isobel Golden **Cmte.** Armed
Services • Small Business
CoS. Margaret Reynolds　　　**LD.** Eric Kanter
Sched. Ainsley Jamieson　　**PS.** Rachel Freed
Dist. Off. Bangor 207.249.7400 • Caribou 207.492.6009 •
Lewiston 207.241.6767

R: 251　**T:** 3rd　53%
Elected Year: 2018

Rep. Chellie M. Pingree (PING-gree)　　　　D-ME-01　　p 202.225.6116

Rm. RHOB 2354 **Web.** pingree.house.gov　**f** 202.225.5590
Bio. 04/02/1955 • Minneapolis • State Legislator • College
of the Atlantic (ME), B.A., 1979 • Lutheran • Se. Donald
Sussman, 3 ch (3 from previous marriage); 3 gr-ch **Cmte.**
Agriculture • Appropriations
CoS. Jesse Connolly (CD)　　**LD.** Evan Johnston
Sched. Karen Sudbay (CD)　**PS.** Victoria Bonney
Dist. Off. Portland 207.774.5019 • Waterville 207.873.5713

R: 89　**T:** 8th　63%
Elected Year: 2008

MARYLAND

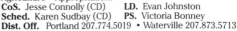

Governor Westley (Wes) Watende Omari Moore ()　　　p 410.974.3901

100 State Circle　　　　　　**C:** Annapolis
Annapolis, MD 21401　　　　**P:** 6,042,718 (19)
Website maryland.gov　　　**A:** 9,707.38 mi^2 (42nd)
Fax 401.974.3275
Term Ends 2027
Lt. Governor
Aruna Miller, **D**

MARYLAND

U.S. Senators
Ben L. Cardin, **D**
Chris J. Van Hollen, **D**
U.S. Representatives
01 / Andy P. Harris, **R**
02 / Dutch Ruppersberger, **D**
03 / John P. Sarbanes, **D**
04 / Glenn F. Ivey, **D**
05 / Steny Hoyer, **D**
06 / David Trone, **D**
07 / Kweisi Mfume, **D**
08 / Jamie Raskin, **D**

⌑ Sen. Ben L. Cardin (KAR-din)   D-MD-Sr.   p 202.224.4524

Rm. HSOB 509 **Web.** cardin.senate.gov   **f** 202.224.1651
Bio. 10/05/1943 • Baltimore • U.S. Representative;
Attorney • Univ. of Pittsburgh (PA), B.A., 1964; Univ. of
Maryland School of Law, J.D., 1967; Villa Julie College (MD),
LL.D., 2007 • Jewish • M. Myrna Edelman Cardin, 2 ch (1
deceased); 2 gr-ch **Cmte.** Environment & Public Works •
Finance • Foreign Relations • Joint Security & Cooperation
in Europe • Small Business & Entrepreneurship
CoS. Christopher W. Lynch   **LD.** Gray Maxwell
Sched. Debbie Yamada   **PS.** Sue Walitsky
Dist. Off. Baltimore 410.962.4436 • Bowie 301.860.0414
• Cumberland 301.777.2957 • Easton 301.860.0414 •
Rockville 301.762.2974

R: 19   **T:** 3rd   65%
Elected Year: 2006
Next Election: 2024

⌑ Sen. Chris J. Van Hollen Jr. (van-HAH-luhn)   D-MD-Jr.   p 202.224.4654

Rm. HSOB 110 **Web.** vanhollen.senate.gov   **f** 202.228.0629
Bio. 01/10/1959 • Karachi • State Senator; Representative
• Swarthmore College (PA), B.A., 1982; John F. Kennedy
School of Government, Harvard Univ., M.P.P., 1985;
Georgetown Univ. (DC), J.D., 1990 • Episcopalian • M.
Katherine Wilkens Van Hollen, 3 ch **Cmte.** Appropriations
• Banking, Housing & Urban Affairs • Budget • Foreign
Relations
CoS. Tricia Russell   **LD.** Sarah Schenning
Sched. Savanna Peterson   **PS.** Francesca Amodeo
Dist. Off. Annapolis 410.263.1325 • Baltimore 667.212.4610
• Cambridge 410.221.2074 • Hagerstown 301.797.2826 •
Largo 301.322.6560 • Rockville 301.545.1500

R: 67   **T:** 2nd   66%
Elected Year: 2016
Next Election: 2028

⌑ Rep. Andy P. Harris (HAIR-iss)   R-MD-01   p 202.225.5311

Rm. LHOB 1536 **Web.** harris.house.gov
Bio. 01/25/1957 • Brooklyn • Johns Hopkins Univ., B.S.,
1977; Johns Hopkins Univ., M.D., 1980; Johns Hopkins Univ.
Bloomburg School of Hygiene and Public Health (MD),
M.H.S., 1995 • Roman Catholic • M. Nicole Harris, 5 ch ; 1
stepch ; 10 gr-ch **Cmte.** Appropriations
CoS. Bryan Shuy   **LD.** Travis Trejo
Sched. Victoria Cesaro   **PS.** Anna Adamian
Dist. Off. Bel Air 410.588.5670 • Chester 410.643.5425 •
Salisbury 443.944.8624

R: 107   **T:** 7th   54%
Elected Year: 2010

⌑ Rep. Steny Hoyer (HOY-yur)   D-MD-05   p 202.225.4131

Rm. LHOB 1705 **Web.** hoyer.house.gov   **f** 202.225.4300
Bio. 06/14/1939 • New York • Attorney; Member, State
Board of Education • Univ. of Maryland, B.S., 1963;
Georgetown Univ. Law Center (DC), J.D., 1966 • Baptist •
W., 3 ch ; 3 gr-ch ; 2 great-gr-ch **Cmte.** Appropriations
CoS. Alexis Covey-Brandt   **LD.** James P. Leuschen
Sched. Harleigh Bean   **PS.** Maya Valentine
Dist. Off. Greenbelt 301.474.0119 • White Plains
301.843.1577

R: 3   **T:** 22nd   66%
Elected Year: 1981

⌑ Rep. Glenn F. Ivey ()   D-MD-04   p 202.225.8699

Rm. LHOB 1529 **Web.** glennivey.com
Bio. 02/27/1961 • Maryland • Princeton Univ. (NJ), A.B.,
1983; Harvard Law School (MA), J.D., 1986 • M. Jolene
Stephenson **Cmte.** Ethics • Homeland Security • Judiciary
CoS. Robin Peguero   **LD.** Brad Kane
Sched. Aaron Harawa   **PS.** Ramon Korionoff
Dist. Off. Largo 301.537.1451

T: 1st   90%
Elected Year: 2022

MARYLAND

⚑ Rep. Kweisi Mfume (oom-FOO-mae)   D-MD-07   p 202.225.4741

Rm. RHOB 2263 **Web.** mfume.house.gov   f 202.225.3178
Bio. 10/24/1948 • Baltimore • Morgan State Univ., B.S., 1976; Johns Hopkins Univ., M.A., 1984 • M. Tiffany McMillan, 5 ch **Cmte.** Oversight & Accountability • Small Business
CoS. Eric Bryant   **LD.** Abigail Cipparone
                    PS. Ryan Lawrence
Dist. Off. Baltimore 410.685.9199 • Catonsville
410.818.2120 • Ellicott City 443.364.5413

R: 98   **T:** 3rd   82%
Elected Year: 2020

⚑ Rep. Jamie Raskin (RAS-kin)   D-MD-08   p 202.225.5341

Rm. RHOB 2242 **Web.** raskin.house.gov
Bio. 12/13/1962 • Washington • Harvard College (MA), B.A., 1983; Harvard Univ. Law School (MA), J.D., 1987 • Unspecified/Other • M. Sarah Raskin, 3 ch (1 deceased)
Cmte. Oversight & Accountability
CoS. Leesa Klepper
Sched. James Montfort   **PS.** Jacob Wilson
Dist. Off. Rockville 301.354.1000

R: 219   **T:** 4th   80%
Elected Year: 2016

⚑ Rep. Dutch Ruppersberger III (ROO-purs-bur-   D-MD-02   p 202.225.3061
gur)

Rm. RHOB 2206 **Web.**   f 202.225.3094
ruppersberger.house.gov
Bio. 01/31/1946 • Baltimore • Member, City Council; Assistant State Attorney • Univ. of Maryland - College Park, B.A., 1967; Univ. of Baltimore School of Law (MD), J.D., 1970 • Methodist • M. Kay Murphy Ruppersberger, 2 ch ; 5 gr-ch
Cmte. Appropriations
CoS. Tara Oursler   **LD.** Walter Gonzales
Sched. Victoria Graham   **PS.** Jaime Lennon (CD)
Dist. Off. Timonium 410.628.2701

R: 51   **T:** 11th   59%
Elected Year: 2002

⚑ Rep. John P. Sarbanes (SAR-baynz)   D-MD-03   p 202.225.4016

Rm. RHOB 2370 **Web.** sarbanes.house.gov   f 202.225.9219
Bio. 05/22/1962 • Baltimore • School Superintendent • Princeton Univ. Woodrow Wilson School of Public and International Affairs (NJ), B.A., 1984; Harvard Univ., J.D., 1988 • Greek Orthodox • M. Dina Sarbanes, 3 ch **Cmte.** Energy & Commerce
CoS. Dvora Lovinger   **LD.** Kathleen Teleky
Sched. Kelly Moura   **PS.** Natalie Young
Dist. Off. Annapolis 410.295.1679 • Columbia 410.832.8890

R: 78   **T:** 9th   60%
Elected Year: 2006

⚑ Rep. David Trone (troan)   D-MD-06   p 202.225.2721

Rm. RHOB 2404 **Web.** trone.house.gov
Bio. 09/21/1955 • Cheverly • Furman Univ. (SC), B.A., 1977; Univ. of Pennsylvania Wharton School of Business (PA), M.B.A., 1985 • Lutheran • M. June Trone, 4 ch **Cmte.** Appropriations • Budget
CoS. Lane Lofton   **LD.** Krista O'Neill
Sched. Juven Jacob   **PS.** Sasha Galbreath
Dist. Off. Cumberland 240.382.6464 • Frederick
240.803.6119 • Gaithersburg 301.926.0300 • Hagerstown
240.382.6464

R: 289   **T:** 3rd   55%
Elected Year: 2018

MASSACHUSETTS

Governor Maura Tracy Healey () p 617.725.4005

Massachusetts State House, Room
280
Boston, MA 02133
Website mass.gov
Fax 617.727.9725
Term Ends 2027
Lt. Governor
Kimberley (Kim) Layne Driscoll, **D**

C: Boston
P: 6,902,149 (15)
A: 7,800.03 mi^2 (45th)

U.S. Senators
Ed Markey, **D**
Elizabeth Warren, **D**
U.S. Representatives
01 / Richard E. Neal, **D**
02 / Jim P. McGovern, **D**
03 / Lori Trahan, **D**
04 / Jake D. Auchincloss, **D**
05 / Katherine Clark, **D**
06 / Seth W. Moulton, **D**
07 / Ayanna Pressley, **D**
08 / Stephen F. Lynch, **D**
09 / Bill R. Keating, **D**

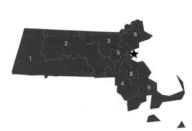

Sen. Ed Markey (MAR-kee) D-MA Jr. p 202.224.2742

Rm. DSOB 255 **Web.** markey.senate.gov
Bio. 07/11/1946 • Malden • Representative • Army
Reserves 1968-73 • Boston College (MA), B.A., 1968; Boston
College Law School (MA), J.D., 1972 • Roman Catholic
• M. Susan Blumenthal **Cmte.** Commerce, Science &
Transportation • Environment & Public Works • Foreign
Relations • Health, Education, Labor & Pensions • Small
Business & Entrepreneurship
CoS. John E. Walsh **LD.** Jeremy D'Aloisio
Sched. Sarah Butler **PS.** Rosemary Boeglin
Dist. Off. Boston 617.565.8519 • Springfield 413.785.4610
R: 55 **T:** 3rd 66%
Elected Year: 2013
Next Election: 2026

Sen. Elizabeth Warren (WAR-ruhn) D-MA-Sr. p 202.224.4543

Rm. HSOB 309 **Web.** warren.senate.gov **f** 202.228.2072
Bio. 06/22/1949 • Oklahoma City • Univ. of Houston (TX),
B.A., 1970; Rutgers Univ. (NJ), J.D., 1976 • Methodist •
M. Bruce H. Mann, 2 ch ; 3 gr-ch **Cmte.** Aging • Armed
Services • Banking, Housing & Urban Affairs • Finance
CoS. Jonathan Donenberg **LD.** Beth Pearson
Sched. Ami Kutzen **PS.** Alex Sarabia
Dist. Off. Boston 617.565.3170 • Springfield 413.788.2690
R: 53 **T:** 2nd 60%
Elected Year: 2012
Next Election: 2024

Rep. Jake D. Auchincloss (AW-kin-klaws) D-MA-04 p 202.225.5931

Rm. LHOB 1524 **Web.** auchincloss.house.gov **f** 202.225.0182
Bio. 01/29/1988 • Newton • Harvard Univ., A.B., 2010;
Massachusetts Institute of Technology, M.B.A., 2016 • Jewish
• M. Michelle Auchincloss **Cmte.** Select China Committee
• Transportation & Infrastructure
CoS. Liz Amster **LD.** Jessica Hatcher
Sched. Joe Valente **PS.** Matt Corridoni
Dist. Off. Attleboro 508.431.1110 • Newton 617.332.3333
R: 299 **T:** 2nd 97%
Elected Year: 2020

MASSACHUSETTS

Rep. Katherine Clark (klark) D-MA-05 p 202.225.2836
Rm. RHOB 2368 **Web.** f 202.226.0092
katherineclark.house.gov
Bio. 07/17/1963 • New Haven • Saint Lawrence Univ., B.A.,
1985; Cornell Univ. Law School (NY), J.D., 1989; Harvard
Univ. John F. Kennedy School of Government (MA), M.P.A.,
1997 • Protestant - Unspecified Christian • M. Rodney
Dowell, 3 ch
CoS. Brooke Scannell **LD.** Steve Thornton
Sched. Judah Piepho **PS.** Kathryn Alexander
Dist. Off. Framingham 508.319.9757 • Malden
617.354.0292
R: 156 **T:** 6th 74%
Elected Year: 2013

Rep. Bill R. Keating (KEE-ting) D-MA-09 p 202.225.3111
Rm. RHOB 2351 **Web.** keating.house.gov f 202.225.5658
Bio. 09/06/1952 • Norwood • Boston College (MA), B.A.,
1974; Boston College (MA), M.B.A., 1982; Suffolk Univ.
School of Law (MA), J.D., 1985 • Roman Catholic • M. Tevis
Keating, 2 ch **Cmte.** Armed Services • Foreign Affairs
CoS. Garrett Donovan **LD.** Ryan Maddock
Sched. David Oleksak **PS.** Lauren McDermott
Dist. Off. Hyannis 508.771.6868 • New Bedford
508.999.6462 • Plymouth 508.746.9000
R: 110 **T:** 7th 59%
Elected Year: 2010

Rep. Stephen F. Lynch (linch) D-MA-08 p 202.225.8273
Rm. RHOB 2109 **Web.** lynch.house.gov f 202.225.3984
Bio. 03/31/1955 • Boston • State Legislator • Wentworth
Institute of Technology (MA), B.S., 1988; Boston College
Law School (MA), J.D., 1991; Harvard Univ. John F. Kennedy
School of Government (MA), M.P.A., 1999 • Roman Catholic
• M. Margaret Shaughnessy Lynch, 1 ch **Cmte.** Financial
Services • Oversight & Accountability
CoS. Kevin Ryan **LD.** Bruce Fernandez
Sched. Maeve McNamara **PS.** Molly Rose Tarpey (CD)
Dist. Off. Boston 617.428.2000 • Brockton 508.586.5555 •
Quincy 617.657.6305
R: 43 **T:** 12th 70%
Elected Year: 2001

Rep. Jim P. McGovern (mih-GUH-vurn) D-MA-02 p 202.225.6101
Rm. CHOB 370 **Web.** mcgovern.house.gov f 202.225.5759
Bio. 11/20/1959 • Worcester • Congressional Aide •
American Univ. (DC), B.A., 1981; American Univ. (DC),
M.P.A., 1984 • Roman Catholic • M. Lisa Murray McGovern,
2 ch **Cmte.** Agriculture • Joint Congressional-Executive
Commission on China • Rules
CoS. Jennifer Chandler **LD.** Cindy Buhl
Sched. Daniel Holt **PS.** Matt Bonaccorsi
Dist. Off. Leominster 978.466.3552 • Northampton
413.341.8700 • Worcester 508.831.7356
R: 27 **T:** 14th 66%
Elected Year: 1996

Rep. Seth W. Moulton (MOAL-tuhn) D-MA-06 p 202.225.8020
Rm. LHOB 1127 **Web.** moulton.house.gov f 202.225.5915
Bio. 10/24/1978 • Salem • Phillips Academy, (MA), M.P.A.,
1997; Harvard Univ., B.S., 2001; Harvard Univ. School of
Business (MA), M.B.A., 2011; Harvard Univ. John F. Kennedy
School of Government (MA), M.P.A., 2011 • Christian - Non-
Denominational • M. Liz Boardman, 1 ch **Cmte.** Armed
Services • Select China Committee • Transportation &
Infrastructure
CoS. Rick Jakious (CD) **LD.** Joey Rodriguez
Sched. Cari Berlin **PS.** Sydney Simon
Dist. Off. Salem 978.531.1669
R: 179 **T:** 5th 63%
Elected Year: 2014

Rep. Richard E. Neal (neel) D-MA-01 p 202.225.5601
Rm. CHOB 372 **Web.** neal.house.gov f 202.225.8112
Bio. 02/14/1949 • Worcester • Mayor (Springfield, MA);
President, Springfield City Council • American International
College (MA), B.A., 1972; Univ. of Hartford Barney School of
Business (CT), M.P.A., 1976 • Roman Catholic • M. Maureen
Conway Neal, 4 ch **Cmte.** Ways & Means
CoS. Elizabeth O'Hara **LD.** Kara Getz
Sched. Timothy Ranstrom **PS.** Jack Chamberland (CD)
Dist. Off. Pittsfield 413.442.0946 • Springfield 413.785.0325
R: 7 **T:** 18th 62%
Elected Year: 1988

MASSACHUSETTS

⊮ Rep. Ayanna Pressley (PRESS-lee)   D-MA-07   p 202.225.5111

Rm. LHOB 1108 **Web.** pressley.house.gov   **f** 202.225.9322
Bio. 02/03/1974 • Cincinnati • Baptist • M. Conan Harris pressley, 1 stepch   **Cmte.** Financial Services
CoS. Sarah Groh   **LD.** Demarquin Johnson
Sched. Lona Watts   **PS.** Ricardo Sanchez
Dist. Off. Hyde Park 617.850.0040

R: 273   **T:** 3rd 85%
Elected Year: 2018

⊮ Rep. Lori Trahan (truh-HAN)   D-MA-03   p 202.225.3411

Rm. RHOB 2439 **Web.** trahan.house.gov
Bio. 10/27/1973 • Lowell • Georgetown Univ. (DC), B.S., 1995 • Catholic • M. David Trahan, 2 ch ; 3 stepch   **Cmte.** Energy & Commerce • Natural Resources
CoS. Mark McDevitt   **LD.** Elya Taichman
Sched. Emma Trittin
Dist. Off. Acton 978.459.0101 • Fitchburg 978.459.0101 • Hudson 978.459.0101 • Lawrence 978.258.1138 • Lowell 978.459.0101

R: 288   **T:** 3rd 64%
Elected Year: 2018

MICHIGAN

MICHIGAN

⊮ Governor Gretchen Whitmer (WHIT-₁₁₁₁₁)   p 517.373.3400

PO Box 30013
Lansing, MI 48909
Website michigan.gov
Fax 517.335.6863
Term Ends 2027
Lt. Governor
Garlin Gilchrist, **D**

C: Lansing
P: 9,995,915 (10)
A: 56,538.85 mi^2 (22nd)

U.S. Senators
Debbie Stabenow, **D**
Gary Peters, **D**
U.S. Representatives
01 / Jack W. Bergman, **R**
02 / John Moolenaar, **R**
03 / Hillary Scholten, **D**
04 / Bill P. Huizenga, **R**
05 / Tim L. Walberg, **R**
06 / Debbie Dingell, **D**
07 / Elissa B. Slotkin, **D**
08 / Dan Kildee, **D**
09 / Lisa McClain, **R**
10 / John E. James, **R**
11 / Haley Stevens, **D**
12 / Rashida Tlaib, **D**
13 / Shri Thanedar, **D**

⊮ Sen. Gary Peters Sr. (PEE-turz)   D-MI-Jr.   p 202.224.6221

Rm. HSOB 724 **Web.** peters.senate.gov   **f** 202.224.7387
Bio. 12/01/1958 • Pontiac • State Legislator; Professor • Navy Reserves • Alma College (MI), B.A., 1980; Univ. of Detroit (MI), M.B.A., 1984; Wayne State Univ. Law School (MI), J.D., 1989; Michigan State Univ., M.A., 2007 • Episcopalian • M. Colleen Ochoa, 3 ch   **Cmte.** Appropriations • Armed Services • Commerce, Science & Transportation • Homeland Security & Government Affairs
CoS. Caitlyn Stephenson   **LD.** Catherine Barrett
Sched. Angeli Chawla   **PS.** Sarah Schakow
Dist. Off. Detroit 313.226.6020 • Grand Rapids 616.233.9150 • Lansing 517.377.1508 • Marquette 906.226.4554 • Pontiac 248.608.8040 • Saginaw 989.754.0112 • Traverse City 231.947.7773

R: 58   **T:** 2nd 50%
Elected Year: 2014
Next Election: 2026

⚑ Sen. Debbie Stabenow (STAB-uh-nou)   D-MI-Sr.   p 202.224.4822

Rm. HSOB 731 **Web.** stabenow.senate.gov   **f** 202.228.0325
Bio. 04/29/1950 • Gladwin • U.S. Representative; State
Legislator; Social Worker • Michigan State Univ., B.A., 1972;
Michigan State Univ., M.S.W., 1975 • Methodist • D., 2 ch ;
4 gr-ch **Cmte.** Agriculture, Nutrition & Forestry • Budget •
Environment & Public Works • Finance • Joint Economic •
Joint Taxation
CoS. Matt VanKuiken   **LD.** Emily Carwell
Sched. Ellen Rodman (CD)   **PS.** Patricia Curran
Dist. Off. Detroit 313.961.4330 • East Lansing 517.203.1760

R: 12   **T:** 4th 52%   • Flint 810.720.4172 • Grand Rapids 616.975.0052 •
Elected Year: 2000   Marquette 906.228.8756 • Traverse City 231.929.1031
Next Election: 2024

⚑ Rep. Jack W. Bergman (BAIRG-mahn)   R-MI-01   p 202.225.4735

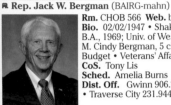

Rm. CHOB 566 **Web.** bergman.house.gov   **f** 202.225.4710
Bio. 02/02/1947 • Shakopee • Gustavus Adolphus College,
B.A., 1969; Univ. of West Florida, M.B.A., 1975 • Lutheran •
M. Cindy Bergman, 5 ch ; 8 gr-ch **Cmte.** Armed Services •
Budget • Veterans' Affairs
CoS. Tony Lis   **LD.** Alec Zender
Sched. Amelia Burns   **PS.** James Hogge
Dist. Off. Gwinn 906.273.2227 • Manistique 906.286.4191
• Traverse City 231.944.7633

R: 198   **T:** 4th 60%
Elected Year: 2016

⚑ Rep. Debbie Dingell (DING-gull)   D-MI-06   p 202.225.4071

Rm. CHOB 102 **Web.**   **f** 202.226.0371
debbiedingell.house.gov
Bio. 11/23/1953 • Detroit • Georgetown Univ. (DC),
B.S., 1975; Georgetown Univ. (DC), M.S., 1996 • Roman
Catholic • W. Hon. John D. Dingell Jr., 4 ch **Cmte.** Energy &
Commerce • Natural Resources
CoS. Dan Black   **LD.** Kevin Rambosk
Sched. Elizabeth Hood   **PS.** Michaela Johnson
Dist. Off. Woodhaven 313.278.2936 • Ypsilanti
734.481.1100

R: 169   **T:** 5th 66%
Elected Year: 2014

⚑ Rep. Bill P. Huizenga (HY-zeng-uh)   R-MI-04   p 202.225.4401

Rm. RHOB 2232 **Web.** huizenga.house.gov   **f** 202.226.0779
Bio. 01/31/1969 • Zeeland • Calvin College (MI), B.A., 1991
• Christian Reformed Church • M. Natalie Huizenga, 5 ch
Cmte. Financial Services • Foreign Affairs
CoS. Todd Whiteman
Sched. Sarah Lisman   **PS.** Brian Patrick

R: 108   **T:** 7th 54%
Elected Year: 2010

⚑ Rep. John E. James ()   R-MI-10   p 202.225.4961

Rm. LHOB 1319 **Web.** johnjamesmi.com
Bio. 06/08/1981 • Southfield • Univ. of Michigan, M.B.A.;
Pennsylvania State Univ., Mast. Deg.; U.S. Military Academy
(NY), B.S., 2004 • Christian Church • M. Elizabeth James,
2 ch **Cmte.** Education & Workforce • Foreign Affairs •
Transportation & Infrastructure
CoS. Jackson Gross
Dist. Off. Warren

R: 395   **T:** 1st 49%
Elected Year: 2022

⚑ Rep. Dan Kildee (KILL-dee)   D-MI-08   p 202.225.3611

Rm. CHOB 200 **Web.** dankildee.house.gov   **f** 202.225.6393
Bio. 08/11/1958 • Flint • Central Michigan Univ., B.S. •
Roman Catholic • M. Jennifer Kildee, 3 ch ; 2 gr-ch **Cmte.**
Budget • Ways & Means
CoS. Mitchell Rivard   **LD.** Jordan Dickinson
Sched. Elizabeth Virga   **PS.** Kelly Montgomery

R: 136   **T:** 6th 53%
Elected Year: 2012

⚑ Rep. Lisa McClain (mih-klain) R-MI-09 p 202.225.2106

Rm. CHOB 444 **Web.** mcclain.house.gov **f** 202.226.1169
Bio. 04/07/1966 • Stockbridge • Lansing Community College, Assc. Deg.; Northwood Univ. (MI), B.A., 1997 • Roman Catholic • M. Mike McClain, 3 ch **Cmte.** Armed Services • Budget • Education & Workforce • Oversight & Accountability
CoS. Nick Hawatmeh **LD.** Erik Kinney
Sched. Jake Ronan **PS.** Dan Wunderlich

R: 330 **T:** 2nd 64%
Elected Year: 2020

⚑ Rep. John Moolenaar (MULL-leh-nar) R-MI-02 p 202.225.3561

Rm. CHOB 246 **Web.** moolenaar.house.gov **f** 202.225.9679
Bio. 05/08/1961 • Midland • Hope College (MI), B.S., 1983; Harvard Univ., M.P.A., 1989 • Christian - Non-Denominational • M. Amy Moolenaar, 6 ch **Cmte.** Appropriations • Select China Committee
CoS. Lindsay Ryan **LD.** Edward Kim
Sched. Michelle Chavez **PS.** David Russell
Dist. Off. Clare 989.802.6040

R: 177 **T:** 5th 64%
Elected Year: 2014

⚐ Rep. Hillary Scholten () D-MI-03 p 202.225.3831

Rm. LHOB 1317 **Web.** hillaryscholten.com
Bio. 02/22/1982 • Michigan • Calvin College, B.A., 2004; Univ. of Maryland School of Law, J.D., 2012 • M. Jesse Holcomb, 2 ch **Cmte.** Small Business • Transportation & Infrastructure
CoS. Craig Kwiecinski **LD.** Andrew Orlebeke
Sched. Matt Campbell **PS.** Isaac Seiler
Dist. Off. Grand Rapids 616.451.8383

R: 425 **T:** 1st 55%
Elected Year: 2022

⚐ Rep. Elissa B. Slotkin (SLAHT-kin) D-MI-07 p 202.225.4872

Rm. RHOB 2245 **Web.** slotkin.house.gov **f** 202.225.5820
Bio. 07/10/1976 • Holly • Columbia Univ. School of International and Public Affairs, Mast. Deg.; Cornell Univ. (NY), B.A., 1998 • Jewish • M. Dave Slotkin, 2 stepch **Cmte.** Armed Services
CoS. Matt Hennessey **LD.** Danielle Most
Sched. Megan Birleson **PS.** Austin Cook

R: 279 **T:** 3rd 52%
Elected Year: 2018

⚐ Rep. Haley Stevens (STEE-vuhnz) D-MI-11 p 202.225.8171

Rm. RHOB 2411 **Web.** stevens.house.gov
Bio. 06/24/1983 • Oakland County • American Univ. (DC), Bach. Deg., 2005; American Univ. (DC), M.A., 2007 • Christian Church • Sc. Rob Gulley **Cmte.** Education & Workforce • Science, Space & Technology • Select China Committee
CoS. Justin German **LD.** Liam Steadman
Sched. John Martin **PS.** Larkin Parker
Dist. Off. Farmington Hills 734.853.3040

R: 285 **T:** 3rd 61%
Elected Year: 2018

⚐ Rep. Shri Thanedar () D-MI-13 p 202.225.5802

Web. thanedar.house.gov **f** 202.225.5739
Bio. 02/22/1955 • India • Karnatak Univ. (India), B.S., 1973; Univ. of Bombay (India), Mast. Deg., 1977; Univ. of Akron, Ph.D., 1982; Fontbonne Univ., M.B.A., 1988 • M. Shashi Thanedar, 2 ch; 1 gr-ch **Cmte.** Homeland Security • Small Business
CoS. Michael McQuerry **LD.** Chi Chukwuka (CD) (CD)
Sched. Linto Thomas (CD)
Dist. Off. Detroit 313.880.2400

R: 430 **T:** 1st 71%
Elected Year: 2022

MICHIGAN

🐦 Rep. Rashida Tlaib (tuh-LEEB)   D-MI-12   p 202.225.5126

Rm. RHOB 2438 **Web.** tlaib.house.gov
Bio. 07/24/1976 • Detroit • Wayne State Univ. (MI), B.A., 1998; Western Michigan Univ., J.D., 2004 • Islam (Muslim) • M. Fayez Tlaib, 2 ch **Cmte.** Financial Services • Natural Resources
CoS. Larissa Richardson   **LD.** Tom Clancy
  (CD)
Sched. Amanda Kaye   **PS.** Derrick Utley
Dist. Off. Detroit 313.463.6220 • Inkster 313.463.6220 •River Rouge

R: 287 **T:** 3rd 71%
Elected Year: 2018

🐦 Rep. Tim L. Walberg (WALL-burg)   R-MI-05   p 202.225.6276

Rm. RHOB 2266 **Web.** walberg.house.gov   **f** 202.225.6281
Bio. 04/12/1951 • Chicago • Minister; College Administrator • Taylor Univ. (IN), B.S., 1975; Fort Wayne Bible College, B.R.E., 1975; Wheaton College (IL), M.A., 1978 • Protestant - Unspecified Christian • M. Susan Walberg, 3 ch ; 2 gr-ch **Cmte.** Education & Workforce • Energy & Commerce
CoS. R.J. Laukitis   **LD.** Joanna Brown
Sched. Mary Elizabeth   **PS.** Mike Rorke
  Stringer
Dist. Off. Jackson 517.780.9075

R: 96 **T:** 7th 62%
Elected Year: 2010

MINNESOTA

MINNESOTA

🐦 Governor Tim J. Walz (wallz)   p 651.201.3400

130 State Capitol, 75 Rev. Dr.   **C:** St. Paul
Martin Luther King Jr. Blvd.   **P:** 5,611,179 (22)
St. Paul, MN 55155   **A:** 79,626.59 mi^2 (14th)
Website state.mn.us
Fax 651.797.1850
Term Ends 2027
Lt. Governor
Peggy Flanagan, **D**

U.S. Senators
Amy Klobuchar, **D**
Tina Smith, **D**
U.S. Representatives
01 / Brad Finstad, **R**
02 / Angie D. Craig, **D**
03 / Dean Phillips, **D**
04 / Betty McCollum, **D**
05 / Ilhan Omar, **D**
06 / Tom Emmer, **R**
07 / Michelle L. Fischbach, **R**
08 / Pete A. Stauber, **R**

🐦 Sen. Amy Klobuchar (KLOE-buh-shar)   D-MN-Sr.   p 202.224.3244

Rm. DSOB 425 **Web.** klobuchar.senate.gov   **f** 202.228.2186
Bio. 05/25/1960 • Plymouth • Attorney; Hennepin County Attorney • Yale Univ. (CT), B.A., 1982; Univ. of Chicago (IL), J.D., 1985 • Congregationalist • M. John Bessler, 1 ch **Cmte.** Agriculture, Nutrition & Forestry • Commerce, Science & Transportation • Joint Economic • Judiciary • Rules & Administration
CoS. Tamara Fucile   **LD.** Lauren Santabar
Sched. Elizabeth Haskell   **PS.** Jane Meyer
Dist. Off. Minneapolis 612.727.5220 • Moorhead 218.287.2219 • Rochester 507.288.5321 • Virginia 218.741.9690

R: 23 **T:** 3rd 60%
Elected Year: 2006
Next Election: 2024

Sen. Tina Smith (smith) — D-MN-Jr. — p 202.224.5641

Rm. HSOB 720 **Web.** smith.senate.gov **f** 202.224.0044
Bio. 03/04/1958 • Albuquerque • Stanford Univ. (CA),
B.A.; Dartmouth College Tuck School of Business (NH),
M.B.A. • M. Archie Smith, 2 ch **Cmte.** Agriculture, Nutrition
& Forestry • Banking, Housing & Urban Affairs • Health,
Education, Labor & Pensions • Indian Affairs
CoS. Jeff Lomonaco **LD.** Tim Everett
Sched. Michael Weiss **PS.** Shea Necheles
Dist. Off. Duluth 218.722.2390 • Moorhead 218.284.8721 •
Rochester 507.288.2003 • Saint Paul 651.221.1016

R: 73 **T:** 3rd 49%
Elected Year: 2018
Next Election: 2026

Rep. Angie D. Craig (krayg) — D-MN-02 — p 202.225.2271

Rm. RHOB 2442 **Web.** craig.house.gov
Bio. 02/14/1972 • West Helena • Univ. of Memphis,
B.A., 1994 • Lutheran • M. Cheryl Greene, 4 ch **Cmte.**
Agriculture • Energy & Commerce
CoS. Nick Coe **LD.** Skylar Borchardt
Sched. Hayden Schutt **PS.** Laura Cottrell
Dist. Off. Burnsville 651.846.2120

R: 241 **T:** 3rd 51%
Elected Year: 2018

Rep. Tom Emmer Jr. (EH-mur) — R-MN-06 — p 202.225.2331

Rm. CHOB 464 **Web.** emmer.house.gov **f** 202.225.6475
Bio. 03/03/1961 • South Bend • Univ. of Alaska, Fairbanks,
B.A., 1984; William Mitchell College of Law (MN), J.D., 1988
• Roman Catholic • M. Jacqueline Samuel Emmer, 7 ch
Cmte. Financial Services
CoS. Sally Fox **LD.** Jeff Kuckuck
Sched. Christine Callaghan **PS.** Theresa Braid
Dist. Off. Otsego 763.241.6848

R: 170 **T:** 5th 62%
Elected Year: 2014

Rep. Brad Finstad () — R-MN-01 — p 202.225.2472

Rm. LHOB 1605 **Web.** finstad.house.gov
Bio. 05/30/1976 • New Ulm • Univ. of Minnesota, B.S., 1998
• M. Jaclyn Finstad, 7 ch **Cmte.** Armed Services
CoS. David FitzSimmons **LD.** Ryan Altman
Sched. Ashlyn **PS.** Abigail Gost
Kammerlocher
Dist. Off. Mankato 507.323.6090 • Rochester 507.323.6090

R: 357 **T:** 2nd 54%
Elected Year: 2022

Rep. Michelle L. Fischbach (FISH-baak) — R-MN-07 — p 202.225.2165

Rm. LHOB 1004 **Web.** fischbach.house.gov **f** 202.225.1593
Bio. 11/03/1965 • Minnesota • St. Cloud State College
(MN), B.A., 1989; William Mitchell College of Law (MN),
J.D., 2011 • Catholic • M. Scott Fischbach, 2 ch **Cmte.**
Agriculture • Budget • Ethics • Rules • Ways & Means
CoS. Emily Hytha **LD.** Sean Murphy
Sched. Eleanor Traynham **PS.** Lauren Weber
Dist. Off. Moorhead 218.422.2090 • Willmar 320.403.6100

R: 311 **T:** 2nd 67%
Elected Year: 2020

Rep. Betty McCollum (mih-KAW-lum) — D-MN-04 — p 202.225.6631

Rm. RHOB 2426 **Web.** mccollum.house.gov **f** 202.225.1968
Bio. 07/12/1954 • Minneapolis • Teacher; Representative •
College of St. Catherine (MN), B.S., 1986 • Roman Catholic
• D., 2 ch **Cmte.** Appropriations • Natural Resources •
Permanent Select on Intelligence
CoS. Joshua Straka (CD) **LD.** Ben Peterson
Sched. Evelyn Humphrey **PS.** Amanda Yanchury
Dist. Off. St. Paul 651.224.9191

R: 41 **T:** 12th 68%
Elected Year: 2000

MINNESOTA

🐦 Rep. Ilhan Omar (O-mar) D-MN-05 p 202.225.4755

Rm. LHOB 1730 **Web.** omar.house.gov
Bio. 10/04/1982 • Mogadishu • North Dakota State Univ.,
B.A., 2011 • Islam (Muslim) • M. Ahmed Hirsi, 3 ch **Cmte.**
Budget • Education & Workforce
CoS. Connor McNutt **LD.** Kelly Misselwitz
PS. Jeremy Slevin
Dist. Off. Minneapolis 612.333.1272

R: 268 **T:** 3rd 74%
Elected Year: 2018

🐦 Rep. Dean Phillips (FIH-lips) D-MN-03 p 202.225.2871

Rm. RHOB 2452 **Web.** phillips.house.gov **f** 202.225.6351
Bio. 01/20/1969 • St. Paul • Brown Univ. (RI), B.A., 1991;
Univ. of Minnesota, M.B.A., 2000 • Jewish • D., 2 ch **Cmte.**
Foreign Affairs • Small Business
CoS. Tim Bertocci **LD.** Trey Webster
Sched. Mae Hougo (CD) **PS.** Bryan Doyle
Dist. Off. Minnetonka 952.656.5176

R: 271 **T:** 3rd 60%
Elected Year: 2018

🐟 Rep. Pete A. Stauber (STAW-bur) R-MN-08 p 202.225.6211

Rm. CHOB 145 **Web.** stauber.house.gov **f** 202.225.0699
Bio. 05/10/1966 • Duluth • Lake Superior State Univ.,
B.S., 1988 • Catholic • M. Jodi Stauber, 4 ch **Cmte.**
Natural Resources • Small Business • Transportation &
Infrastructure
CoS. Desiree Koetzle **LD.** Allie Esau
Sched. Carolyn Lowrance **PS.** Eli Mansour
Dist. Off. Brainerd 218.355.0862 • Cambridge 763.310.6208
• Chisholm 218.355.0726 • Hermantown 218.481.6396

R: 282 **T:** 3rd 57%
Elected Year: 2018

MISSISSIPPI

🐟 Governor Tate Reeves (reevz) p 601.359.3150

PO Box 139 **C:** Jackson
Jackson, MS 39205 **P:** 2,986,530 (35)
Website mississippi.gov **A:** 46,923.36 mi^2 (31st)
Fax 601.359.3741
Term Ends 2024
Lt. Governor
Delbert Hosemann, **R**

U.S. Senators
Roger F. Wicker, **R**
Cindy Hyde-Smith, **R**
U.S. Representatives
01 / Trent Kelly, **R**
02 / Bennie G. Thompson, **D**
03 / Michael P. Guest, **R**
04 / Mike Ezell, **R**

♣ Sen. Cindy Hyde-Smith ("hide" smith)   R-MS-Jr.   p 202.224.5054

Rm. HSOB 702 **Web.** hydesmith.senate.gov **f** 202.224.5321
Bio. 05/10/1959 • Brookhaven • Copiah-Lincoln
Community College (MS), A.A., 1979; Univ. of Southern
Mississippi, A.A., 1981 • Baptist • M. Michael Smith, 1 ch
Cmte. Agriculture, Nutrition & Forestry • Appropriations •
Energy & Natural Resources • Rules & Administration
CoS. Doug E. Davis   **LD.** Tim Wolverton
Sched. Lindsey Funderburg   **PS.** Chris Gallegos
Dist. Off. Brookhaven 601.748.8024 • Gulfport
228.867.9710 • Jackson 601.965.4459 • Oxford 662.236.1018

R: 74 **T:** 4th 54%
Elected Year: 2018
Next Election: 2026

♣ Sen. Roger F. Wicker (WIH-kur)   R-MS-Sr.   p 202.224.6253

Rm. DSOB 555 **Web.** wicker.senate.gov **f** 202.228.0378
Bio. 07/05/1951 • Pontotoc • State Senator; Attorney • Air
Force 1976-80 • Univ. of Mississippi, B.A., 1973; Univ. of
Mississippi, J.D., 1975 • M. Gayle Long Wicker, 3
ch ; 5 gr-ch **Cmte.** Armed Services • Commerce, Science
& Transportation • Environment & Public Works • Rules &
Administration
CoS. Michelle Barlow
Richardson
Sched. Jen Jett   **PS.** Phillip Waller
Dist. Off. Gulfport 228.871.7017 • Hernando 662.429.1002
• Jackson 601.965.4644 • Tupelo 662.844.5010

R: 27 **T:** 4th 59%
Elected Year: 2007
Next Election: 2024

♣ Rep. Mike Ezell ()   R-MS-04   p 202.225.5772

Rm. CHOB 443 **Web.** ezell.house.gov
Bio. Pascagoula • Univ. of Southern Mississippi, Bach.
Deg., 1997 • Baptist • M. Suzette Ezell, 1 ch ; 1 gr-ch **Cmte.**
Homeland Security • Transportation & Infrastructure
CoS. Joe Nicholson   **LD.** Al David Saab
Sched. Sara Catherine   **PS.** Josh Riggs
Joseph
Dist. Off. Pensacola

R: 381 **T:** 1st 73%
Elected Year: 2022

♣ Rep. Michael P. Guest ("guest")   R-MS-03   p 202.225.5031

Rm. CHOB 450 **Web.** guest.house.gov **f** 202.225.5797
Bio. 02/04/1970 • Woodbury • Mississippi State Univ., B.A.,
1992; Univ. of Mississippi, J.D., 1995 • Baptist • M. Haley
Guest, 2 ch **Cmte.** Appropriations • Ethics • Homeland
Security
CoS. Jordan Downs   **LD.** Elizabeth Joseph
Sched. Debra Boutwell   **PS.** Rob Pillow
(CD)
Dist. Off. Brandon 769.241.6120 • Brookhaven
601.823.3400 • Meridian 601.693.6681 • Starkville
662.324.0007

R: 254 **T:** 3rd 71%
Elected Year: 2018

♣ Rep. Trent Kelly (KEH-lee)   R-MS-01   p 202.225.4306

Rm. RHOB 2243 **Web.** trentkelly.house.gov **f** 202.225.3549
Bio. 03/01/1966 • Union • East Central Community College
(MS), A.A., 1986; Univ. of Mississippi Business School, B.A.,
1989; Univ. of Mississippi Law School, J.D., 1994; Army War
College, M.A., 2010 • Methodist • M. Sheila Kelly Hampton,
3 ch **Cmte.** Agriculture • Armed Services • Permanent
Select on Intelligence
Sched. Stewart Samples   **PS.** Susan Parker (CD)
Dist. Off. Columbus 662.327.0748 • Corinth 662.687.1525
• Eupora 662.687.1545 • Hernando 662.687.0576 • Oxford
662.687.1540 • Tupelo 662.841.8808

R: 187 **T:** 5th 73%
Elected Year: 2015

ᴴ Rep. Bennie G. Thompson (TOMP-suhn) D-MS-02 p 202.225.5876

Rm. RHOB 2466 **Web.** f 202.225.5898
benniethompson.house.gov
Bio. 01/28/1948 • Bolton • County Supervisor, Hinds Co.,
MS; Mayor (Bolton, MS) • Tougaloo College (MS), B.A.,
1968; Jackson State Univ. (MS), M.S., 1972 • Methodist
• M. London Johnson Thompson, 1 ch ; 2 gr-ch **Cmte.**
Homeland Security
CoS. Timla Washington
Sched. Earvin Miers **PS.** Alexus Hunter
Dist. Off. Bolton 601.866.9003 • Greenville 662.335.9003 •
Greenwood 662.455.9003 • Jackson 601.946.9003 • Marks
662.326.9003 • Mound Bayou 662.741.9003

R: 17 **T:** 16th 60%
Elected Year: 1993

MISSOURI

ᴿ Governor Michael L. Parson (PAR-suhn) p 573.751.3222

State Capitol **C:** Jefferson City
PO Box 720 **P:** 6,126,452 (18)
Jefferson City, MO 65102-9500 **A:** 68,741.60 mi^2 (18th)
Website mo.gov
Fax 573.526.3291
Term Ends 2025
Lt. Governor
Mike Kehoe, **R**

U.S. Senators
Josh Hawley, **R**
Eric S. Schmitt, **R**
U.S. Representatives
01 / Cori Bush, **D**
02 / Ann L. Wagner, **R**
03 / Blaine Luetkemeyer, **R**
04 / Mark Alford, **R**
05 / Emanuel Cleaver, **D**
06 / Sam B. Graves, **R**
07 / Eric Burlison, **R**
08 / Jason T. Smith, **R**

ᴿ Sen. Josh Hawley (Haw - l ee) R-MO-Sr. p 202.224.6154

Rm. RSOB 115 **Web.** hawley.senate.gov f 202.228.0526
Bio. 12/31/1979 • Springdale • Stanford Univ. (CA), A.B.,
2002; Yale Law School (CT), J.D., 2006 • Evangelical • M.
Erin Morrow, 3 ch **Cmte.** Energy & Natural Resources •
Homeland Security & Government Affairs • Judiciary •
Small Business & Entrepreneurship
CoS. Chris Weihs **LD.** Michael Velchik
Sched. Ellen James **PS.** Abigail Marone
Dist. Off. Cape Girardeau 573.334.5995 • Columbia
573.554.1919 • Kansas City 816.960.4694 • Springfield
417.869.4433 • St. Louis 314.354.7060

R: 81 **T:** 1st 51%
Elected Year: 2018
Next Election: 2024

ᴿ Sen. Eric S. Schmitt () R-MO-Jr. p 202.224.5721

Rm. RSOB B11 **Web.** schmittforsenate.com
Bio. 06/20/1975 • Bridgeton • Truman State Univ. (MO),
B.A., 1997; Sant Louis Univ. School of Law, J.D., 2000 • M.
Jaime Forrester, 3 ch **Cmte.** Armed Services • Commerce,
Science & Transportation • Joint Economic
CoS. Jimmy Peacock **LD.** Drew Dziedzie
  PS. Will O'Grady
Dist. Off. Columbia 573.514.8680 • Springfield
417.290.5000 • St. Louis 314.230.7263

R: 98 **T:** 1st 55%
Elected Year: 2022
Next Election: 2028

⬛ Rep. Mark Alford ()   R-MO-04   p 202.225.2876

Rm. LHOB 1516 **Web.** alford.house.gov
Bio. 10/04/1963 • Baytown • Univ. of Texas as Austin, Bach.
Deg., 1988 • M. Leslie Adkins, 3 ch **Cmte.** Armed Services
• Small Business
CoS. Michael Martin   **LD.** Tom Dolan
Sched. Elle Stevens   **PS.** Andrew Leppert
Dist. Off. Columbia • Lebanon • Raymore 816.441.6318

R: 362 **T:** 1st 71%
Elected Year: 2022

⬛ Rep. Eric Burlison ()   R-MO-07   p 202.225.6536

Rm. LHOB 1108 **Web.** burlison.house.gov
Bio. 10/02/1976 • Springfield • Missouri State Univ., B.A.,
2000; Missouri State Univ., M.B.A., 2002 • Christian - Non-
Denominational • M. Angie Burlison, 2 ch **Cmte.** Education
& Workforce • Oversight & Accountability • Transportation
& Infrastructure
CoS. Aaron Calkins   **LD.** Kyle McKay
Sched. David Brown   **PS.** Matthew Esguerra
Dist. Off. Joplin 417.781.1041 • Springfield 417.889.1800

R: 367 **T:** 1st 71%
Elected Year: 2022

🔹 Rep. Cori Bush (bush)   D-MO-01   p 202.225.2406

Rm. RHOB 2463 **Web.** bush.house.gov f 202.226.0711
Bio. 07/21/1976 • St. Louis • Christian Non-
Denominational D., 2 ch **Cmte.** Judiciary • Oversight &
Accountability
CoS. Abbas Alawieh   **LD.** Lynese Wallace
Sched. Stephanie Herndon   **PS.** Marina Chafa
Dist. Off. St. Louis 314.955.9980

R: 304 **T:** 2nd 73%
Elected Year: 2020

🔹 Rep. Emanuel Cleaver II (KLEE-vur)   D-MO-05   p 202.225.4535

Rm. RHOB 2217 **Web.** cleaver.house.gov f 202.225.4403
Bio. 10/26/1944 • Waxahachie • Pastor; Mayor (Kansas City,
MO) • Prairie View Agricultural and Mechanical Univ. (TX),
B.S., 1972; St. Paul School of Theology, Kansas City (MO),
M.Div., 1974 • Methodist • M. Dianne Cleaver, 4 ch (twins); 3
gr-ch **Cmte.** Financial Services
CoS. Christina Mahoney   **LD.** Harden Spencer
Sched. Domonique Bell   **PS.** Matthew Helfant
(CD)
Dist. Off. Higginsville 660.584.7373 • Independence
816.833.4545 • Kansas City 816.842.4545

R: 56 **T:** 10th 61%
Elected Year: 2004

⬛ Rep. Sam B. Graves Jr. (grayvz)   R-MO-06   p 202.225.7041

Rm. LHOB 1135 **Web.** graves.house.gov f 202.225.8221
Bio. 11/07/1952 • Tarkio • State Representative • Univ.
of Missouri, Columbia, School of Agriculture, B.S., 1986 •
Baptist • M. Lesley Graves, 3 ch **Cmte.** Armed Services •
Transportation & Infrastructure
CoS. Nick Christensen
Sched. Tucker Brown   **PS.** Bryan Nichols (CD)
Dist. Off. Hannibal 573.221.3400 • Kansas City
816.792.3976 • St. Joseph 816.749.0800

R: 39 **T:** 12th 70%
Elected Year: 2000

⬛ Rep. Blaine Luetkemeyer (LOOT-keh-my-ur)   R-MO-03   p 202.225.2956

Rm. RHOB 2230 **Web.** f 202.225.5712
luetkemeyer.house.gov
Bio. 05/07/1952 • Jefferson City • State Representative;
Banker • Lincoln Univ. (MO), B.A., 1974 • Catholic •
M. Jackie Luetkemeyer, 3 ch ; 4 gr-ch **Cmte.** Financial
Services • Select China Committee • Small Business
CoS. Chad Ramey   **LD.** Meghan Schmidtlein
Sched. Ann Vogel   **PS.** Georgeanna Sullivan
Dist. Off. Jefferson City 573.635.7232 • Washington
636.239.2276 • Wentzville 636.327.7055

R: 87 **T:** 8th 65%
Elected Year: 2008

MISSOURI

♞ Rep. Jason T. Smith (smith)   R-MO-08   p 202.225.4404

Rm. LHOB 1011 **Web.** jasonsmith.house.gov **f** 202.226.0326
Bio. 06/16/1980 • St. Louis • Missouri State Univ., B.S.,
2001; Oklahoma City Univ. Law School (OK), J.D., 2004 •
Assembly of God • NS. **Cmte.** Ways & Means
CoS. Matthew Meyer   **LD.** Hilary Pinegar
Sched. Marshall Stallings
Dist. Off. Cape Girardeau 573.335.0101 • Farmington
573.756.9755 • Poplar Bluff 573.609.2996 • Rolla
573.364.2455 • West Plains 417.255.1515

R: 155   **T:** 6th 76%
Elected Year: 2013

♞ Rep. Ann L. Wagner (WAG-nur)   R-MO-02   p 202.225.1621

Rm. RHOB 2350 **Web.** wagner.house.gov **f** 202.225.2563
Bio. 09/13/1962 • St. Louis • Univ. of Missouri, B.S., 1984 •
Roman Catholic • M. Raymond T. Wagner Jr., 3 ch **Cmte.**
Financial Services • Foreign Affairs
CoS. Charlie Keller   **LD.** Molly Joseph
Sched. Emily Ann Smith   **PS.** Arthur Bryant
Dist. Off. Ballwin 636.779.5449

R: 150   **T:** 6th 55%
Elected Year: 2012

MONTANA

♞ Governor Greg Gianforte (JEE-uhn-for-tay)   p 406.444.3111

Montana State Capitol Building   **C:** Helena
PO Box 200801   **P:** 1,062,305 (44)
Helena, MT 59620-0801   **A:** 145,545.78 mi^2 (4th)
Website mt.gov
Fax 406.444.5529
Term Ends 2025
Lt. Governor
Kristen Juras, R

U.S. Senators
Jon Tester, **D**
Steve Daines, **R**
U.S. Representatives
01 / Ryan K. Zinke, R
02 / Matt M. Rosendale, R

♞ Sen. Steve Daines (daynz)   R-MT-Jr.   p 202.224.2651

Rm. HSOB 320 **Web.** daines.senate.gov **f** 202.228.1236
Bio. 08/20/1962 • Van Nuys • Montana State Univ.,
Bozeman, B.S., 1984 • Presbyterian • M. Cindy Daines, 4 ch
Cmte. Banking, Housing & Urban Affairs • Energy & Natural
Resources • Finance • Indian Affairs
CoS. Darin C. Thacker   **LD.** Dan Gerig
Sched. Caitlin Affolter   **PS.** Katie Schoettler
Dist. Off. Billings 406.245.6822 • Bozeman 406.587.3446
• Great Falls 406.453.0148 • Helena 406.443.3189 •
Kalispell 406.257.3765 • Missoula 406.549.8198 • Sidney
406.482.9010

R: 62   **T:** 2nd 55%
Elected Year: 2014
Next Election: 2026

MONTANA

⚑ Sen. Jon Tester (TEHSS-tur)   D-MT-Sr.   p 202.224.2644

Rm. HSOB 311 **Web.** tester.senate.gov   **f** 202.224.8594
Bio. 08/21/1956 • Havre • Farmer • Univ. of Great Falls
(MT), B.Mus., 1978 • Christian Church • M. Sharla Tester,
2 ch ; 2 gr-ch **Cmte.** Appropriations • Banking, Housing
& Urban Affairs • Commerce, Science & Transportation •
Indian Affairs • Veterans' Affairs
CoS. Dylan Laslovich   **LD.** Justin Folsom
Sched. Corine Weiler   **PS.** Sarah Feldman
Dist. Off. Billings 406.252.0550 • Bozeman 406.586.4450
• Butte 406.723.3277 • Great Falls 406.452.9585 •
Helena 406.449.5401 • Kalispell 406.257.3360 • Missoula
406.728.3003

R: 25   **T:** 3rd   50%
Elected Year: 2006
Next Election: 2024

⚑ Rep. Matt M. Rosendale Sr. (RO-zuhn-dayl)   R-MT-02   p 202.225.3211

Rm. LHOB 1023 **Web.** rosendale.house.gov
Bio. 07/07/1960 • Baltimore • Catholic • M. Jean
Rosendale, 3 ch **Cmte.** Natural Resources • Veterans'
Affairs
CoS. Trevor Whetstone   **LD.** Babs Hough
Sched. Aashka Varma   **PS.** Grace Davis

R: 340   **T:** 2nd   57%
Elected Year: 2020

⚑ Rep. Ryan K. Zinke (ZINK)   R-MT-01   p 202.225.5628

Rm. CHOB 512 **Web.** ryanzinke.com
Bio. 11/01/1961 • Bozeman • Univ. of Oregon, B.S., 1984;
National Univ. (CA), M.B.A., 1991; Univ. of San Diego, M.S.,
2003 • Lutheran • M. Lolita Hand, 2 ch; 1 stepch (wife had/
w prev marriage); 1 gr-ch **Cmte.** Appropriations
CoS. Heather Swift   **LD.** Ben Van Sickle
Sched. Ashley Bianco   **PS.** Colton Snedecor
Dist. Off. Whitefish 406.442.6633

R: 361   **T:** 1st   50%
Elected Year: 2022

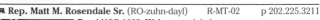

NEBRASKA

⚑ Governor James (Jim) D. Pillen ()   p 402.471.2244

State Capitol
PO Box 94848
Lincoln, NE 68509-4848
Website nebraska.gov
Fax 402.471.6031
Term Ends 2027
Lt. Governor
Joseph (Joe) Patrick Kelly, R

C: Lincoln
P: 1,929,268 (38)
A: 76,824.26 mi^2 (15th)

U.S. Senators
Deb Fischer, **R**
Pete Ricketts, **R**
U.S. Representatives
01 / Mike Flood, **R**
02 / Don J. Bacon, **R**
03 / Adrian M. Smith, **R**

NEBRASKA

NEBRASKA

♟ Sen. Deb Fischer (FIH-shur)   R-NE-Sr.   p 202.224.6551

Rm. RSOB 454 **Web.** fischer.senate.gov   **f** 202.228.1325
Bio. 03/01/1951 • Lincoln • Univ. of Nebraska, Lincoln, B.S.,
1988 • Presbyterian • M. Bruce G. Fischer, 3 ch ; 3 gr-ch
Cmte. Agriculture, Nutrition & Forestry • Appropriations •
Armed Services • Commerce, Science & Transportation •
Ethics • Rules & Administration
CoS. Emily Leviner   **LD.** Laura Lee Burkett
Sched. Abigail G. Stahl   **PS.** Nathaniel Sizemore
Dist. Off. Kearney 308.234.2361 • Lincoln 402.441.4600 •
Omaha 402.391.3411 • Scottsbluff 308.630.2329

R: 54 **T:** 2nd 58%
Elected Year: 2012
Next Election: 2024

♟ Sen. Pete Ricketts ()   R-NE-Jr.   p 202.224.4224

Rm. DSOB 40D **Web.** ricketts.senate.gov
Bio. 08/19/1964 • Nebraska City • Univ. of Chicago (IL),
B.S.; Univ. of Chicago (IL), M.B.A. • Roman Catholic • M.
Susanne Shore, 3 ch **Cmte.** Aging • Environment & Public
Works • Judiciary

R: 100 **T:** 1st
Elected Year: 2023
Next Election: 2026

♟ Rep. Don J. Bacon (BAY-kun)   R-NE-02   p 202.225.4155

Rm. RHOB 2104 **Web.** bacon.house.gov
Bio. 08/16/1963 • Momence • Northern Illinois Univ., B.A.,
1984; Univ. of Phoenix, M.S., 1995; National War College
(DC), Mast. Deg., 2004; Univ. of Virginia Darden School of
Business, M.S., 2009 • Christian - Non-Denominational • M.
Angie Bacon, 4 ch **Cmte.** Agriculture • Armed Services
CoS. Mark Edward Dreiling   **LD.** Jeff Kratz
                                PS. Danielle Jensen (CD)
Dist. Off. Omaha 402.938.0300

R: 195 **T:** 4th 51%
Elected Year: 2016

♟ Rep. Mike Flood ()   R-NE-01   p 202.225.4806

Rm. CHOB 343 **Web.** flood.house.gov   **f** 202.225.5686
Bio. 02/23/1975 • Omaha • Univ. of Notre Dame (IN), B.A.,
1997; Univ. of Nebraska Law School, Lincoln, J.D., 2001
• Catholic • M. Mandi Guernsey, 2 ch **Cmte.** Financial
Services
CoS. Jake Dumas   **LD.** Curt Bliamptis
Sched. Shelby McKee   **PS.** Taylor Gage
Dist. Off. Lincoln 402.438.1598

R: 356 **T:** 2nd 58%
Elected Year: 2022

♟ Rep. Adrian M. Smith (smith)   R-NE-03   p 202.225.6435

Rm. CHOB 502 **Web.** adriansmith.house.gov **f** 202.225.0207
Bio. 12/19/1970 • Scottsbluff • State Legislator; Realtor •
Univ. of Nebraska, Lincoln, B.S., 1993 • Evangelical • M.
Andrea Smith, 1 ch **Cmte.** Ways & Means
CoS. Monica Didiuk   **LD.** Joshua Jackson
Sched. Becca Salter   **PS.** Tiffany Haverly
Dist. Off. Grand Island 308.384.3900 • Scottsbluff
308.633.6333

R: 79 **T:** 9th 78%
Elected Year: 2006

NEVADA

🏛 Governor Joseph (Joe) Michael Lombardo ()   p 775.684.5670

State Capitol
101 N. Carson St.
Carson City, NV 89701
Website nv.gov
Fax 775.684.5683
Term Ends 2027
Lt. Governor
Stavros S. Anthony, **R**

C: Carson City
P: 3,034,392 (33)
A: 109,781.15 mi² (7th)

U.S. Senators
Catherine Cortez Masto, **D**
Jacky S. Rosen, **D**
U.S. Representatives
01 / Dina Titus, **D**
02 / Mark E. Amodei, **R**
03 / Susie K. Lee, **D**
04 / Steven A. Horsford, **D**

🔟 Sen. Catherine Cortez Masto (kor-TEZ-MASS-toe) D-NV-Sr.   p 202.224.3542

Bio. 03/29/1964 • Las Vegas • Univ. of Nevada, Reno, B.S., 1986; Gonzaga Univ. School of Law, J.D., 1990 • Catholic • M. Paul Masto **Cmte.** Banking, Housing & Urban Affairs • Energy & Natural Resources • Finance • Indian Affairs
CoS. Scott Fairchild (CD)   **LD.** Bridget Kelleher (CD)
                                 PS. Tony Hernandez (CD)
Dist. Off. Las Vegas 702.388.5020 • Reno 775.686.5750

R: 72 **T:** 2nd 49%
Elected Year: 2016
Next Election: 2028

🔟 Sen. Jacky S. Rosen (RO-zuhn)   D-NV-Jr.   p

Web. rosen.senate.gov
Bio. 08/02/1957 • Chicago • Univ. of Minnesota, B.A., 1979 • Jewish • M. Larry Rosen, 1 ch **Cmte.** Armed Services • Commerce, Science & Transportation • Homeland Security & Government Affairs • Small Business & Entrepreneurship
CoS. Dara Cohen (CD)   **LD.** Grant Dubler (CD)
Sched. Nicole Echeto (CD) **PS.** Renzo Olivari (CD)
Dist. Off. Las Vegas 702.388.0205 • Reno 775.337.0110

R: 78 **T:** 1st 50%
Elected Year: 2018
Next Election: 2024

🏛 Rep. Mark E. Amodei (AM-uh-day)   R-NV-02   p 202.225.6155

Rm. CHOB 104 **Web.** amodei.house.gov   **f** 202.225.5679
Bio. 06/12/1958 • Carson City • Univ. of Nevada, Reno, B.A., 1980; Univ. of the Pacific McGeorge School of Law (CA), J.D., 1983 • Presbyterian • D., 2 ch **Cmte.** Appropriations
CoS. Molly Cutrona   **LD.** Ken Brooke
Sched. Marie Jackson
Dist. Off. Elko 775.777.7705 • Reno 775.686.5760

R: 118 **T:** 7th 60%
Elected Year: 2011

NEVADA

⌐ Rep. Steven A. Horsford (HORSS-furd)   D-NV-04   p 202.225.9894

Rm. CHOB 406 **Web.** horsford.house.gov   **f** 202.225.9783
Bio. 04/29/1973 • Las Vegas • NV State Senator • Univ. of
Nevada, Reno, B.A., 2014 • Baptist • M. Dr. Sonya Horsford,
3 ch   **Cmte.** Armed Services • Financial Services
CoS. Asha Jones (CD)   **LD.** LaVontae Brooks
Sched. Larissa Fernandez   **PS.** Miguel Ayala
Dist. Off. North Las Vegas 702.963.9360

R: 234   **T:** 3rd 52%
Elected Year: 2018

⌐ Rep. Susie K. Lee (lee)   D-NV-03   p 202.225.3252

Rm. CHOB 365 **Web.** susielee.house.gov   **f** 202.225.2185
Bio. 11/07/1966 • Canton • Carnegie Mellon Univ., B.S.,
1989; Carnegie Mellon Univ., M.P.A., 1990 • Catholic • M.
Dan Lee, 2 ch   **Cmte.** Appropriations
CoS. Lauren Toy   **LD.** Bowen Peard
Sched. Katherine   **PS.** Henry Novak
  Zimmermann
Dist. Off. Las Vegas 702.963.9336

R: 261   **T:** 3rd 52%
Elected Year: 2018

⌐ Rep. Dina Titus (TY-tuhs)   D-NV-01   p 202.225.5965

Rm. RHOB 2464 **Web.** titus.house.gov   **f** 202.225.3119
Bio. 05/23/1950 • Thomasville • State Legislator; Professor
• College of William and Mary (VA), A.B., 1970; Univ.
of Georgia, M.A., 1973; Florida State Univ., Ph.D., 1976
• Greek Orthodox • M. Thomas Clayton Wright **Cmte.**
Foreign Affairs • Homeland Security • Transportation &
Infrastructure
CoS. Jay Gertsema   **LD.** Mitchell Moonier
    PS. Ryan Radulovacki
Dist. Off. Las Vegas 702.220.9823

R: 123   **T:** 6th 52%
Elected Year: 2012

NEW HAMPSHIRE

NEW HAMPSHIRE

⌐ Governor Chris Sununu (suh-NOO-noo)   p 603.271.2121

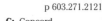

State House   **C:** Concord
107 N. Main St.   **P:** 1,356,458 (42)
Concord, NH 03301   **A:** 8,952.55 mi^2 (44th)
Website nh.gov
Fax 603.271.7640
Term Ends 2025

U.S. Senators
Jeanne Shaheen, **D**
Maggie Hassan, **D**
U.S. Representatives
01 / Chris C. Pappas, **D**
02 / Ann McLane Kuster, **D**

⚑ Sen. Maggie Hassan (HAS-suhn)　　　D-NH-Jr.　　p 202.224.3324

Rm. HSOB 324　**Web.** hassan.senate.gov　　**f** 202.228.0581
Bio. 02/27/1958 • Boston • Brown Univ. (RI), A.B., 1980;
Northeastern Univ. Law School (MA), J.D., 1985 • United
Church of Christ • M. Thomas Hassan, 2 ch　**Cmte.** Finance
• Health, Education, Labor & Pensions • Homeland Security
& Government Affairs • Joint Economic • Veterans' Affairs
CoS. Marc Goldberg　　　　**LD.** Dave Christie
Sched. Catherine Toner　　　**PS.** Laura Epstein
Dist. Off.　Berlin 603.752.6190 • Concord 603.622.2204
• Manchester 603.622.2204 • Nashua 603.622.2204 •
Portsmouth 603.433.4445

R: 70　**T:** 2nd　54%
Elected Year: 2016
Next Election: 2028

⚑ Sen. Jeanne Shaheen (shuh-HEEN)　　　D-NH-Sr.　　p 202.224.2841

Rm. HSOB 506　**Web.** shaheen.senate.gov　　**f** 202.228.3194
Bio. 01/28/1947 • St. Charles • Governor, NH; State
Legislator; Teacher • Shippensburg Univ. (PA), B.A., 1969;
Univ. of Mississippi, M.S., 1973 • Protestant - Unspecified
Christian • M. William Shaheen, 3 ch ; 7 gr-ch　**Cmte.**
Appropriations • Armed Services • Ethics • Foreign
Relations • Small Business & Entrepreneurship
CoS. Jennifer MacLellan　　**LD.** Ariel Marshall
Sched. Meaghan D'Arcy　　　**PS.** Sarah Weinstein
Dist. Off.　Berlin 603.752.6300 • Claremont 603.542.4872
• Dover 603.750.3004 • Keene 603.358.6604 • Manchester
603.647.7500 • Nashua 603.883.0196

R: 28　**T:** 3rd　57%
Elected Year: 2008
Next Election: 2026

⚑ Rep. Ann McLane Kuster (mih-KLAIN-KUM-ster)　　D-NH-02　p 202.225.5206

Rm. RHOB 2201　**Web.** kuster.house.gov　　**f** 202.225.2946
Bio. 09/05/1956 • Concord • Dartmouth College, A.B.,
1978; Georgetown Univ. Law Center (DC), J.D., 1984 •
Christian Church • M. Brad Kuster, 2 ch　**Cmte.** Agriculture
• Energy & Commerce
CoS. Patrick Devney　　　**LD.** Will Pisano
Sched. Miriam Young　　　　**PS.** Annie Lentz
Dist. Off.　Concord 603.226.1002 • Littleton 603.444.7700 •
Nashua 603.595.2006

R: 138　**T:** 6th　56%
Elected Year: 2012

⚑ Rep. Chris C. Pappas (PAP-puhss)　　　D-NH-01　　p 202.225.5456

Rm. CHOB 452　**Web.** pappas.house.gov
Bio. 06/04/1980 • Manchester • Harvard College (MA),
B.A., 2002 • Greek Orthodox • E. Vann Bentley　**Cmte.** Small
Business • Transportation & Infrastructure • Veterans' Affairs
CoS. Steven Carlson　　　**LD.** Nandini Narayan
Sched. Alex Siegal　　　　**PS.** Kristen Morris
Dist. Off.　Dover 603.285.4300 • Manchester 603.935.6710

R: 269　**T:** 3rd　54%
Elected Year: 2018

NEW JERSEY

⚑ Governor Phil Murphy (MUR-fee)　　　　　　　p 609.292.6000

The State House
PO Box 001
Trenton, NJ 08625
Website nj.gov
Fax 609.292.3454
Term Ends 2026
Lt. Governor
Sheila Oliver, **D**

C: Trenton
P: 8,908,520 (11)
A: 7,354.08 mi^2 (46th)

NEW JERSEY

U.S. Senators
Bob Menendez, **D**
Cory Booker, **D**
U.S. Representatives
01 / Donald W. Norcross, **D**
02 / Jefferson Van Drew, **R**
03 / Andy Kim, **D**
04 / Chris H. Smith, **R**
05 / Josh S. Gottheimer, **D**
06 / Frank J. Pallone, **D**
07 / Thomas H. Kean, **R**
08 / Robert J. Menendez, **D**
09 / Bill J. Pascrell, **D**
10 / Donald M. Payne, **D**
11 / Mikie Sherrill, **D**
12 / Bonnie Watson Coleman, **D**

🔊 Sen. Cory Booker ("BOOK"-ur)　　　　D-NJ-Jr.　　p 202.224.3224

Rm. HSOB 717　**Web.** booker.senate.gov　**f** 202.224.8378
Bio. 04/27/1969 • Washington • Stanford Univ. (CA), B.A.,
1991; Stanford Univ. (CA), M.A., 1992; Yale Law School (CT),
J.D., 1997 • Baptist • S.　**Cmte.** Agriculture, Nutrition &
Forestry • Foreign Relations • Judiciary • Small Business &
Entrepreneurship
CoS. Veronica Duron　　　　**LD.** Leah Hill
Sched. Andrew Serrano　　　**PS.** Jeff Giertz
Dist. Off. Camden 856.338.8922 • Newark 973.639.8700

R: 56　**T:** 3rd 57%
Elected Year: 2013
Next Election: 2026

🔊 Sen. Bob Menendez (meh-NEN-dehz)　　　D-NJ-Sr.　　p 202.224.4744

Rm. HSOB 528　**Web.** menendez.senate.gov　**f** 202.228.2197
Bio. 01/01/1954 • New York • State Senator; Mayor of Union
City • St. Peter's College (NJ), B.A., 1976; Rutgers Univ.
Law School (NJ), J.D., 1979 • Roman Catholic • M. Nadine
Arslanian, 2 ch (2 from previous marriage)　**Cmte.** Banking,
Housing & Urban Affairs • Finance • Foreign Relations
CoS. Jason Tuber　　　　　**LD.** Rebecca Schatz
Sched. Maria Almeida (CD)　**PS.** Francisco Pelayo
Dist. Off. Barrington 856.757.5353 • Jersey City
973.645.3030

R: 18　**T:** 3rd 54%
Elected Year: 2006
Next Election: 2024

🔊 Rep. Josh S. Gottheimer (GAHT-hy-mur)　　D-NJ-05　　p 202.225.4465

Rm. CHOB 203　**Web.** gottheimer.house.gov　**f** 202.225.9048
Bio. 03/08/1975 • Livingston • Univ. of Pennsylvania, B.A.,
1997; Harvard Law School (MA), J.D., 2004 • Jewish • M.
Marla Brooke Tusk Gottheimer, 2 ch　**Cmte.** Financial
Services • Permanent Select on Intelligence
CoS. Chelsea Brossard　　　　**LD.** Eliza Ramirez
Sched. Jonathan Older　　　　**PS.** Christopher D'Aloia
Dist. Off. Glen Rock 201.389.1100 • Hackensack
973.814.4076 • Newton 973.940.1117 • Ringwood
973.814.4076 • Vernon Township 973.814.4076

R: 210　**T:** 4th 55%
Elected Year: 2016

🔊 Rep. Thomas H. Kean Jr. ()　　　　R-NJ-07　　p 202.225.5361

Rm. CHOB 251　**Web.** kean.house.gov
Bio. 09/05/1968 • Livingston • Tufts Univ. Fletcher School
of Law and Diplomacy (MA), M.A.; Dartmouth College, B.A.,
1990 • Episcopalian • M. Rhonda Kean, 2 ch　**Cmte.** Foreign
Affairs • Science, Space & Technology • Transportation &
Infrastructure
CoS. Danielle Stewart　　　　**LD.** Christopher Hall
Sched. Samantha Moore　　　**PS.** Dan Scharfenberger
Dist. Off. Bridgewater 908.547.3307

R: 397　**T:** 1st 51%
Elected Year: 2022

⚑ Rep. Andy Kim (kim) D-NJ-03 p 202.225.4765

Rm. RHOB 2444 **Web.** kim.house.gov **f** 202.225.0778
Bio. 07/12/1982 • Boston • Univ. of Chicago (IL), B.A., 2004; Oxford Univ. (UK), M.Phil, 2007; Univ. of Oxford (UK), Ph.D., 2010 • Presbyterian • M. Kammy Kim, 2 ch **Cmte.** Armed Services • Foreign Affairs • Select China Committee
CoS. Amy Pfeiffer **LD.** Thomas Carnes
Sched. Hafiza Kazi **PS.** Forrest Rilling
Dist. Off. Willingboro 856.703.2700

R: 260 **T:** 3rd 56%
Elected Year: 2018

⚑ Rep. Robert J. Menendez Jr. () D-NJ-08 p 202.225.7919

Rm. LHOB 1007 **Web.** menendez.house.gov
Bio. 07/12/1985 • • Univ. of North Carolina at Chapel Hill, B.A.; Rutgers Law School (NJ), J.D., 2011 • M. Alex Banfich, 2 ch **Cmte.** Homeland Security • Transportation & Infrastructure
CoS. Claudia Urrabazo-Beckelman
Sched. Mitchell Dunn **PS.** Michael Zhadanovsky
Dist. Off. Jersey City 201.309.0301

R: 411 **T:** 1st 73%
Elected Year: 2022

⚑ Rep. Donald W. Norcross (NOR-krawss) D-NJ-01 p 202.225.6501

Rm. RHOB 2427 **Web.** norcross.house.gov **f** 202.225.0442
Bio. 12/13/1958 • Camden • Camden County College (NJ), A.S. 1979; Ironworan • M. Andrea Doran, 3 ch; 3 gr-ch **Cmte.** Armed Services • Education & Workforce
CoS. Todd Sloves **LD.** Hannah Cooper
Sched. Kyle McCarthy **PS.** Britton Burdick
Dist. Off. Camden 856.427.7000 • Cherry Hill 856.427.7000

R: 158 **T:** 6th 62%
Elected Year: 2014

⚑ Rep. Frank J. Pallone Jr. (puh-LOAN) D-NJ-06 p 202.225.4671

Rm. RHOB 2107 **Web.** pallone.house.gov **f** 202.225.9665
Bio. 10/30/1951 • Long Branch • State Senator; Member, City Council • Middlebury College (VT), B.A., 1973; Tufts Univ. Fletcher School of Law and Diplomacy (MA), M.A., 1974; Rutgers Univ. Law School (NJ), J.D., 1978 • Roman Catholic • M. Sarah Hospodor Pallone, 3 ch **Cmte.** Energy & Commerce
CoS. Liam Fitzsimmons **LD.** James Johnson
Sched. Saman Haider **PS.** Mary Werden
Dist. Off. Long Branch 732.571.1140 • New Brunswick 732.249.8892

R: 6 **T:** 18th 58%
Elected Year: 1988

⚑ Rep. Bill J. Pascrell Jr. (PASS-krell) D-NJ-09 p 202.225.5751

Rm. RHOB 2409 **Web.** pascrell.house.gov **f** 202.225.5782
Bio. 01/25/1937 • Paterson • Attorney • Army 1961-62; Army Reserves 1962-67 • Fordham Univ. (NY), B.S., 1959; Fordham Univ. (NY), M.A., 1961 • Roman Catholic • M. Elsie Marie Botto Pascrell, 3 ch ; 3 gr-ch **Cmte.** Ways & Means
CoS. Benjamin Rich **LD.** Dylan Sodaro
Sched. Francesco Hanson **PS.** Mark Greenbaum
Dist. Off. Englewood 201.935.2248 • Lyndhurst 201.935.2248 • Passaic 973.472.4510 • Paterson 973.523.5152

R: 28 **T:** 14th 55%
Elected Year: 1996

⚑ Rep. Donald M. Payne Jr. (pain) D-NJ-10 p 202.225.3436

Rm. CHOB 106 **Web.** payne.house.gov **f** 202.225.4160
Bio. 12/17/1958 • Newark • Baptist • M. Bea Payne, 3 ch (triplets) **Cmte.** Homeland Security • Transportation & Infrastructure
CoS. LaVerne Alexander **LD.** Sam Morgante
Sched. Wendy Featherson **PS.** Patrick Wright
Dist. Off. Hillside 862.229.2994 • Jersey City 201.369.0392 • Newark 973.645.3213

R: 122 **T:** 7th 78%
Elected Year: 2012

NEW JERSEY

☙ Rep. Mikie Sherrill (SHAIR-uhl) D-NJ-11 p 202.225.5034

Rm. LHOB 1427 **Web.** sherrill.house.gov **f** 202.225.3186
Bio. 01/19/1972 • Alexandria • U.S. Naval Academy (MD),
B.S., 1994; London School of Economics and Political
Science, Mast. Deg., 2003; Georgetown Univ. (DC), J.D.,
2007 • Catholic • M. Jason Hedberg, 4 ch **Cmte.** Armed
Services • Select China Committee
CoS. Alex Ball **LD.** Isaac Loeb
Sched. Harlow Poteete **PS.** Charlotte Laracy
Dist. Off. Parsippany 973.526.5668

R: 278 **T:** 3rd 59%
Elected Year: 2018

☙ Rep. Chris H. Smith (smith) R-NJ-04 p 202.225.3765

Rm. RHOB 2373 **Web.** chrissmith.house.gov **f** 202.225.7768
Bio. 03/04/1953 • Rahway • State Legislator; Wholesaler
• Trenton State College (NJ), B.A., 1975 • Roman Catholic
• M. Marie Hahn Smith, 4 ch **Cmte.** Foreign Affairs • Joint
Congressional-Executive Commission on China
CoS. Mary Noonan
Sched. Kathryn Latona **PS.** Michael Finan
Dist. Off. Middletown 732.780.3035 • Toms River
732.504.0567

R: 2 **T:** 22nd 67%
Elected Year: 1980

☙ Rep. Jefferson Van Drew (van-DROO) R-NJ-02 p 202.225.6572

Rm. RHOB 2447 **Web.** vandrew.house.gov
Bio. 02/23/1953 • New York • Rutgers Univ. Cook College
(NJ), B.S., 1975; Fairleigh Dickinson Univ. School of Dentistry
(NJ), D.D.S., 1979 • Catholic • M. Ricarda Drew, 2 ch **Cmte.**
Judiciary • Transportation & Infrastructure
CoS. Allison Murphy **LD.** Trevor Ray
Sched. Alyson Kerr (CD) **PS.** Ashley Brown
Dist. Off. Northfield 609.625.5008

R: 291 **T:** 3rd 59%
Elected Year: 2018

☙ Rep. Bonnie Watson Coleman (WAHT-suhn KOAL-muhn) D-NJ-12 p 202.225.5801

Rm. CHOB 168 **Web.** **f** 202.225.6025
watsoncoleman.house.gov
Bio. 02/06/1945 • Camden • Thomas Edison State College
(NJ), B.A., 1985 • Baptist • M. William E. Coleman Jr., 1 ch ;
2 stepch ; 3 gr-ch **Cmte.** Appropriations
CoS. Alex Huang
Sched. Jaimee Gilmartin **PS.** Owen Stidman
(CD)
Dist. Off. Ewing 609.883.0026

R: 185 **T:** 5th 63%
Elected Year: 2014

NEW MEXICO

☙ Governor Michelle Lujan Grisham (LOO-hahn GRIH-shuhm) p 505.476.2200

State Capitol
490 Old Sante Fe Trail, Room 400
Santa Fe, NM 87501
Website newmexico.gov
Fax 505.476.2226
Term Ends 2027
Lt. Governor
Howie Morales, **D**

C: Santa Fe
P: 2,095,428 (37)
A: 121,298.19 mi^2 (5th)

U.S. Senators
Martin T. Heinrich, **D**
Ben Ray Luján, **D**
U.S. Representatives
01 / Melanie A. Stansbury, **D**
02 / Gabe Vasquez, **D**
03 / Teresa Isabel Leger
Fernandez, **D**

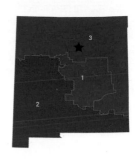

🔷 Sen. Martin T. Heinrich (HYN-rihk)　　　　D-NM-Sr.　p 202.224.5521

Rm. HSOB 303 **Web.** heinrich.senate.gov　**f** 202.228.2841
Bio. 10/17/1971 • Fallon • Businessman • Univ. of Missouri,
B.S., 1995 • Lutheran • M. Julie Heinrich, 2 ch **Cmte.**
Appropriations • Energy & Natural Resources • Intelligence
• Joint Economic
CoS. Rebecca Avitia
LD. Dominic Saavedra
PS. Whitney Potter
Dist. Off. Albuquerque 505.346.6601 • Farmington
505.325.5030 • Las Cruces 575.523.6561 • Roswell
575.622.7113 • Santa Fe 505.988.6647

R: 49　**T:** 2nd 54%
Elected Year: 2012
Next Election: 2024

🔷 Sen. Ben Ray Luján Jr. (LOO-hahn)　　　　D-NM-Jr.　p 202.224.6621

Rm. RSOB 498　　　　　　　　　　**f** 202.224.3370
Bio. 06/07/1972 • Santa Fe • Chairman, New Mexico Public
Regulation Commission • New Mexico Highlands Univ.,
B.B.A., 2007 • Roman Catholic • S. **Cmte.** Agriculture,
Nutrition & Forestry • Budget • Commerce, Science &
Transportation • Health, Education, Labor & Pensions •
Indian Affairs
CoS. Carlos Sanchez
LD. Graham Mason
Sched. Rebekah Kirkwood
PS. Katherine Schneider
Dist. Off. Las Cruces 575.526.5475 • Las Vegas • Portales
575.252.6188 • Santa Fe

R: 84　**T:** 1st 52%
Elected Year: 2020
Next Election: 2026

🔷 Rep. Teresa Isabel Leger Fernandez (LEDGE-er　D-NM-03　p 202.225.6190
fehr-NAHN-dess)

Rm. LHOB 1510 **Web.** fernandez.house.gov　**f** 202.225.1528
Bio. 07/01/1959 • Las Vegas • Yale Univ. (CT), B.A., 1982;
Stanford Law School (CA), J.D., 1987 • Catholic • D., 3 ch
Cmte. Education & Workforce • Natural Resources • Rules
CoS. Nathan Schelble
LD. Elizabeth Arevalo
Sched. Chris Garcia
PS. Nairka Trevino Muller
Dist. Off. Las Vegas 505.570.7558 • Santa Fe 505.428.4680

R: 325　**T:** 2nd 58%
Elected Year: 2020

🔷 Rep. Melanie A. Stansbury ()　　　　　D-NM-01　p 202.225.6316

Rm. LHOB 1421 **Web.** stansbury.house.gov
Bio. 01/31/1979 • Albuquerque • Saint Mary's College
of California, B.S.; Cornell Univ. (NY), M.S.; Cornell Univ.
(NY), Ph.D. • NS. **Cmte.** Natural Resources • Oversight &
Accountability
CoS. Scott Forrester
LD. Ian Fluellen
Sched. Libertie Green
PS. Julia Friedmann
Dist. Off. Albuquerque 505.346.6781

R: 351　**T:** 2nd 56%
Elected Year: 2021

NEW MEXICO

Rep. Gabe Vasquez () D-NM-02 p 202.225.2365

Rm. LHOB 1517 **Web.** gabeforcongress.com
Bio. 08/03/1984 • El Paso • New Mexico State Univ., Bach.
Deg., 2008 • **Cmte.** Armed Services
LD. Austin Yager
Sched. Audrey Jimenez **PS.** Valeria Ojeda-Avitia
Dist. Off. Las Cruces

R: 433 **T:** 1st 50%
Elected Year: 2022

NEW YORK

NEW YORK

Governor Kathy Hochul () p 518.474.8390

State Capitol **C:** Albany
Executive Chambers **P:** 19,542,209 (4)
Albany, NY 12224 **A:** 47,126.45 mi^2 (30th)
Website ny.gov
Fax 518.474.1513
Term Ends 2026
Lt. Governor
Antonio Ramon Delgado, D

U.S. Senators
Chuck E. Schumer, **D**
Kirsten E. Gillibrand, **D**
U.S. Representatives
01 / Nicholas J. LaLota, **R**
02 / Andrew R. Garbarino, **R**
03 / George Santos, **R**
04 / Anthony P. D'Esposito, **R**
05 / Gregory W. Meeks, **D**
06 / Grace Meng, **D**
07 / Nydia M. Velazquez, **D**
08 / Hakeem Jeffries, **D**
09 / Yvette D. Clarke, **D**
10 / Daniel Goldman, **D**
11 / Nicole Malliotakis, **R**
12 / Jerry L. Nadler, **D**
13 / Adriano Espaillat, **D**
14 / Alexandria Ocasio-Cortez, **D**
15 / Ritchie John Torres, **D**
16 / Jamaal A. Bowman, **D**
17 / Michael V. Lawler, **R**
18 / Patrick Ryan, **D**
19 / Marcus J. Molinaro, **R**
20 / Paul D. Tonko, **D**
21 / Elise Stefanik, **R**
22 / Brandon Williams, **R**
23 / Nicholas A. Langworthy, **R**
24 / Claudia Tenney, **R**
25 / Joseph D. Morelle, **D**
26 / Brian M. Higgins, **D**

Sen. Kirsten E. Gillibrand (JIH-luh-brand) D-NY-Jr. p 202.224.4451

Rm. RSOB 478 **Web.** gillibrand.senate.gov **f** 202.228.4977
Bio. 12/09/1966 • Albany • Attorney • Dartmouth College,
B.A., 1988; Univ. of California, Los Angeles, J.D., 1991 •
Roman Catholic • M. Jonathan Gillibrand, 2 ch **Cmte.**
Aging • Agriculture, Nutrition & Forestry • Armed Services •
Intelligence
CoS. Jess C. Fassler **LD.** Gilbert Ruiz
Sched. Jennifer Dean **PS.** Evan T. Lukaske
Dist. Off. Albany 518.431.0120 • Buffalo 716.854.9725
• Lowville 315.376.6118 • Melville 631.249.2825 • New
York 212.688.6262 • Rochester 585.263.6250 • Syracuse
315.448.0470 • Yonkers 845.875.4585

R: 33 **T:** 4th 67%
Elected Year: 2009
Next Election: 2024

⚑ Sen. Chuck E. Schumer (SHOO-mur) D-NY-Sr. p 202.224.6542

Rm. HSOB 322 **Web.** schumer.senate.gov **f** 202.228.3027
Bio. 11/23/1950 • Brooklyn • U.S. Representative; Attorney
• Harvard Univ., B.A., 1971; Harvard Univ., J.D., 1974 •
Jewish • M. Iris Weinshall, 2 ch ; 2 gr-ch **Cmte.** Intelligence
• Rules & Administration
CoS. Michael Lynch **LD.** Meghan Taira
Sched. Kellie Karney **PS.** Allison Biasotti
Dist. Off. Albany 518.431.4070 • Binghamton 607.772.6792
• Buffalo 716.846.4111 • Melville 631.753.0978 • New
York 212.486.4430 • Peekskill 914.734.1532 • Rochester
585.263.5866 • Syracuse 315.423.5471

R: 9 **T:** 5th 57%
Elected Year: 1998
Next Election: 2028

⚑ Rep. Jamaal A. Bowman (BO-muhn) D-NY-16 p 202.225.2464

Rm. CHOB 345 **Web.** bowman.house.gov **f** 202.225.5513
Bio. 04/01/1976 • New York City • Potomac State Junior
College, M.A.; Sayreville War Memorial High School, M.A.;
Univ. of New Haven, B.A., 1999; Mercy College of New
York, M.A., 2007; Manhattanville College, Ed.D., 2019 •
Unspecified/Other • M. Melissa Oppenheimer, 3 ch **Cmte.**
Education & Workforce • Science, Space & Technology
CoS. Sarah Iddrissu **LD.** Rajiv Sicora
Sched. Daniel Maher **PS.** WanJira Banfield
Dist. Off. Mount Vernon 914.371.9220 • White Plains
914.323.5550

R: 303 **T:** 2nd 64%
Elected Year: 2020

⚑ Rep. Yvette D. Clarke (klark) D-NY-09 p 202.225.6231

Rm. RHOB 2058 **Web.** clarke.house.gov **f** 202.226.0112
Bio. 11/01/1964 • Brooklyn • State Representative • African
Methodist Episcopal • S. **Cmte.** Energy & Commerce •
Homeland Security
CoS. Christopher Cox **LD.** Steven Blattner
Sched. Rachel St. Louis **PS.** Brian Phillips
Dist. Off. Brooklyn 718.287.1142

R: 71 **T:** 9th 82%
Elected Year: 2006

⚑ Rep. Anthony P. D'Esposito () R-NY-04 p 202.225.5516

Rm. LHOB 1508 **Web.** desposito.house.gov
Bio. 02/22/1982 • Island Park • Hofstra Univ., B.A., 2004 •
Catholic • **Cmte.** Administration • Homeland Security •
Transportation & Infrastructure
CoS. Robert Gies **LD.** Sarah Talmage
Sched. Ashley Sapraicone **PS.** Matthew Capp
Dist. Off. Garden City 516.739.3008

R: 375 **T:** 1st 52%
Elected Year: 2022

⚑ Rep. Adriano Espaillat (eh-spy-YAHT) D-NY-13 p 202.225.4365

Rm. RHOB 2332 **Web.** espaillat.house.gov **f** 202.226.9731
Bio. 09/27/1954 • Santiago • Univ. of New York Queens
College (NY), B.S., 1978 • Roman Catholic • M. Marthera
Madera Espaillat, 2 ch **Cmte.** Appropriations
CoS. Aneiry Batista **LD.** Monica Garay
Sched. Justin Ramos **PS.** Jose Acosta (CD)
Dist. Off. Bronx 646.740.3632 • New York 212.407.5959 •
New York 212.663.3900

R: 204 **T:** 4th 100%
Elected Year: 2016

⚑ Rep. Andrew R. Garbarino (gar-ba-REE-noh) R-NY-02 p 202.225.7896

Rm. RHOB 2344 **Web.** garbarino.house.gov **f** 202.226.2279
Bio. 09/27/1984 • West Islip • George Washington Univ.
(DC), B.A., 2006; Hofstra Univ. School of Law, J.D., 2009 •
Roman Catholic • S. **Cmte.** Ethics • Financial Services •
Homeland Security
Sched. Nicholas Keddy **PS.** Kristen Cianci
Dist. Off. Patchogue 631.541.4225

R: 314 **T:** 2nd 61%
Elected Year: 2020

NEW YORK

⌁ Rep. Daniel Goldman ()   D-NY-10   p 202.225.7944

Rm. CHOB 245 **Web.** goldman.house.gov
Bio. 02/26/1976 • Washington • Yale Univ. (CT), B.A. • M.
Corinne Levy, 5 ch **Cmte.** Homeland Security • Oversight &
Accountability
CoS. Haley Scott   **LD.** Erin Meegan
Sched. Christopher Bannon   **PS.** Simone Kanter
Dist. Off. Brooklyn

R: 387   **T:** 1st   84%
Elected Year: 2022

⌁ Rep. Brian M. Higgins (HIH-guhnz)   D-NY-26   p 202.225.3306

Rm. RHOB 2269 **Web.** higgins.house.gov   **f** 202.226.0347
Bio. 10/06/1959 • Buffalo • Member, State Assembly;
Member, City Council • Buffalo State College (NY), B.S.,
1984; Buffalo State College (NY), M.A., 1985; Harvard Univ.
John F. Kennedy School of Government (MA), M.A., 1996
• Catholic • M. Mary Jane Hannon, 2 ch **Cmte.** Budget •
Ways & Means
CoS. Matthew Fery   **LD.** Lyndsey Barnes
Sched. Colin Maczka   **PS.** Haley Panek
Dist. Off. Buffalo 716.852.3501 • Niagara Falls 716.282.1274

R: 61   **T:** 10th   64%
Elected Year: 2004

⌁ Rep. Hakeem Jeffries (JEHF-reez)   D-NY-08   p 202.225.5936

Rm. RHOB 2433 **Web.** jeffries.house.gov   **f** 202.225.1018
Bio. 08/04/1970 • Brooklyn • State Univ. of New York,
Binghamton, B.A., 1992; Georgetown Univ. (DC), M.P.P.,
1994; New York Univ. Law School, J.D., 1997 • Baptist • M.
Kennisandra Jeffries, 2 ch
CoS. Tasia Jackson   **LD.** Zoe Oreck
Sched. Lauren Milnes   **PS.** Andy Eichar
Dist. Off. Brooklyn 718.237.2211 • Brooklyn 718.373.0033

R: 134   **T:** 6th   77%
Elected Year: 2012

⌁ Rep. Nicholas J. LaLota ()   R-NY-01   p 202.225.3826

Rm. LHOB 1530 **Web.** lalota.house.gov
Bio. 06/23/1978 • Bay Shore • U.S. Naval Academy (MD),
Bach. Deg., 2000; Hofstra Univ. - Zarb School of Business
(NY), M.B.A., 2012; Hofstra Univ. School of Law, J.D., 2020 •
M. Kaylie LaLota, 3 ch **Cmte.** Armed Services • Homeland
Security • Small Business
               LD. Mary Hrinkevich
Dist. Off. Huntington 631.289.1097

R: 400   **T:** 1st   56%
Elected Year: 2022

⌁ Rep. Nicholas A. Langworthy ()   R-NY-23   p 202.225.3161

Web. nicklangworthy.com
Bio. 02/27/1981 • Jamestown • Niagara Univ., B.A., 2003
• M. Erin Baker, 1 ch **Cmte.** Oversight & Accountability •
Rules
CoS. Jessica Proud (CD)   **LD.** William Smith (CD)
Sched. Hannah Jahreis   **PS.** Molly Safreed (CD)
(CD)
Dist. Off. Corning 607.377.3130 • Jamestown 716.488.8111
• Olean • Williamsville 716.547.6844

R: 402   **T:** 1st   65%
Elected Year: 2022

⌁ Rep. Michael V. Lawler ()   R-NY-17   p 202.225.6506

Rm. LHOB 1013 **Web.** lawler.house.gov
Bio. • Manhattan College, B.B.A., 2009 • M. Doina Lawler,
1 ch **Cmte.** Financial Services • Foreign Affairs
CoS. Andrea Grace   **LD.** James McNamee
Sched. Ashley Brown
Dist. Off. Pearl River 845.213.3253

R: 403   **T:** 1st   50%
Elected Year: 2022

Rep. Nicole Malliotakis (MAL-ee-uh-TAHK-uhs) R-NY-11 p 202.225

Rm. CHOB 351 **Web.** malliotakis.house.gov
Bio. 11/11/1980 • New York • Seton Hall Univ. (NJ), B.A.,
2001; Wagner College, M.B.A., 2010 • Greek Orthodox • S.
Cmte. Ways & Means
CoS. Alex B. Bolton   **LD.** Michael DeFilippis
Sched. Courtney Watson   **PS.** Natalie Baldassarre
Dist. Off. Brooklyn 718.306.1620 • Staten Island
718.568.2870

R: 327   **T:** 2nd 62%
Elected Year: 2020

Rep. Gregory W. Meeks (meeks) D-NY-05 p 202.225.3461

Rm. RHOB 2310 **Web.** meeks.house.gov   **f** 202.226.4169
Bio. 09/25/1953 • Harlem • Assistant District Attorney; State
Legislator • Adelphi Univ. (NY), B.A., 1975; Howard Univ.
Law School (DC), J.D., 1978 • African Methodist Episcopal •
M. Simone-Marie Meeks, 3 ch **Cmte.** Financial Services •
Foreign Affairs
CoS. Kayla Williams   **LD.** Megan Hannigan
Sched. Bobby Bivens   **PS.** Ayanna Young
Dist. Off. Arverne 347.230.4032 • Jamaica 718.725.6000

R: 31   **T:** 13th 75%
Elected Year: 1998

Rep. Grace Meng (mehng) D-NY-06 p 202.225.2601

Rm. RHOB 2209 **Web.** meng.house.gov   **f** 202.225.1589
Bio. 10/01/1975 • Queens • Univ. of Michigan, B.A., 1997;
Yeshiva Univ. Benjamin N. Cardozo School of Law (NY),
J.D., 2002 • Christian Church • M. Wayne Kye, 2 ch **Cmte.**
Appropriations
CoS. Maeve Healy   **LD.** Mark Olson
Sched. Aaron Feldman   **PS.** Nathan Easington
Dist. Off. Flushing 718.358.6364 • Forest Hills 718.358.6364

R: 140   **T:** 6th 64%
Elected Year: 2012

Rep. Marcus J. Molinaro () R-NY-19 p 202.225.5441

Rm. LHOB 1207 **Web.** marcforus.com
Bio. Yonkers • Dutchess Community College (NY), A.A.,
1995 • Christian Reformed Church • M. Corinne Adams, 4
ch **Cmte.** Small Business • Transportation & Infrastructure
CoS. Jeff Bishop   **LD.** Connor Torossian
Sched. Rick Yackel   **PS.** Dan Kranz
Dist. Off. Binghamton 607.242.0200

R: 414   **T:** 1st 49%
Elected Year: 2022

Rep. Joseph D. Morelle (mor-REH-lee) D-NY-25 p 202.225.3615

Rm. CHOB 570 **Web.** morelle.house.gov   **f** 202.225.7822
Bio. 04/29/1957 • Utica • State Univ. of New York
(Geneseo), B.A., 1986 • Roman Catholic • M. Mary Beth
Morelle, 3 ch (1 deceased) **Cmte.** Administration •
Appropriations
CoS. Abbie Sorrendino   **LD.** Joanne Stiles
Sched. Elena Bernstein   **PS.** Dana Hipolito (CD)
Dist. Off. Rochester 585.232.4850

231   **T:** 4th 54%
cted Year: 2018

---

ep. Jerry L. Nadler (NAD-lur) D-NY-12 p 202.225.5635

Rm. RHOB 2132 **Web.** nadler.house.gov   **f** 202.225.6923
Bio. 06/13/1947 • Brooklyn • State Representative; NY State
Legislative Staffer • Columbia Univ. (NY), Bach. Deg., 1969;
Fordham Univ. School of Law (NY), J.D., 1978 • Jewish • M.
Joyce L. Miller, 1 ch **Cmte.** Judiciary
CoS. John Doty   **LD.** Andrew Heineman
Sched. Asha Armstrong   **PS.** Daniel Rubin
Dist. Off. New York 212.367.7350

Rep. Alexandria Ocasio-Cortez (o-kah-SEE-o R-tehz)   D-NY-14   p 202.225.3965

Rm. CHOB 250 **Web.** ocasio-cortez.house.gov
Bio. 10/13/1989 • Bronx • Boston Univ. (MA), B.A., 2011 • Catholic • E. Riley Roberts **Cmte.** Natural Resources • Oversight & Accountability
CoS. Gerardo Bonilla Chavez   **LD.** Aya Saed
Sched. Alejandra Escobar Serrano   **PS.** Lauren Hitt
Dist. Off. The Bronx 718.662.5970

R: 267   **T:** 3rd
Elected Year: 2018

Rep. Patrick Ryan ()   D-NY-18   p 202.225.5614

Rm. LHOB 1030 **Web.** patryan.house.gov
Bio. 03/28/1982 • Kingston • U.S. Military Academy (NY), B.S., 2004; Georgetown Univ. (DC), M.A., 2013 • M. Rebecca Ryan, 2 ch **Cmte.** Armed Services • Transportation & Infrastructure
CoS. Robert Dougherty   **LD.** Kana Smith
Sched. Ashley Therien   **PS.** Sam Silverman
Dist. Off. Kingston 845.443.2930

R: 359   **T:** 2nd 49%
Elected Year: 2022

Rep. George Santos ()   R-NY-03   p 202.225.3335

Rm. LHOB 1117 **Web.** santos.house.gov
Bio. 07/22/1988 • • Catholic • M. Matt Santos
   PS. Gabrielle Lipsky
Dist. Off. Douglaston 718.631.0400

R: 424   **T:** 1st 54%
Elected Year: 2022

Rep. Elise Stefanik (steh-FAH-nik)   R-NY-21   p 202.225.4611

Rm. RHOB 2211 **Web.** stefanik.house.gov   **f** 202.226.0621
Bio. 07/02/1984 • Albany • Harvard Univ., A.B., 2006 • Roman Catholic • M. Matthew Manda, 1 ch **Cmte.** Armed Services • Education & Workforce • Permanent Select on Intelligence
CoS. Patrick Stewart Hester   **LD.** Jim Robertson
Sched. Lauren Homeyer   **PS.** Palmer Brigham
Dist. Off. Glens Falls 518.743.0964 • Plattsburgh 518.561.2324 • Watertown 315.782.3150

R: 183   **T:** 5th 59%
Elected Year: 2014

Rep. Claudia Tenney (TEH-nee)   R-NY-24   p 202.225.3665

Rm. RHOB 2349 **Web.** tenney.house.gov   **f** 202.225.1891
Bio. 02/04/1961 • New Hartford • Colgate Univ., B.A., 1983; Univ. of Cincinnati, J.D., 1987 • Presbyterian • D., 1 ch
Cmte. Science, Space & Technology • Ways & Means
CoS. Nick Stewart   **LD.** George Iverson
Sched. Noah Larsen   **PS.** Meg Deneen
Dist. Off. Binghamton 607.242.0200 • Utica 315.732.0713

R: 298   **T:** 2nd 66%
Elected Year: 2020

Rep. Paul D. Tonko (TAHN-ko)   D-NY-20   p 202.225

Rm. RHOB 2369 **Web.** tonko.house.gov   **f** 202.22
Bio. 06/18/1949 • Amsterdam • Engineer • Clarkson (NY), B.S., 1971 • Roman Catholic • S. **Cmte.** Energy Commerce • Natural Resources
CoS. Jeff Morgan   **LD.** Emily Silverbe
Sched. David Mastrangelo   **PS.** Rachel Dejea
Dist. Off. Albany 518.465.0700 • Saratoga Spri 518.374.4547

R: 92   **T:** 8th 55%
Elected Year: 2008

🕊 Rep. Ritchie John Torres (toe-ress)   D-N

Rm. LHOB 1414 **Web.**
ritchietorres.house.gov
Bio. 03/12/1988 • Bronx • Christian - Non-D
S. **Cmte.** Financial Services • Select China C
CoS. Angel Vazquez   **LD.** Zach Gross
Dist. Off. Bronx 718.503.9610

R: 346 **T:** 2nd 83%
Elected Year: 2020

🕊 Rep. Nydia M. Velazquez (veh-LAS-kez)   D-NY-07   p 202.225.2361

Rm. RHOB 2302 **Web.** velazquez.house.gov **f** 202.226.0327
Bio. 03/28/1953 • Yabucoa • Director, Dept. of Puerto Rican
Community Affairs; Congressional Staffer • Univ. of Puerto
Rico (Rio Piedras), B.A., 1974; New York Univ., M.A., 1976 •
Roman Catholic • M. Paul Bader **Cmte.** Financial Services
• Natural Resources • Small Business
CoS. Melissa Jung   **LD.** Renata Beca-Barragan
Sched. Timothy McWade   **PS.** Chris Garcia
Dist. Off. Brooklyn 718.599.3658

R: 16 **T:** 16th 73%
Elected Year: 1992

📛 Rep. Brandon Williams ()   R-NY-22   p 202.225.3701

Rm. LHOB 1022 **Web.**
brandonforcongressny22.com
Bio. Dallas • Wharton School (PA), M.B.A.; Pepperdine
Univ., B.A., 1990 • M. Stephanie McRee, 2 ch **Cmte.**
Education & Workforce • Science, Space & Technology •
Transportation & Infrastructure
CoS. Michael Gordon   **LD.** Ryan Sweeney
Sched. Megan Paulsen   **PS.** Sarah Selip
Dist. Off. Syracuse •Utica

R: 434 **T:** 1st 51%
Elected Year: 2022

NORTH CAROLINA

🕊 Governor Roy Cooper (KOO-pur)   p 919.814.2000

Office of the Governor, 20301 Mail **C:** Raleigh
Service Center   **P:** 10,383,620 (9)
Raleigh, NC 27699-0301   **A:** 48,617.96 mi^2 (29th)
Website nc.gov
Fax 919.733.2120
Term Ends 2025
Lt. Governor
Mark Robinson, **R**

U.S. Senators
Thom R. Tillis, **R**
Ted P. Budd, **R**
U.S. Representatives
01 / Don Davis, **D**
02 / Deborah K. Ross, **D**
03 / Gregory F. Murphy, **R**
04 / Valerie P. Foushee, **D**
05 / Virginia A. Foxx, **R**
06 / Kathy E. Manning, **D**

07 / David C. Rouzer, **R**   11 / Chuck Edwards, **R**
08 / Dan Bishop, **R**   12 / Alma S. Adams, **D**
09 / Richard Hudson, **R**   13 / Wiley Nickel, **D**
0 / Patrick T. McHenry, **R**   14 / Jeff Jackson, **D**

NORTH CAROLINA

ud")   R-NC-Jr.   p 202.224.3154

Rm. RSOB B85 **Web.** budd.senate.gov
Bio. 10/21/1971 • Winston-Salem • Appalachian State
Univ. (NC), B.S., 1994; Dallas Theological Seminary (TX),
M.Th., 1998; Wake Forest Univ. (NC), M.B.A., 2007 • Christian
- Non-Denominational • M. Amy Kate, 3 ch **Cmte.**
Armed Services • Commerce, Science & Transportation •
Health, Education, Labor & Pensions • Small Business &
Entrepreneurship

CoS. Tucker Knott	**LD.** Caitlin Miller
Sched. Elizabeth Dews-Haymore	**PS.** Curtis Kalin

Dist. Off. Asheville •Wilmington

95 **T:** 1st 51%
Elected Year: 2022
Next Election: 2028

R Sen. Thom R. Tillis (TIH-liss)   R-NC-Sr.   p 202.224.6342

Rm. DSOB 113 **Web.** tillis.senate.gov   **f** 202.228.2563
Bio. 08/30/1960 • Jacksonville • Univ. of Maryland Univ.
College, B.S., 1996 • Catholic • M. Susan Tillis, 2 ch **Cmte.**
Banking, Housing & Urban Affairs • Finance • Judiciary •
Veterans' Affairs

CoS. Shil Patel	**LD.** Corey Weber
Sched. Angela Schulze	**PS.** Adam Webb

Dist. Off. Charlotte 704.509.9087 • Greenville 252.329.0371
• Hendersonville 828.693.8750 • High Point 336.885.0685 •
Raleigh 919.856.4630

R: 64 **T:** 2nd 49%
Elected Year: 2014
Next Election: 2026

Rep. Alma S. Adams (AD-uhmz)   D-NC-12   p 202.225.1510

Rm. RHOB 2436 **Web.** adams.house.gov   **f** 202.225.1512
Bio. 05/27/1946 • High Point • West Side High School,
Newark (NJ), Univ.; North Carolina Agricultural and
Technical State Univ., B.S., 1968; North Carolina Agricultural
and Technical State Univ., M.S., 1972; Ohio State Univ.,
Ph.D., 1981 • Baptist • D., 2 ch; 4 gr-ch **Cmte.** Agriculture •
Education & Workforce

CoS. Adrienne Christian	**LD.** Ben Owens
	PS. Sam Spencer (CD)

Dist. Off. Charlotte 704.344.9950

R: 157 **T:** 6th 63%
Elected Year: 2014

R Rep. Dan Bishop (BIH-shuhp)   R-NC-08   p 202.225.1976

Rm. RHOB 2459 **Web.** danbishop.house.gov
Bio. 07/01/1964 • Charlotte • Univ. of North Carolina, B.S.,
1986; Univ. of North Carolina School of Law, J.D., 1990 • M.
Jo bishop, 1 ch **Cmte.** Homeland Security • Judiciary

CoS. James Hampson	**LD.** Travis Rowland
Sched. Austin Hoffman	**PS.** Alexandra McCandless

Dist. Off. Monroe 704.218.5300 • Salisbury 704.218.5300

R: 294 **T:** 3rd 70%
Elected Year: 2019

Rep. Don Davis ()   D-NC-01   p 202.225.3101

Rm. LHOB 1123 **Web.** dondavis.house.gov
Bio. 08/29/1971 • Snow Hill • United States Air Force
Academy, B.S.; Central Michigan Univ., M.S.; East Carolina
Univ., M.A.; East Carolina Univ., Ed.D. • Presbyterian • M.
Yuvonka Shawnte Batts, 3 ch **Cmte.** Armed Services

CoS. Hannah Spengler	**LD.** Delia Kashat
Sched. John Bonus	**PS.** D'Andre Henderson

Dist. Off. Greenville 252.999.7600

R: 376 **T:** 1st 52%
Elected Year: 2022

ℝ Rep. Chuck Edwards () R-N⃫

Web. edwards.house.gov
Bio. 09/13/1960 • Western • M. Teresa E⃫
Cmte. Budget • Oversight & Accountability
& Infrastructure
CoS. Bronwyn E. Lance **LD.** Ryan Dierk⃫
(CD)
Dist. Off. Hendersonville 828.435.7310

R: 380 **T:** 1st 54%
Elected Year: 2022

Rep. Valerie P. Foushee () D-NC-04 p 202.225.1784

Web. foushee.house.gov
Bio. 05/07/1956 • Chapel Hill • Univ. of North Carolina
Chapel Hill (UNC), Bach. Deg. • Baptist • M. Stan Foushee,
2 ch; 1 gr-ch **Cmte.** Science, Space & Technology •
Transportation & Infrastructure
CoS. Anna Nunn (CD) **LD.** Elizabeth Adkins (CD)
Sched. Seth Washington **PS.** Jennifer Putney (CD)
(CD)
Dist. Off. Durham 919.967.7924

R: 382 **T:** 1st 67%
Elected Year: 2022

ℝ Rep. Virginia A. Foxx (fahks) R-NC-05 p 202.225.2071

Rm. RHOB 2462 **Web.** foxx.house.gov **f** 202.225.2995
Bio. 06/29/1943 • Bronx • Business Owner; Board of
Education • Univ. of North Carolina Chapel Hill (UNC),
Bach. Deg., 1968; Univ. of North Carolina Chapel Hill (UNC),
M.A., 1972; Univ. of North Carolina, Greensboro, Ed.D.,
1985 • Roman Catholic • M. Thomas A. Foxx, 1 ch ; 2 gr-ch
Cmte. Education & Workforce • Oversight & Accountability
CoS. Carson Middleton **LD.** Bryan McVae
Sched. Hannah Cooke **PS.** Alex Ives
Dist. Off. Boone 828.265.0240 • Clemmons 336.778.0211

R: 59 **T:** 10th 63%
Elected Year: 2004

ℝ Rep. Richard Hudson Jr. (HUD-suhn) R-NC-09 p 202.225.3715

Rm. RHOB 2112 **Web.** hudson.house.gov **f** 202.225.4036
Bio. 11/04/1971 • Franklin • Univ. of North Carolina,
Charlotte, B.A., 1996 • Methodist • M. Renee Hudson, 1 ch
Cmte. Energy & Commerce
CoS. Elliott Guffin **LD.** Alex Stepahin
Sched. Emma Balkin **PS.** Emma Hogan

R: 132 **T:** 6th 57%
Elected Year: 2012

Rep. Jeff Jackson () D-NC-14 p 202.225.5634

Rm. LHOB 1318 **Web.** jeffjacksonnc.com
Bio. 09/12/1982 • • Emory Univ. - Atlanta (GA), Mast. Deg.,
2004; Emory Univ. - Atlanta (GA), Bach. Deg., 2004; Univ. of
North Carolina School of Law, J.D., 2009 • Presbyterian •
M. Marisa Jackson, 3 ch **Cmte.** Armed Services • Science,
Space & Technology
CoS. Dylan Arant **LD.** Brian Duckworth
Sched. Thomas Cromie
Dist. Off. Charlotte

R: 393 **T:** 1st 58%
Elected Year: 2022

Rep. Kathy E. Manning (MAN-ing) D-NC-06 p 202.225.3065

Rm. CHOB 307 **Web.** manning.house.gov **f** 202.225.8611
Bio. 12/03/1956 • Detroit • Harvard Univ., A.B., 1978; Univ.
of Michigan Law School, J.D., 1981 • Jewish • M. Randall
Kaplan, 3 ch **Cmte.** Education & Workforce • Foreign
Affairs
CoS. Sarah Curtis **LD.** Daniel Marrow
Sched. Josie Ansbacher **PS.** Hailey Barringer
Dist. Off. Greensboro 336.333.5005

...enry (mik-HEN-ree) R-NC-10 p 202.225.2576
Rm. RHOB 2134 **Web.** mchenry.house.gov **f** 202.225.0316
Bio. 10/22/1975 • Charlotte • Realtor; Campaign Aide •
Belmont Abbey College (NC), B.A., 2000 • Roman Catholic •
M. Giulia Cangiano McHenry, 3 ch **Cmte.** Financial Services
CoS. Jeff Butler **LD.** Doug Nation
Sched. Grace Tricomi **PS.** Taylor Theodossiou
Dist. Off. Hickory 828.327.6100 • Mooresville 800.477.2576

R: 63 **T:** 10th 73%
Elected Year: 2004

A Rep. Gregory F. Murphy (MUR-fee) R-NC-03 p 202.225.3415

Rm. CHOB 407 **Web.** gregmurphy.house.gov **f** 202.225.3286
Bio. 03/05/1963 • Raleigh • Davidson College, B.S., 1985;
Univ. of North Carolina School of Medicine, Chapel Hill,
M.D., 1989 • M. Wendy Murphy, 3 ch **Cmte.** Administration
• Veterans' Affairs • Ways & Means
CoS. Kris Skrzycki **LD.** Luke Wallwork
Sched. Jessica Santos **PS.** Jack Colonnetta
Dist. Off. Greenville 252.931.1003 • Jacksonville
910.937.6929 • Manteo 252.230.3549 • New Bern
252.636.6612

R: 295 **T:** 3rd 67%
Elected Year: 2019

♩ Rep. Wiley Nickel () D-NC-13 p 202.225.4531

Web. wileynickelforcongress.com
Bio. 11/23/1975 • Tulane Univ. (LA), B.A., 1998;
Pepperdine Univ. School of Law (CA), J.D., 2005 • M.
Caroline Nickel, 2 ch **Cmte.** Financial Services
Sched. Freedom
Richardson (CD)
Dist. Off. Washington 919.501.0745

R: 418 **T:** 1st 52%
Elected Year: 2022

♩ Rep. Deborah K. Ross (rawss) D-NC-02 p 202.225.3032

Rm. LHOB 1221 **Web.** ross.house.gov **f** 202.225.0181
Bio. 06/20/1963 • Philadelphia • Brown Univ. (RI), A.B.,
1985; Univ. of North Carolina in Chapel Hill, J.D., 1990 •
Unitarian • M. Stephen (Steve) J. Wrinn **Cmte.** Ethics •
Judiciary • Science, Space & Technology
CoS. Matt Lee **LD.** Katie Paulson
Sched. Maura Haydin **PS.** Josie Feron
Dist. Off. Raleigh 919.334.0840

R: 341 **T:** 2nd 65%
Elected Year: 2020

A Rep. David C. Rouzer (ROU-zur) R-NC-07 p 202.225.2731

Rm. RHOB 2333 **Web.** rouzer.house.gov **f** 202.225.5773
Bio. 02/16/1972 • Landstuhl • North Carolina State
Univ., B.A., 1994; North Carolina State Univ., B.S., 1994 •
Southern Baptist • S. **Cmte.** Agriculture • Transportation &
Infrastructure
CoS. Anna McCormack **LD.** Joseph White
  PS. Erin McBride
Dist. Off. Bolivia 910.253.6111 • Lumberton 910.702.6140
• Wilmington 910.395.0202

R: 182 **T:** 5th 58%
Elected Year: 2014

NORTH DAKOTA

A Governor Doug Burgum (BUR-guhm) p 701.328.2200

600 E. Boulevard Ave. **C:** Bismarck
Bismarck, ND 58505-0001 **P:** 760,077 (48)
Website nd.gov **A:** 69,000.67 mi^2 (
Fax 701.328.2205
Term Ends 2024
Lt. Governor
Tammy J. Miller, **R**

U.S. Senators
John H. Hoeven, **R**
Kevin J. Cramer, **R**
U.S. Representatives
01 / Kelly M. Armstrong, **R**

⊞ Sen. Kevin J. Cramer (KRAY-mur) R-ND-Jr. p 202.224.2043

Rm. HSOB 330 **Web.** cramer.senate.gov
Bio. 01/21/1961 • Rolette • Concordia College (MN), B.A., 1983; Univ. of Mary (ND), M.A., 2003 • Evangelical • M. Kris Neumann, 5 ch (1 deceased); 5 gr-ch **Cmte.** Armed Services • Banking, Housing & Urban Affairs • Environment & Public Works • Veterans' Affairs
CoS. Mark Gruman   **LD.** Micah Chambers
Sched. Rachel Buening   **PS.** Abbey Schieffer
Dist. Off. Bismarck 701.699.7020 • Fargo 701.232.5094 • Grand Forks 701.699.7030 • Minot 701.837.6141 • Williston 701.441.7230

R: 77 **T:** 1st 55%
Elected Year: 2018
Next Election: 2024

⊞ Sen. John H. Hoeven III (HO-vuhn) R-ND-Sr. p 202.224.2551

Rm. RSOB 338 • **Web.** hoeven.senate.gov   **f** 202.224.7999
Bio. 03/13/1957 • Bismarck • Former Chair, Gov.'s Ethanol Coalition; Chair, Midwestern Governors Assn.; Chair, District 47 North Dakota Republican Party; Chair, Interstate Oil and Gas Compact Commission • Dartmouth College, Hanover (NH), B.A., 1979; Northwestern Univ. Kellogg School Management (IL), M.B.A., 1981 • Roman Catholic • M. Mikey Hoeven, 2 ch **Cmte.** Agriculture, Nutrition & Forestry • Appropriations • Energy & Natural Resources • Indian Affairs
CoS. Tony Eberhard   **LD.** Daniel Auger
Sched. Sydney Fitzpatrick   **PS.** Kami Capener
Dist. Off. Bismarck 701.250.4618 • Fargo 701.239.5389 • Grand Forks 701.746.8972 • Minot 701.838.1361 • Watford City 701.609.2727

R: 38 **T:** 3rd 56%
Elected Year: 2010
Next Election: 2028

⊞ Rep. Kelly M. Armstrong (ARM-strong) R-ND-01 p 202.225.2611

Rm. RHOB 2267 **Web.** armstrong.house.gov **f** 202.226.3410
Bio. 10/08/1976 • Dickinson • Univ. of North Dakota, B.A., 2000; Univ. of North Dakota School of Law, J.D., 2003 • Lutheran • M. Kjersti Armstrong, 2 ch **Cmte.** Energy & Commerce • Oversight & Accountability
CoS. Rosalyn Leighton   **LD.** Nicholas Tortorici
            PS. Conner Swanson
Dist. Off. Bismarck 701.354.6700 • Fargo 701.353.6665

R: 236 **T:** 3rd 62%
Elected Year: 2018

OHIO

⊞ Governor Mike DeWine (duh-WINE)   p 614.466.3555

Riffe Center
77 S. High St., 30th Floor
Columbus, OH 43215
Website ohio.gov
Fax 614.466.9354
Term Ends 2027
Lt. Governor
Jon A. Husted, **R**

C: Columbus
P: 11,689,442 (7)
A: 40,860.79 mi^2 (35th)

OHIO

...ves
...nan, **D**
...enstrup, **R**
. Beatty, **D**
Jordan, **R**
...E. Latta, **R**
. Johnson, **R**
...ax L. Miller, **R**
Warren Davidson, **R**
. / Marcy C. Kaptur, **D**
10 / Mike R. Turner, **R**
11 / Shontel Brown, **D**
12 / Troy Balderson, **R**
13 / Emilia Sykes, **D**
14 / Dave P. Joyce, **R**
15 / Mike Carey, **R**

Sen. Sherrod C. Brown ("brown") D-OH-Sr. p 202.224.2315

Rm. HSOB 503 **Web.** brown.senate.gov **f** 202.228.6321
Bio. 11/09/1952 • Mansfield • Professor; Representative •
Yale Univ. (CT), B.A., 1974; Ohio State Univ., M.A., 1979; Ohio
State Univ., M.P.A., 1981 • Lutheran • M. Connie Schultz,
2 ch ; 2 stepch ; 6 gr-ch **Cmte.** Agriculture, Nutrition &
Forestry • Banking, Housing & Urban Affairs • Finance •
Veterans' Affairs
CoS. Trudy Perkins **LD.** Jeremy Hekhuis
Sched. Diana Baron **PS.** Katie Quintela
Dist. Off. Cincinnati 513.684.1021 • Cleveland
216.522.7272 • Columbus 614.469.2083 • Lorain
440.242.4100

R: 21 **T:** 3rd 53%
Elected Year: 2006
Next Election: 2024

Sen. J.D. Vance , (AAKC AE) () R-OH-Jr. p 202.224.3353

Rm. DSOB B40C **Web.**
ohiovaluesproject.com
Bio. 08/02/1984 • Middletown • Ohio State Univ., B.A.; Yale
Law School (CT), J.D. • Roman Catholic • M. Usha Chilukuri
Vance, 3 ch **Cmte.** Aging • Banking, Housing & Urban
Affairs • Commerce, Science & Transportation • Foreign
Relations • Joint Economic
CoS. Jacob Reses **LD.** James Braid
Sched. Abby Delahoyde **PS.** Will Martin
Dist. Off. Cleveland • Columbus •Toledo

R: 97 **T:** 1st 53%
Elected Year: 2022
Next Election: 2028

Rep. Troy Balderson (ball-dur-sun) R-OH-12 p 202.225.5355

Rm. RHOB 2429 **Web.** balderson.house.gov **f** 202.226.4523
Bio. 01/16/1962 • Zanesville • Christian Church • D. Angie
Albright, 1 ch **Cmte.** Agriculture • Energy & Commerce
CoS. Laura Engquist **LD.** Nate Zimpher
Sched. Katie Tomko **PS.** Clark Siddle (CD)
Dist. Off. Worthington 614.523.2555

R: 229 **T:** 4th 69%
Elected Year: 2018

Rep. Joyce B. Beatty (BAY-dee) D-OH-03 p 202.225.4324

Rm. RHOB 2079 **Web.** beatty.house.gov **f** 202.225.1984
Bio. 03/12/1950 • Dayton • Central State Univ. (OH), B.A.,
1972; Wright State Univ. (OH), M.S., 1974 • Baptist • M.
Justice Otto Beatty Jr., 2 stepch ; 2 gr-ch **Cmte.** Financial
Services
CoS. Todd Valentine **LD.** Nicholas Semanko
Dist. Off. Columbus 614.220.0003

R: 125 **T:** 6th 70%
Elected Year: 2012

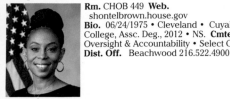

❧ Rep. Shontel Brown ("brown") D-OH-11 p 202.2

Rm. CHOB 449 **Web.** f 202.22
shontelbrown.house.gov
Bio. 06/24/1975 • Cleveland • Cuyahoga Community
College, Assc. Deg., 2012 • NS. **Cmte.** Agriculture •
Oversight & Accountability • Select China Committee
Dist. Off. Beachwood 216.522.4900

R: 353 **T:** 2nd 78%
Elected Year: 2021

❧ Rep. Mike Carey (KAIR-ree) R-OH-15 p 202.225.2015

Rm. LHOB 1433 **Web.** carey.house.gov
Bio. 03/13/1971 • Sabina • Marion Military Institute,
A.S., 1991; Ohio State Univ., B.A., 1993 • Christian -
Non-Denominational • M. Meghan Carey, 3 ch **Cmte.**
Administration • Ways & Means
Dist. Off. Columbus 614.927.6902

R: 354 **T:** 2nd 57%
Elected Year: 2021

❧ Rep. Warren Davidson (DAY-vid-suhn) R-OH-08 p 202.225.6205

Rm. RHOB 2113 **Web.** davidson.house.gov f 202.225.0704
Bio. 03/01/1970 • Troy • Univ. of Notre Dame (IN),
M.B.A.; U.S. Military Academy at West Point, B.A., 1995
• Unspecified/Other • M. Lisa Davidson, 2 ch **Cmte.**
Financial Services • Foreign Affairs
CoS. Connor White
Dist. Off. Cincinnati 513.779.5400 • Springfield
937.322.1120 • West Chester 937.339.1524

R: 189 **T:** 5th 65%
Elected Year: 2016

❧ Rep. Bill Johnson (JAHN-suhn) R-OH-06 p 202.225.5705

Rm. RHOB 2082 **Web.** billjohnson.house.gov f 202.225.5907
Bio. 11/10/1954 • Roseboro • Troy Univ. (AL), B.S., 1979;
Georgia Institute of Technology, M.S., 1984 • Protestant -
Unspecified Christian • M. LeeAnn Johnson, 4 ch ; 6 gr-ch
Cmte. Energy & Commerce
CoS. Mike Smullen   **LD.** Sam Hattrup
Sched. McKenna Simpson   **PS.** Alyssa Gulick
Dist. Off. Cambridge 740.432.2366 • Ironton 740.534.9431
• Marietta 740.376.0868 • Salem 330.337.6951

R: 109 **T:** 7th 68%
Elected Year: 2010

❧ Rep. Jim D. Jordan (JOR-duhn) R-OH-04 p 202.225.2676

Rm. RHOB 2056 **Web.** jordan.house.gov f 202.226.0577
Bio. 02/17/1964 • Urbana • State Representative • Univ. of
Wisconsin, B.S., 1986; Ohio State Univ., M.A., 1991; Capital
Univ. (OH), J.D., 2001 • Evangelical • M. Polly Jordan, 4 ch ;
2 gr-ch **Cmte.** Judiciary • Oversight & Accountability
CoS. Kevin Christopher   **LD.** Jared Dilley
Eichinger
Sched. Emma Summers   **PS.** Russell Dye
Dist. Off. Lima 419.999.6455 • Mansfield 419.669.3015

R: 75 **T:** 9th 69%
Elected Year: 2006

❧ Rep. Dave P. Joyce (joyss) R-OH-14 p 202.225.5731

Rm. RHOB 2065 **Web.** joyce.house.gov f 202.225.3307
Bio. 03/17/1957 • Cleveland • Univ. of Dayton (OH), B.S.,
1979; Univ. of Dayton (OH), J.D., 1982 • Roman Catholic • M.
Kelly Joyce, 3 ch **Cmte.** Appropriations • Ethics
CoS. Anna Romeo
Dist. Off. Mentor 440.352.3939 • Twinsburg 330.357.4139

%

Marcy C. Kaptur (KAP-tur)   D-OH-09   p 202.225.4146

Rm. RHOB 2186 **Web.** kaptur.house.gov   **f** 202.225.7711
Bio. 06/17/1946 • Toledo • Domestic Policy Staffer,
President Jimmy Carter; Urban Planner • Univ. of
Wisconsin, 1968; Univ. of Michigan, M.A., 1974 •
Catholic • S. **Cmte.** Agriculture • Appropriations
CoS. Steve Katich (CD)
Dist. Off. Cleveland 216.767.5933 • Lorain 440.288.1500 •
Toledo 419.259.7500

R: 4   **T:** 21st 57%
Elected Year: 1982

🐦 Rep. Greg Landsman ()   D-OH-01   p 202.225.2216

Rm. LHOB 1432 **Web.**
landsmanforcongress.com
Bio. 12/04/1976 • Cincinnati • Ohio Univ., B.A., 1999;
Harvard Univ., M.Th., 2004 • M. Sarah Landsman, 2 ch
Cmte. Small Business • Veterans' Affairs
CoS. Leslie Waldron Grubb   **LD.** Dominque Wardell
Sched. Emma Treadway   **PS.** Alexa Helwig (CD)
Dist. Off. Lebanon

R: 401   **T:** 1st 53%
Elected Year: 2022

🏛 Rep. Bob E. Latta (LAT-uh)   R-OH-05   p 202.225.6405

Rm. RHOB 2467 **Web.** latta.house.gov   **f** 202.225.1985
Bio. 04/18/1956 • Bluffton • State Legislator; Attorney •
Bowling Green State Univ. (OH), B.A., 1978; Univ. of Toledo
College of Law (OH), J.D., 1981 • Roman Catholic • M.
Marcia Sloan Latta, 2 ch **Cmte.** Energy & Commerce
CoS. Rebecca Angelson   **LD.** Mike Davin
Sched. Andrew Henthorn   **PS.** Claire Hurley
Dist. Off. Bowling Green 419.354.8700 • Findlay
419.422.7791

R: 80   **T:** 9th 67%
Elected Year: 2006

🏛 Rep. Max L. Miller ()   R-OH-07   p 202.225.3876

Rm. CHOB 143 **Web.** votemaxmiller.com
Bio. 11/13/1988 • • Cleveland State Univ. (OH), B.A. • M.
Emily Moreno **Cmte.** Science, Space & Technology
CoS. Joe Ellis   **LD.** Steve Hansen
              PS. Tiffany Boguslawski
Dist. Off. Medina • Parma

R: 412   **T:** 1st 55%
Elected Year: 2022

🐦 Rep. Emilia Sykes ()   D-OH-13   p 202.225.6265

Rm. LHOB 1217 **Web.**
emiliasykesforcongress.com
Bio. 01/04/1986 • Akron • Kent State Univ. (OH), B.A.;
Univ. of Florida Levin College of Law, J.D.; Univ. of Florida
College of Public Health and Health Professions, M.PH •
NS. **Cmte.** Science, Space & Technology • Transportation &
Infrastructure
CoS. Kathryn Mitchell
Thomas
Sched. Mark Hamilton
Dist. Off. Akron

R: 429   **T:** 1st 53%
Elected Year: 2022

🏛 Rep. Mike R. Turner (TUR-nur)   R-OH-10   p 202.225.646

Rm. RHOB 2082 **Web.** turner.house.gov   **f** 202.225.67
Bio. 01/11/1960 • Dayton • Corporate Counsel; Mayor
(Dayton, OH) • Ohio Northern Univ., B.A., 1982; Case
Western Reserve Univ. School of Law, J.D., 1985; Univ.
Dayton (OH), M.B.A., 1992; Georgetown Univ. (DC), D
Deg., 2022 • Presbyterian • D. Majida Mourad, 2 ch
Armed Services • Oversight & Accountability • Perr
Select on Intelligence
CoS. Jason Galanes   **LD.** Maggie Ward
Dist. Off. Dayton 937.225.2843

R: 54   **T:** 11th 62%
Elected Year: 2002

⚑ Rep. Brad R. Wenstrup (WEN-strup)   R-OH-02   p 202.225.3164

Rm. RHOB 2335 **Web.** wenstrup.house.gov   **f** 202.225.1992
Bio. 06/17/1958 • Cincinnati • St. Xavier High School (OH), B.S., 1976; Univ. of Cincinnati, B.A., 1980; Rosalind Franklin Univ. (IL), B.S., 1985 • Roman Catholic • M. Monica Klein, 2 ch   **Cmte.** Permanent Select on Intelligence • Ways & Means
CoS. Greg Brooks   **LD.** Alexandra Igleheart
Sched. Anna Waterkotte   **PS.** Barbara Boland
Dist. Off. Cincinnati 513.474.7777 • Peebles 513.605.1380

R: 152   **T:** 6th 75%
Elected Year: 2012

⚑ Governor Kevin Stitt (stit)   p 405.521.2342

State Capitol Building
2300 N. Lincoln Blvd., Room 212
Oklahoma City, OK 73105
Website ok.gov
Fax 405.521.3353
Term Ends 2027
Lt. Governor
Matt Pinnell, **R**

C: Oklahoma City
P: 3,943,079 (28)
A: 68,594.88 mi^2 (19th)

U.S. Senators
James P. Lankford, **R**
Markwayne Mullin, **R**
U.S. Representatives
01 / Kevin R. Hern, **R**
02 / Josh Brecheen, **R**
03 / Frank D. Lucas, **R**
04 / Tom J. Cole, **R**
05 / Stephanie Bice, **R**

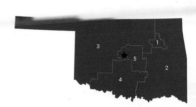

⚑ Sen. James P. Lankford (LANK-furd)   R-OK-Sr.   p 202.224.5754

Rm. HSOB 316 **Web.** lankford.senate.gov   **f** 202.228.1015
Bio. 03/04/1968 • Dallas, TX • Univ. of Texas, B.S., 1990; Southwestern Theological Baptist Seminary (TX), M.Div., 1994 • Baptist • M. Cindy Lankford, 2 ch   **Cmte.** Ethics • Finance • Homeland Security & Government Affairs • Intelligence
CoS. Michelle Altman   **LD.** Sarah Seitz
Sched. Jaclyn Newton   **PS.** Aly Beley
Dist. Off. Oklahoma City 405.231.4941 • Tulsa 918.581.7651

R: 60   **T:** 3rd 64%
Elected Year: 2014
Next Election: 2028

⚑ Sen. Markwayne Mullin (MUHL-luhn)   R-OK-Jr.   p 202.224.4721

Rm. RSOB B33 **Web.** mullin.senate.gov
Bio. 07/26/1977 • Tulsa • Oklahoma State Univ. Institute of Technology, Assc. Deg., 2010 • Assembly of God • M. Christie Mullin, 6 ch   **Cmte.** Armed Services • Environment & Public Works • Health, Education, Labor & Pensions • Indian Affairs
CoS. Benjamin Cantrell   **LD.** Kaitlynn Quaofio
                                  PS. Kate Currie
Dist. Off. Oklahoma City 405.208.8841 • Tulsa 918.748.5111

R: 94   **T:** 1st 62%
Elected Year: 2022
Next Election: 2026

OKLAHOMA

🏛 Rep. Stephanie Bice (bais)   R-OK-05   p 202.225.2132

Rm. RHOB 2437 **Web.** bice.house.gov
Bio. 11/11/1973 • Oklahoma City • Oklahoma State Univ.,
B.S., 1995 • Catholic • M. Geoffrey Bice, 2 ch **Cmte.**
Administration • Appropriations • Budget • Science, Space
& Technology
CoS. Amy Albro (CD)
Dist. Off. Oklahoma City 405.300.6890

R: 301   **T:** 2nd   59%
Elected Year: 2020

🏛 Rep. Josh Brecheen ()   R-OK-02   p 202.225.2701

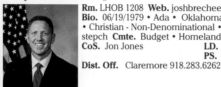

Rm. LHOB 1208 **Web.** joshbrecheen.com
Bio. 06/19/1979 • Ada • Oklahoma State Univ., Bach. Deg.
• Christian - Non-Denominational • M. Kacie Ann, 1 ch ; 2
stepch **Cmte.** Budget • Homeland Security
CoS. Jon Jones   **LD.** Sean McAndrews
                  PS. Ben Decatur
Dist. Off. Claremore 918.283.6262

R: 365   **T:** 1st   73%
Elected Year: 2022

🏛 Rep. Tom J. Cole (koal)   R-OK-04   p 202.225.6165

Rm. RHOB 2207 **Web.** cole.house.gov   **f** 202.225.3512
Bio. 04/28/1949 • Shreveport • Chief of Staff, Republican
National Committee; Secretary of State • Grinnell College
(IA), B.A., 1971; Institute for Historical Research - London
(England), B.A., 1972; Yale Univ. (CT), M.A., 1974; Univ.
of Oklahoma (OK), Ph.D., 1984 • Methodist • M. Ellen
Elizabeth Decker Cole, 1 ch **Cmte.** Appropriations • Rules
CoS. Josh Grogis   **LD.** Shane Hand
Sched. Sabrina Parker   **PS.** Sarah A. Corley
Dist. Off. Ada 580.436.5375 • Lawton 580.357.2131 •
Norman 405.329.6500

R: 47   **T:** 11th   67%
Elected Year: 2002

🏛 Rep. Kevin R. Hern (hurn)   R-OK-01   p 202.225.2211

Rm. LHOB 1019 **Web.** hern.house.gov   **f** 202.225.9187
Bio. 12/04/1961 • Belton • Univ. of Arkansas-Little Rock,
B.S., 1986; Univ. of Arkansas-Little Rock, M.B.A., 1999 •
Evangelical • M. Tammy Hern, 3 ch **Cmte.** Ways & Means
CoS. Cameron Foster   **LD.** Dominique Yelinski
                  PS. Miranda Dabney
Dist. Off. Tulsa 918.935.3222

R: 230   **T:** 4th   61%
Elected Year: 2018

🏛 Rep. Frank D. Lucas (LOO-kuhss)   R-OK-03   p 202.225.5565

Rm. RHOB 2405 **Web.** lucas.house.gov   **f** 202.225.8698
Bio. 01/06/1960 • Cheyenne • State Representative; Farmer/
Rancher • Oklahoma State Univ., B.S., 1982 • Baptist • M.
Lynda Bradshaw Lucas, 3 ch ; 2 gr-ch **Cmte.** Financial
Services • Science, Space & Technology
CoS. Stacey Glasscock (CD)   **LD.** Alison Slagell
Sched. Courtney Trigg   **PS.** Patrick Bond
Dist. Off. Yukon 405.373.1958

R: 18   **T:** 15th   75%
Elected Year: 1994

OREGON

🏵 **Governor Tina Kotek ()**   p 503.378.4582

160 State Capitol
900 Court St. NE, Rm. 160
Salem, OR 97301-4047
Website oregon.gov
Fax 503.378.8970
Term Ends 2027

C: Salem
P: 4,190,713 (27)
A: 95,988.05 mi^2 (10th)

U.S. Senators
Ron Wyden, **D**
Jeff A. Merkley, **D**
U.S. Representatives
01 / Suzanne M. Bonamici, **D**
02 / Cliff S. Bentz, **R**
03 / Earl Blumenauer, **D**
04 / Valerie T. Hoyle, **D**
05 / Lori Chavez-DeRemer, **R**
06 / Andrea Salinas, **D**

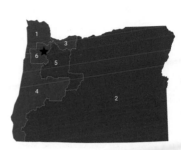

🏵 **Sen. Jeff A. Merkley** (MURK-lee)   D-OR-Jr.   p 202.224.3753

Rm. HSOB 531 **Web.** merkley.senate.gov   **f** 202.228.3997
Bio. 10/24/1956 • Myrtle Creek • State Legislator • Stanford
Univ. (CA), B.A., 1979; Princeton Univ. Woodrow Wilson
School of Public and International Affairs (NJ), M.P.P., 1982 •
Lutheran • M. Mary Sorteberg, 2 ch **Cmte.** Appropriations
• Budget • Environment & Public Works • Foreign Relations
• Joint Congressional-Executive Commission on China •
Rules & Administration
CoS. Michael Zamore   **LD.** Elvia Montoya
Sched. Lucky Sasiphong   **PS.** Martina McLennan
Dist. Off. Baker City 541.278.1129 • Bend 541.318.1298 •

R: 31   **T:** 3rd 57%
Elected Year: 2008
Next Election: 2026

Eugene 541.465.6750 • Medford 541.608.9102 • Portland
503.326.3386 • Salem 503.362.8102

🏵 **Sen. Ron Wyden** (WY-duhn)   D-OR-Sr.   p 202.224.5244

Rm. DSOB 221 **Web.** wyden.senate.gov   **f** 202.228.2717
Bio. 05/03/1949 • Wichita • Senior Citizen Advocacy
Group State Director; Professor, Gerontology • Univ. of
California, B.A., 1969; Stanford Univ. (CA), B.A., 1971; Univ.
of Oregon Law School, J.D., 1974 • Jewish • M. Nancy Bass
Wyden, 5 ch (2 from previous marriage) **Cmte.** Budget •
Energy & Natural Resources • Finance • Intelligence • Joint
Economic • Joint Taxation
CoS. Jeffrey Michels   **LD.** Isaiah Akin
                 PS. Keith Chu

R: 5   **T:** 6th 56%
Elected Year: 1996
Next Election: 2028

Dist. Off. Bend 541.330.9142 • Eugene 541.431.0229 • La
Grande 541.962.7691 • Medford 541.858.5122 • Portland
503.326.7525 • Salem 503.589.4555

🏵 **Rep. Cliff S. Bentz** (behnts)   R-OR-02   p 202.225.6730

Rm. CHOB 409 **Web.** bentz.house.gov   **f** 202.225.5774
Bio. 01/12/1952 • Salem • Eastern Oregon State College,
B.S., 1974; Northwestern School of Law, Lewis and Clark
College (OR), J.D., 1977 • Roman Catholic • M. Dr. Lindsay
Norman, 2 ch **Cmte.** Judiciary • Natural Resources
Dist. Off. Medford 541.776.4646 • Ontario 541.709.2040

R: 300   **T:** 2nd 68%
Elected Year: 2020

OREGON

🐦 Rep. Earl Blumenauer (BLOO-meh-nou-ur)   D-OR-03   p 202.225.4811
     Rm. LHOB 1111 **Web.**   f 202.225.8941
     blumenauer.house.gov
     Bio. 08/16/1948 • Portland • Attorney • Lewis & Clark
     College (OR), B.A., 1970; Northwestern Law School, Lewis
     and Clark College (OR), J.D., 1976 • Unspecified/Other •
     M. Margaret Kirkpatrick Blumenauer, 2 ch **Cmte.** Budget •
     Ways & Means
     CoS. Willie Smith (CD)   **LD.** Jon Bosworth
     Sched. Zoe Walker   **PS.** Hunter Spence
     Dist. Off. Portland 503.231.2300

R: 22   **T:** 15th   70%
Elected Year: 1996

🐦 Rep. Suzanne M. Bonamici (baw-nuh-MEE-chee) D-OR-01   p 202.225.0855
     Rm. RHOB 2231 **Web.** bonamici.house.gov   f 202.225.9497
     Bio. 10/14/1954 • Detroit • State Legislator; Attorney •
     Lane Community College (OR), A.A., 1978; Univ. of Oregon,
     B.A., 1980; Univ. of Oregon, School of Journalism, B.A., 1980;
     Univ. of Oregon Law School, J.D., 1983 • Episcopalian • M.
     Michael H. Simon, 2 ch **Cmte.** Education & Workforce •
     Science, Space & Technology
     CoS. Rachael Bornstein   **LD.** Joshua Izaak
     Sched. Audrey Hazel   **PS.** Natalie Crofts
     Dist. Off. Beaverton 503.469.6010

R: 119   **T:** 7th   68%
Elected Year: 2012

🐦 Rep. Lori Chavez-DeRemer ()   R-OR-05   p 202.225.5711
     Rm. LHOB 1722 **Web.**
     lorichavezderemer.com
     Bio. 04/07/1968 • • California State Univ., Fresno,
     B.B.A., 1990 • M. Dr. Shawn DeRemer, 2 ch (twins) **Cmte.**
     Education & Workforce • Transportation & Infrastructure
     CoS. Jihun Han   **LD.** Marcus Brubaker
     Sched. Peyton Smith   **PS.** Aaron Britt
     Dist. Off. Oregon City 903.732.0334

R: 370   **T:** 1st   51%
Elected Year: 2022

🐦 Rep. Valerie T. Hoyle ()   D-OR-04   p 202.225.6416
     Rm. LHOB 1620 **Web.** valhoyle.com
     Bio. 02/14/1964 • Travis Air Force Base • Emmanuel
     College, B.A., 1992 • Catholic • M. Dr. Shawn DeRemer, 2 ch
     Cmte. Natural Resources • Transportation & Infrastructure
     CoS. Karmen Fore   **LD.** Bobby Puckett
     Sched. David C. Martinez   **PS.** Sophia MonDragon
     Dist. Off. Eugene 458.215.1817

R: 390   **T:** 1st   51%
Elected Year: 2022

🐦 Rep. Andrea Salinas ()   D-OR-06   p 202.225.5643
     Rm. CHOB 109 **Web.**
     andreasalinasfororegon.com
     Bio. 12/06/1969 • Pleasant Hill • Univ. of California,
     Berkeley, B.A., 1994 • M. Chris Salinas, 1 ch **Cmte.**
     Science, Space & Technology
     CoS. Shannon Geison   **LD.** Kelly Nickel
     Sched. Alma Baker   **PS.** Teddy Lake
     Dist. Off. Salem 503.385.0906

R: 423   **T:** 1st   50%
Elected Year: 2022

PENNSYLVANIA

PENNSYLVANIA

🐦 Governor Joshua Shapiro ()   p 717.787.2500

     Main Capitol Building, Rm. 225   **C:** Harrisburg
     Harrisburg, PA 17120   **P:** 12,807,060 (5)
     Website pa.gov   **A:** 44,742.66 mi^2 (32nd)
     Fax 717.772.8284
     Term Ends 2027
     Lt. Governor
     Austin Davis, **D**

PENNSYLVANIA

U.S. Senators
Bob Casey, **D**
John K. Fetterman, **D**
U.S. Representatives
01 / Brian Fitzpatrick, **R**
02 / Brendan F. Boyle, **D**
03 / Dwight Evans, **D**
04 / Madeleine Dean, **D**
05 / Mary Gay Scanlon, **D**
06 / Chrissy Jampoler Houlahan, **D**
07 / Susan Ellis Wild, **D**
08 / Matt Cartwright, **D**
09 / Dan P. Meuser, **R**

10 / Scott Perry, **R**
11 / Lloyd K. Smucker, **R**
12 / Summer Lee, **D**
13 / John Joyce, **R**
14 / Guy Reschenthaler, **R**
15 / Glenn W. Thompson, **R**
16 / Mike Kelly, **R**
17 / Chris Deluzio, **D**

Sen. Bob Casey Jr. (KAY-see)　　　　D-PA-Sr.　　p 202.224.6324

Rm. RSOB 393 **Web.** casey.senate.gov　　**f** 202.228.0604
Bio. 04/13/1960 • Scranton • Teacher; Attorney • College of The Holy Cross (MA), B.A., 1982; Catholic Univ. of America (DC), J.D., 1988 • Roman Catholic • M. Terese Foppiano Casey, 4 ch ; 1 gr-ch　**Cmte.** Aging • Finance • Health, Education, Labor & Pensions • Intelligence
CoS. Kristen E. Gentile　　**LD.** Derek J. Miller
Sched. Landy Wade　　**PS.** Mairead Lynn
Dist. Off. Allentown 610.782.9470 • Bellefonte 814.357.0314 • Erie 814.874.5080 • Harrisburg 717.231.7540 • Philadelphia 215.405.9660 • Pittsburgh 412.803.7370 • Scranton 570.941.0930

R: 22　**T:** 3rd　56%
Elected Year: 2006
Next Election: 2024

Sen. John K. Fetterman ()　　　　D-PA-Jr.　　p 202.224.6551

Rm. DSOB B40B **Web.** johnfetterman.com
Bio. 08/15/1969 • Reading • Albright College, Bach. Deg., 1991; Univ. of Connecticut, M.B.A., 1993; Harvard Univ. Kennedy School of Government (MA), M.P.P., 1999 • M. Gisele Barreto Almeida, 3 ch　**Cmte.** Aging • Agriculture, Nutrition & Forestry • Banking, Housing & Urban Affairs • Environment & Public Works • Joint Economic
CoS. Adam Jentleson　　**LD.** Tre Easton
　　　　　　　　　　PS. Joe Calvello
Dist. Off. Philadelphia 215.241.1090

R: 96　**T:** 1st　51%
Elected Year: 2022
Next Election: 2028

Rep. Brendan F. Boyle (BOY-uhl)　　　　D-PA-02　　p 202.225.6111

Rm. LHOB 1502 **Web.** boyle.house.gov　　**f** 202.226.0611
Bio. 02/06/1977 • Philadelphia • Univ. of Notre Dame (IN), B.A., 1999; Harvard Univ. John F. Kennedy School of Government (MA), M.P.P., 2005 • Roman Catholic • M. Jennifer Morgan, 1 ch　**Cmte.** Budget
CoS. Tim Barnes
Sched. David Beer　　**PS.** Sean Tobin
Dist. Off. Philadelphia 215.426.4616 • Philadelphia 215.982.1156

R: 165　**T:** 5th　76%
Elected Year: 2014

Rep. Matt Cartwright (KART-rite)　　　　D-PA-08　　p 202.225.5546

Rm. RHOB 2102 **Web.** cartwright.house.gov　**f** 202.226.0996
Bio. 05/01/1961 • Erie • Hamilton College (NY), A.B., 1983; Univ. of Pennsylvania, J.D., 1986 • Roman Catholic • M. Marion Munley, 2 ch　**Cmte.** Appropriations
CoS. Hunter Ridgway　　**LD.** Rachel Cohen
Sched. Tammy Aita (CD)　　**PS.** Colleen Gerrity (CD)
Dist. Off. Hawley 570.576.8005 • Hazleton 570.751.0050 • Tannersville 570.355.1818

R: 129　**T:** 6th　51%
Elected Year: 2012

PENNSYLVANIA

🐦 Rep. Madeleine Dean (deen)   D-PA-04   p 202.225.4731

Rm. CHOB 120 **Web.** dean.house.gov
Bio. 06/06/1959 • Glenside • Montgomery County
Community College, B.A.; La Salle Univ. (PA), B.A., 1981;
Widener Univ. (DE), J.D., 1984 • Christian Church • M.
Patrick J. Cunnane, 3 ch; 1 gr-ch **Cmte.** Foreign Affairs •
Judiciary
CoS. Colleen Carlos
Sched. Meghan Janoson   **PS.** Tim Mack
(CD)
Dist. Off. Glenside 215.884.4300

R: 245   **T:** 3rd   61%
Elected Year: 2018

🐦 Rep. Chris Deluzio ()   D-PA-17   p 202.225.2301

Rm. LHOB 1222 **Web.** chrisforpa.com
Bio. 07/13/1984 • Pittsburgh • U.S. Naval Academy (MD),
B.S.; Georgetown Univ. Law Center (DC), J.D. • M. Zoe
Bunnell, 3 ch **Cmte.** Armed Services • Veterans' Affairs
CoS. Matthew Koos   **LD.** Christopher Jerrolds
                     PS. Zoe Bluffstone
Dist. Off. Monaca • Pittsburg

R: 378   **T:** 1st   53%
Elected Year: 2022

🐦 Rep. Dwight Evans (EH-vuhnz)   D-PA-03   p 202.225.4001

Rm. LHOB 1105 **Web.** evans.house.gov   **f** 202.225.5392
Bio. 05/16/1954 • Philadelphia • Community College of
Philadelphia, A.A., 1973; La Salle College (PA), B.A., 1975 •
Baptist • S. **Cmte.** Ways & Means
                     LD. Gillian Mueller
                     PS. Ben Turner
Dist. Off. Philadelphia 215.276.0340

R: 191   **T:** 5th   95%
Elected Year: 2016

♟ Rep. Brian Fitzpatrick (fits-PAT-rik)   R-PA-01   p 202.225.4276

Rm. CHOB 271 **Web.**   **f** 202.225.9511
brianfitzpatrick.house.gov
Bio. 12/17/1973 • Levittown • LaSalle Univ., Bach. Deg.,
1996; Pennsylvania State Univ., M.B.A., 2001; Penn State Univ.
Dickinson School of Law (PA), J.D., 2001 • Roman Catholic
• S. **Cmte.** Permanent Select on Intelligence • Ways &
Means
CoS. Joseph Knowles
Sched. Emery Boylan   **PS.** Reagan McCarthy
Dist. Off. Langhorne 215.579.8102

R: 206   **T:** 4th   55%
Elected Year: 2016

🐦 Rep. Chrissy Jampoler Houlahan (HOO-luh-han) D-PA-06   p 202.225.4315

Rm. LHOB 1727 **Web.** houlahan.house.gov
Bio. 06/05/1967 • Patuxent River • Stanford Univ. (CA), B.S.,
1989; Massachusetts Institute of Technology, M.S., 1994 •
Unspecified/Other • M. Bart Houlahan, 2 ch **Cmte.** Armed
Services • Permanent Select on Intelligence
                     LD. Kat Cosgrove
Sched. Ron Washington   **PS.** Aubrey Stuber (CD)
Dist. Off. Reading 610.295.0815 • West Chester
610.883.5050

R: 257   **T:** 3rd   58%
Elected Year: 2018

♟ Rep. John Joyce (joyss)   R-PA-13   p 202.225.2431

Rm. CHOB 152 **Web.** johnjoyce.house.gov   **f** 202.225.2486
Bio. 02/08/1957 • Altoona • Pennsylvania State Univ., Bach.
Deg., 1979; Temple Univ. (PA), M.D., 1983 • Catholic • M.
Alice Joyce, 3 ch **Cmte.** Energy & Commerce
Dist. Off. Abbottstown 717.357.6320 • Altoona
814.656.6081 • Chambersburg 717.753.6344 • Johnstown
814.485.6020

R: 259   **T:** 3rd   100%
Elected Year: 2018

♺ Rep. Mike Kelly Jr. (KEH-lee)   R-PA-16   p 202.225.5406

Rm. LHOB 1707 **Web.** kelly.house.gov   **f** 202.225.3103
Bio. 05/10/1948 • Pittsburgh • Univ. of Notre Dame (IN), B.A., 1970 • Roman Catholic • M. Victoria Kelly, 4 ch ; 10 gr-ch   **Cmte.** Ways & Means
Sched. Michael Guido (CD)   **PS.** Matt Knoeller

R: 111   **T:** 7th   59%
Elected Year: 2010

♺ Rep. Summer Lee ()   D-PA-12   p 202.225.2135

Rm. CHOB 243 **Web.** summerlee.house.gov
Bio. 11/26/1987 • North Braddock • Pennsylvania State Univ., B.J., 2009; Howard Univ. Law School (DC), J.D., 2015 • NS. **Cmte.** Oversight & Accountability • Science, Space & Technology
CoS. Wasiullah Mohamed
Dist. Off. Pittsburgh

R: 405   **T:** 1st   100%
Elected Year: 2022

♺ Rep. Dan P. Meuser (MYOO-zur)   R-PA-09   p 202.225.6511

Rm. CHOB 350 **Web.** meuser.house.gov
Bio. 02/10/1954 • Babylon • Cornell Univ. (NY), B.A., 1976 • Catholic • M. Shelley Van Acker, 3 ch **Cmte.** Financial Services • Small Business
Dist. Off. Palmyra 717.473.5375 • Pottsville 570.871.6370 • Reading 610.568.9959

R: 264   **T:** 3rd   69%
Elected Year: 2018

♺ Rep. Scott Perry (PAIR-ree)   R-PA-10   p 202.225.5836

Rm. RHOB 2160 **Web.** perry.house.gov   **f** 202.226.1000
Bio. 05/27/1962 • San Diego • U.S. Army War College (PA), M.S.; Pennsylvania State Univ., Harrisburg, 1991 • Church of the United Brethren in Christ • M. Christy Perry, 2 ch **Cmte.** Foreign Affairs • Oversight & Accountability • Transportation & Infrastructure
CoS. Lauren Muglia   **LD.** Patrick Schilling
Sched. Carol Wiest (CD)   **PS.** Jay Ostrich (CD)
Dist. Off. Harrisburg 717.603.4980 • York 717.893.7868

R: 141   **T:** 6th   54%
Elected Year: 2012

♺ Rep. Guy Reschenthaler (REH-shen-thaw-lur)   R-PA-14   p 202.225.2065

Rm. CHOB 409 **Web.**   **f** 202.225.5709
reschenthaler.house.gov
Bio. 04/17/1983 • Pittsburgh • Pennsylvania State Univ., B.A., 2004; Duquesne Univ., J.D., 2007 • Christian Church • S. **Cmte.** Appropriations • Rules
CoS. Ashley Menzler   **LD.** Michael D'Orazio
Sched. Abbey Obourn   **PS.** Alexa Vance
Dist. Off. Greensburg 724.219.4200 • Washington 724.206.4800

R: 274   **T:** 3rd   100%
Elected Year: 2018

♺ Rep. Mary Gay Scanlon (scan-lin)   D-PA-05   p 202.225.2011

Rm. LHOB 1227 **Web.** scanlon.house.gov   **f** 202.226.0280
Bio. 08/30/1959 • Syracuse • Colgate Univ., B.A., 1980; Univ. of Pennsylvania Law School, J.D., 1984 • Catholic • M. Mark Scanlon, 3 ch **Cmte.** Judiciary • Rules
CoS. Armita Pedramrazi   **LD.** Keanu Rivera
Sched. Tessa Cate   **PS.** Carina Figliuzzi
Dist. Off. Chester 610.626.2020

R: 232   **T:** 4th   65%
Elected Year: 2018

PENNSYLVANIA

⚑ Rep. Lloyd K. Smucker (SMUH-kur)   R-PA-11   p 202.225.2411

Rm. CHOB 302 **Web.** smucker.house.gov   **f** 202.225.2013
Bio. 01/23/1964 • Lancaster • Lutheran • M. Cynthia Smucker, 3 ch **Cmte.** Budget • Education & Workforce • Ways & Means
CoS. Kate Bonner
Sched. Karen Cologne   **PS.** Eric Reath (CD)
Dist. Off. Hanover 717.969.6132 • Red Lion 717.969.6133

R: 221 **T:** 4th 62%
Elected Year: 2016

⚑ Rep. Glenn W. Thompson Jr. (TOMP-suhn)   R-PA-15   p 202.225.5121

Rm. CHOB 400 **Web.** thompson.house.gov   **f** 202.225.5796
Bio. 07/27/1959 • Bellefonte • School Board Member; Health Care Executive • Pennsylvania State Univ., B.S., 1981; Temple Univ. (PA), M.Ed., 1998 • Protestant - Unspecified Christian • M. Penny Thompson, 3 ch **Cmte.** Agriculture • Education & Workforce
CoS. Renee Gamela
Sched. Cindy Kunes (CD)   **PS.** Maddison Stone
Dist. Off. Ebensburg 814.419.8583

R: 91 **T:** 8th 70%
Elected Year: 2008

🐦 Rep. Susan Ellis Wild ("wild")   D-PA-07   p 202.225.6411

Rm. LHOB 1027 **Web.** wild.house.gov
Bio. 06/07/1957 • Wiesbaden • American Univ. (DC), B.A., 1978; George Washington Univ. (DC), J.D., 1982 • Jewish • D., 2 ch **Cmte.** Education & Workforce • Ethics • Foreign Affairs
CoS. Jed Ober
PS. Olivia Taylor-Puckett
Dist. Off. Allentown 484.781.6000 • Easton 610.333.1170 • Stroudsburg 570.807.0333

R: 233 **T:** 4th 51%
Elected Year: 2018

RHODE ISLAND

🐦 Governor Daniel McKee (mih-KEE)   p 401.222.2371

82 Smith St.
Providence, RI 02903
Website ri.gov
Fax 401.222.2012
Term Ends 2027
Lt. Governor
Sabina Matos, **D**

C: Providence
P: 1,057,315 (45)
A: 1,033.98 mi^2 (51st)

U.S. Senators
Jack F. Reed, **D**
Sheldon Whitehouse, **D**
U.S. Representatives
01 / David Cicilline, **D**
02 / Seth Magaziner, **D**

Sen. Jack F. Reed (reed)   D-RI-Sr.   p 202.224.4642

Rm. HSOB 728 **Web.** reed.senate.gov   **f** 202.224.4680
Bio. 11/12/1949 • Cranston • Attorney; Professor at West Point • Army 1967-79 • U.S. Military Academy (NY), B.S., 1971; Harvard Univ. John F. Kennedy School of Government (MA), M.P.P., 1973; Harvard Univ. School of Law (MA), J.D., 1982 • Roman Catholic • M. Julia Hart Reed, 1 ch **Cmte.** Appropriations • Armed Services • Banking, Housing & Urban Affairs • Intelligence
CoS. Neil Campbell   **LD.** Steven Keenan
Sched. Cara Gilbert   **PS.** Chip Unruh
Dist. Off. Cranston 401.943.3100 • Providence 401.528.5200

R: 7   T: 5th   67%
Elected Year: 1996
Next Election: 2026

Sen. Sheldon Whitehouse (WHITE-house)   D-RI-Jr.   p 202.224.2921

Rm. HSOB 530 **Web.** whitehouse.senate.gov **f** 202.228.6362
Bio. 10/20/1955 • New York City • Attorney • Yale Univ. (CT), B.Arch., 1978; Univ. of Virginia Law School, J.D., 1982 • Episcopalian • M. Sandra Thornton Whitehouse, 2 ch **Cmte.** Budget • Environment & Public Works • Finance • Judiciary
CoS. Monalisa Dugue   **LD.** Chris Gorud
Sched. Rebecca Tulloch   **PS.** Stephen DeLeo
Dist. Off. Providence 401.453.5294

R: 24   T: 3rd   61%
Elected Year: 2006
Next Election: 2024

Rep. David Cicilline (sih-sih-LEE-nee)   D-RI-01   p 202.225.4911

Rm. RHOB 2233 **Web.** cicilline.house.gov   **f** 202.225.3290
Bio. 07/15/1961 • Providence • Narragansett High School, J.D.; Brown Univ. (RI), B.A., 1983; Georgetown Univ. Law Center (DC), J.D., 1986 • Jewish • S. **Cmte.** Foreign Affairs • Judiciary
CoS. Peter Karafotas
Sched. Leo Confalone   **PS.** Jennifer Bell
Dist. Off. Pawtucket 401.729.5600

R: 100   T: 7th   64%
Elected Year: 2010

Rep. Seth Magaziner ()   D-RI-02   p 202.225.2735

Rm. LHOB 1218 **Web.** sethmagaziner.com
Bio. 07/22/1983 • Bristol • Brown Univ. (RI), A.B., 2006; Yale Univ. School of Management, M.B.A., 2010 • M. Julia McDowell, 1 ch **Cmte.** Homeland Security • Natural Resources
CoS. Clay Schroers   **LD.** Emily Mercado
Sched. Selin Ciesielski   **PS.** Matt Fidel
Dist. Off. Warwick 401.244.1201

R: 408   T: 1st   50%
Elected Year: 2022

SOUTH CAROLINA

Governor Henry McMaster (mik-MASS-tur)   p 803.734.2100

Office of the Governor
1205 Pendleton St.
Columbia, SC 29201
Website sc.gov
Fax 803.734.5167
Term Ends 2027
Lt. Governor
Pamela Evette, **R**

C: Columbia
P: 5,084,127 (23)
A: 30,060.74 mi^2 (40th)

SOUTH CAROLINA

U.S. Senators
Lindsey Graham, **R**
Tim E. Scott, **R**
U.S. Representatives
01 / Nancy Mace, **R**
02 / Joe Wilson, **R**
03 / Jeff D. Duncan, **R**
04 / William R. Timmons, **R**
05 / Ralph W. Norman, **R**
06 / James E. Clyburn, **D**
07 / Russell W. Fry, **R**

⚑ Sen. Lindsey Graham (gram) R-SC-Sr. p 202.224.5972

Rm. RSOB 290 **Web.** lgraham.senate.gov **f** 202.224.3808
Bio. 07/09/1955 • Central • U.S. Representative • Air Force
Judge Advocate General Corps 1982-88; South Carolina Air
National Guard 1989-95, Air Force Reserve 1995-present
• The Univ. of South Carolina, B.S., 1977; The Univ. of
South Carolina, M.P.A., 1978; Univ. of South Carolina School
of Law, J.D., 1981 • Baptist • S. **Cmte.** Appropriations •
Budget • Environment & Public Works • Judiciary
CoS. Richard S. Perry **LD.** Craig R. Abele
Sched. Edward Mercer (CD) **PS.** Alice James
Dist. Off. Columbia 803.933.0112 • Florence 843.669.1505
• Greenville 864.250.1417 • Mount Pleasant 843.849.3887 •
Pendleton 864.646.4090 • Rock Hill 803.366.2828

R: 16 T: 4th 54%
Elected Year: 2002
Next Election: 2026

⚑ Sen. Tim E. Scott (skaht) R-SC-Jr. p 202.224.6121

Rm. HSOB 104 **Web.** scott.senate.gov **f** 202.228.5143
Bio. 09/19/1965 • North Charleston • Charleston Southern
Univ. (SC), B.S., 1988 • Evangelical • S. **Cmte.** Aging
• Banking, Housing & Urban Affairs • Finance • Small
Business & Entrepreneurship
CoS. Neri A. Martinez **LD.** Adam Farris
Sched. Molly Venegas **PS.** Katie Vincentz
Dist. Off. Columbia 803.771.6112 • Greenville
864.233.5366 • North Charleston 843.727.4525

R: 45 T: 4th 63%
Elected Year: 2013
Next Election: 2028

⚑ Rep. James E. Clyburn (KLY-burn) D-SC-06 p 202.225.3315

Rm. CHOB 274 **Web.** clyburn.house.gov **f** 202.225.2313
Bio. 07/21/1940 • Sumter • SC Human Affairs
Commissioner; Gubernatorial Assistant • South Carolina
State Univ., B.S., 1962; Univ. of South Carolina School of Law,
B.S., 1974 • African Methodist Episcopal • W. Emily England
Clyburn, 3 ch ; 4 gr-ch
CoS. Yelberton R. Watkins
Sched. Lindy Birch Kelly **PS.** Quadri Bell (CD)
Dist. Off. Columbia 803.799.1100 • Kingstree 843.355.1211
• Santee 803.854.4700

R: 13 T: 16th 62%
Elected Year: 1992

⚑ Rep. Jeff D. Duncan (DUN-kuhn) R-SC-03 p 202.225.5301

Rm. RHOB 2229 **Web.** jeffduncan.house.gov **f** 202.225.3216
Bio. 01/07/1966 • Greenville • Clemson Univ. (SC), B.A.,
1988 • Baptist • M. Melody Duncan, 3 ch **Cmte.** Energy &
Commerce
CoS. Allen Klump **LD.** Joshua Gross
Sched. Thomas McAllister **PS.** Emily Wood
Dist. Off. Anderson 864.224.7401 • Clinton 864.681.1028

R: 103 T: 7th 98%
Elected Year: 2010

☗ Rep. Russell W. Fry () R-SC-07 p 202.225.9895

Rm. LHOB 1626 **Web.** fryforhouse.com
Bio. 01/31/1985 • Surfside Beach • The Univ. of South
Carolina, B.A., 2007; Charleston School of Law, J.D., 2011 •
Methodist • M. Bronwen Burson, 1 ch **Cmte.** Judiciary •
Oversight & Accountability
CoS. Matt Orr **LD.** Annie Barletta
Sched. Anna Clark **PS.** Hannah Nine
Dist. Off. Surfside Beach 843.650.9137

R: 384 **T:** 1st 65%
Elected Year: 2022

☗ Rep. Nancy Mace (mace) R-SC-01 p 202.225.3176

Rm. LHOB 1728 **Web.** mace.house.gov
Bio. 12/04/1977 • Fayetteville • The Citadel Univ., B.S.,
1999; Univ. of Georgia, M.S., 2004 • Christian - Non-
Denominational • E. Curtis Jackson, 2 ch **Cmte.** Armed
Services • Oversight & Accountability • Veterans' Affairs
CoS. Daniel Hanlon **LD.** Madison Van Every
 PS. John Seibels
Dist. Off. Beaufort 843.521.2530 • Mount Pleasant
843.352.7572

R: 326 **T:** 2nd 56%
Elected Year: 2020

☗ Rep. Ralph W. Norman Jr. (NOR-muhn) R-SC-05 p 202.225.5501

Rm. CHOB 569 **Web.** norman.house.gov **f** 202.225.0464
Bio. 06/20/1953 • York County • Rock Hill High School,
B.S., 1971; Presbyterian College (SC), B.S., 1975 •
Presbyterian • M. Elaine Rice, 4 ch ; 16 gr-ch **Cmte.** Budget
• Financial Services • Rules
CoS. Mark Piland **LD.** Hali Gruber
 PS. Nicole McGrath (CD)
Dist. Off. Rock Hill 803.327.1114

R: 225 **T:** 4th 64%
Elected Year: 2017

☗ Rep. William R. Timmons IV (TIH-muhnz) R-SC-04 p 202.225.6030

Rm. CHOB 267 **Web.** timmons.house.gov
Bio. 04/30/1984 • Greenville • George Washington Univ.
(DC), B.A., 2006; The Univ. of South Carolina, Mast. Deg.,
2009; The Univ. of South Carolina, J.D., 2010 • Church
of Christ • S. **Cmte.** Financial Services • Oversight &
Accountability
 PS. Heather K. Smith
Dist. Off. Greer 864.241.0175

R: 286 **T:** 3rd 91%
Elected Year: 2018

☗ Rep. Joe Wilson (WILL-suhn) R-SC-02 p 202.225.2452

Rm. LHOB 1436 **Web.** joewilson.house.gov **f** 202.225.2455
Bio. 07/31/1947 • Charleston • State Senator; Attorney,
Founding Partner; Judge, Springdale • Army Reserve
1972-75; SC Army National Guard 1975-03 • Washington
and Lee Univ. (VA), B.A., 1969; The Univ. of South Carolina,
J.D., 1972 • Presbyterian • M. Roxanne Dusenbury McCrory
Wilson, 4 ch; 7 gr-ch **Cmte.** Armed Services • Education &
Workforce • Foreign Affairs • Joint Security & Cooperation
in Europe
CoS. Jonathan Day **LD.** Drew Kennedy
 PS. David Snider
R: 44 **T:** 12th 60% **Dist. Off.** Aiken 803.642.6416 • West Columbia
Elected Year: 2001 803.939.0041

SOUTH DAKOTA

SOUTH DAKOTA

R Governor Kristi Lynn Noem (noam)　　　　p 605.773.3212

State Capitol
500 E. Capitol Ave.
Pierre, SD 57501-5070
Website sd.gov
Fax 605.773.4711
Term Ends 2027
Lt. Governor
Larry Rhoden, **R**

C: Pierre
P: 882,235 (47)
A: 75,811.13 mi^2 (16th)

U.S. Senators
John Thune, **R**
Mike Rounds, **R**
U.S. Representatives
01 / Dusty Johnson, **R**

R Sen. Mike Rounds (rounz)　　　　R-SD-Jr.　　p 202.224.5842

Rm. HSOB 716 **Web.** rounds.senate.gov　　**f** 202.224.7482
Bio. 10/24/1954 • Huron • Majority Leader, SD Senate;
Mbr., SD Senate • South Dakota State Univ., B.S., 1977 •
Roman Catholic • W. Jean Vedvei Rounds, 4 ch ; 6 gr-ch
Cmte. Armed Services • Banking, Housing & Urban Affairs
• Foreign Relations • Indian Affairs • Intelligence • Veterans'
Affairs
CoS. Kyle Chase
Sched. Danielle Quercia　　**PS.** Dezmond Ward
Dist. Off. Aberdeen 605.225.0366 • Pierre 605.224.1450 •
Rapid City 605.343.5035 • Sioux Falls 605.336.0486

R: 63 **T:** 2nd 66%
Elected Year: 2014
Next Election: 2026

R Sen. John Thune (thoon)　　　　R-SD-Sr.　　p 202.224.2321

Rm. DSOB 511 **Web.** thune.senate.gov　　**f** 202.228.5429
Bio. 01/07/1961 • Pierre • U.S. Representative;
Congressional Aide • Biola Univ., B.B.A., 1983; Univ. of
South Dakota, M.B.A., 1984 • Evangelical • M. Kimberley
Joe Weems Thune, 2 ch ; 2 gr-ch **Cmte.** Agriculture,
Nutrition & Forestry • Commerce, Science & Transportation
• Finance
CoS. Ryan Nelson　　　　　**LD.** Jessica McBride
Sched. Amy Barrera　　　　**PS.** Ryan Wrasse
Dist. Off. Aberdeen 605.225.8823 • Rapid City
605.348.7551 • Sioux Falls 605.334.9596

R: 17 **T:** 4th 70%
Elected Year: 2004
Next Election: 2028

R Rep. Dusty Johnson (JAHN-suhn)　　R-SD-01　　p 202.225.2801

Rm. LHOB 1714 **Web.**
dustyjohnson.house.gov
Bio. 09/30/1976 • Pierre • Univ. of South Dakota, B.A.,
1999; Univ. of Kansas Stene Center, M.P.A., 2002 • Christian
Church • M. Jacquelyn Johnson, 3 ch **Cmte.** Agriculture •
Select China Committee • Transportation & Infrastructure
CoS. Jazmine Kemp　　　　**LD.** Elizabeth Lloyd
Sched. Alana Lomis　　　　**PS.** Kristen Kurtz
Dist. Off. Aberdeen 605.622.1060 • Rapid City
605.646.6454 • Sioux Falls 605.275.2868

R: 258 **T:** 3rd 77%
Elected Year: 2018

TENNESSEE

⚑ Governor Bill Lee (lee)   p 615.741.2001

Tennessee State Capitol, 1st Floor
Nashville, TN 37243
Website tennessee.gov
Fax 615.532.9711
Term Ends 2027
Lt. Governor
Randy McNally, **R**

C: Nashville
P: 6,770,010 (16)
A: 41,234.92 mi^2 (34th)

U.S. Senators
Marsha Blackburn, **R**
Bill Hagerty, **R**
U.S. Representatives
01 / Diana Harshbarger, **R**
02 / Tim Burchett, **R**
03 / Chuck J. Fleischmann, **R**
04 / Scott E. DesJarlais, **R**
05 / Andy Ogles, **R**
06 / John W. Rose, **R**
07 / Mark E. Green, **R**
08 / David F. Kustoff, **R**
09 / Steve I. Cohen, **D**

⚑ Sen. Marsha Blackburn (BLAK-burn)   R-TN-Sr.   p 202.224.3344

Rm. DSOB 357 **Web.** blackburn.senate.gov **f** 202.228.0566
Bio. 06/06/1952 • Laurel • Small Business Owner; State
Senator • Mississippi State Univ., B.S., 1973 • Presbyterian
• M. Chuck Blackburn, 2 ch ; 2 gr-ch **Cmte.** Commerce,
Science & Transportation • Finance • Judiciary • Veterans'
Affairs
CoS. Sean Farrell   **LD.** Jon M. Adame
Sched. Grace Burch (CD)   **PS.** Spencer Hurwitz
Dist. Off. Chattanooga 423.541.2939 • Jackson
731.660.3971 • Jonesborough 423.753.4009 • Knoxville
865.540.3781 • Memphis 901.527.9199 • Nashville
629.800.6600

R: 75 **T:** 1st 55%
Elected Year: 2018
Next Election: 2024

⚑ Sen. Bill Hagerty (HAG-gur-tee)   R-TN-Jr.   p 202.224.4944

Rm. RSOB 248 **Web.** hagerty.senate.gov   **f** 202.228.3398
Bio. 08/14/1959 • Gallatin • Vanderbilt Univ. (TN),
B.S., 1981; Vanderbilt Univ. Law School (TN), J.D.,
1984 • Episcopalian • M. Chrissy Hagerty, 4 ch **Cmte.**
Appropriations • Banking, Housing & Urban Affairs • Foreign
Relations • Rules & Administration
CoS. Adam Telle   **LD.** Natalie McIntyre
Sched. Walton Stivender   **PS.** Audrey Traynor
Dist. Off. Blountville 423.325.6240 • Chattanooga
423.752.5337 • Cookeville 931.981.4874 • Jackson
731.234.9358 • Knoxville 865.545.4253 • Memphis
901.544.4224 • Nashville 615.736.5129

R: 88 **T:** 1st 62%
Elected Year: 2020
Next Election: 2026

⚑ Rep. Tim Burchett (BUR-chuht)   R-TN-02   p 202.225.5435

Rm. LHOB 1122 **Web.** burchett.house.gov   **f** 202.225.6440
Bio. 08/25/1964 • Knoxville • Univ. of Tennessee, B.S., 1988
• Presbyterian • M. Kelly Burchett, 1 ch **Cmte.** Foreign
Affairs • Oversight & Accountability • Transportation &
Infrastructure
CoS. Michael Grider   **LD.** Kelsey Wolfgram
Sched. Whitney Hutson   **PS.** Rachel Partlow
Dist. Off. Knoxville 865.523.3772 • Maryville 865.984.5464

238 **T:** 3rd 68%
ted Year: 2018

Rep. Steve I. Cohen (KO-uhn)   D-TN-09   p 202.225.3265

Rm. RHOB 2268 **Web.** cohen.house.gov   **f** 202.225.5663
Bio. 05/24/1949 • Memphis • Attorney; State Representative • Vanderbilt Univ. (TN), B.A., 1971; Memphis State Univ. - Cecil C. Humphreys School of Law (TN), J.D., 1973 • Jewish • S. **Cmte.** Judiciary • Natural Resources • Transportation & Infrastructure
CoS. Marilyn Dillihay   **LD.** Reisha Buster
Sched. Patti Marsh   **PS.** Bart Sullivan
Dist. Off. Memphis 901.544.4131

R: 72   **T:** 9th 70%
Elected Year: 2006

Rep. Scott E. DesJarlais (deh-zhar-LAY)   R-TN-04   p 202.225.6831

Rm. RHOB 2304 **Web.** desjarlais.house.gov   **f** 202.226.5172
Bio. 02/21/1964 • Des Moines • Univ. of South Dakota, B.S., 1987; Univ. of South Dakota School of Medicine, M.D., 1991 • Episcopalian • M. Amy DesJarlais, 4 ch (1 from previous marriage) **Cmte.** Agriculture • Armed Services
CoS. Richard Vaughn   **LD.** Hannah Russell
Sched. MeKenna Carman   **PS.** Alex Swisher
Dist. Off. Cleveland 423.472.7500 • Columbia 931.381.9920 • Murfreesboro 615.896.1986 • Winchester 931.962.3180

R: 102   **T:** 7th 71%
Elected Year: 2010

Rep. Chuck J. Fleischmann (FLYSH-muhn)   R-TN-03   p 202.225.3271

Rm. RHOB 2187 **Web.** fleischmann.house.gov   **f** 202.225.3494
Bio. 10/11/1962 • New York • Univ. of Illinois, B.A., 1983; Univ. of Tennessee College of Law, Knoxville, J.D., 1986 • Roman Catholic • M. Brenda Fleischmann, 3 ch **Cmte.** Appropriations
Dist. Off. Athens 423.745.4671 • Chattanooga 423.756.2342 • Oak Ridge 865.576.1976

R: 104   **T:** 7th 68%
Elected Year: 2010

Rep. Mark E. Green (green)   R-TN-07   p 202.225.2811

Rm. RHOB 2446 **Web.** markgreen.house.gov **f** 202.225.3004
Bio. 11/08/1964 • Jacksonville • U.S. Military Academy - West Point (NY), B.S., 1986; Univ. of Southern California, Mast. Deg., 1987; Wright State Univ. (OH), M.D., 1999 • Christian Church • M. Camilla Joy Guenther, 2 ch **Cmte.** Foreign Affairs • Homeland Security
CoS. Stephen Siao   **LD.** Jay Kronzer
Sched. Merry Holland   **PS.** Rachel del Guidice
Dist. Off. Clarksville 931.266.4483 • Franklin 629.223.6050

R: 253   **T:** 3rd 60%
Elected Year: 2018

Rep. Diana Harshbarger (HARSH-bar-gur)   R-TN-01   p 202.225.6356

Rm. CHOB 167 **Web.** harshbarger.house.gov
Bio. 01/01/1960 • Kingsport • East Tennessee State Univ., Bach. Deg.; Mercer Univ. (GA), Pharm.D., 1987 • Baptist • M. Robert Harshbarger, 1 ch **Cmte.** Energy & Commerce
CoS. Zachary Rutherford   **LD.** Susan Falconer
Sched. Natalia Gutierrez   **PS.** Britney Dickerson
Dist. Off. Kingsport 423.398.5186 • Morristown 423.254.1400

R: 319   **T:** 2nd 78%
Elected Year: 2020

Rep. David F. Kustoff (KUS-tawf)   R-TN-08   p 202.225.4

Rm. CHOB 560   **f** 202.225
Bio. 10/08/1966 • Memphis • Univ. of Memphis, B.B.A. 1989; Univ. of Memphis School of Law, J.D., 1992 • Jew M. Roberta Kustoff, 2 ch **Cmte.** Ways & Means
CoS. Justin E. Melvin   **LD.** Eliana Goodman
Dist. Off. Dyersburg 731.412.1037 • Jackson 731. • Martin 731.412.1043 • Memphis 901.682.4422

R: 216   **T:** 4th 74%
Elected Year: 2016

℞ Rep. Andy Ogles () R-TN-05 p 202.225.4311

Rm. CHOB 151 **Web.** andyogles.com
Bio. 06/18/1971 • Nashville • Middle Tennessee State
Univ., Bach. Deg. • M. Monica Ogles, 3 ch **Cmte.** Financial
Services
CoS. Grant Henry **LD.** Christopher A.
 Fernandez
Sched. Erin Drummy
Dist. Off. Columbia 931.683.2272

R: 420 **T:** 1st 56%
Elected Year: 2022

℞ Rep. John W. Rose (roaz) R-TN-06 p 202.225.4231

Rm. LHOB 2238 **Web.** johnrose.house.gov **f** 202.225.6887
Bio. 02/23/1965 • Cookeville • Tennessee Tech Univ., B.S.,
1988; Purdue Univ. (IN), M.S., 1990; Vanderbilt Univ. (TN),
J.D., 1993 • Christian Church • M. Chelsea Rose, 2 ch (1
deceased) **Cmte.** Financial Services
Dist. Off. Cookeville 931.854.9430 • Gallatin 615.206.8204

R: 275 **T:** 3rd 66%
Elected Year: 2018

TEXAS

℞ Governor Greg Abbott (A-buht) p 512.403.2000

PO Box 12428
Austin, TX 78711-2428
Website texas.gov
Fax 512.463.5571
Term Ends 2027
Lt. Governor
Dan Patrick, **R**

C: Austin
P: 28,701,845 (2)
A: 261,231.59 mi^2 (2nd)

U.S. Senators
John Cornyn, **R**
Ted Cruz, **R**
U.S. Representatives
01 / Nathaniel Moran, **R**
02 / Daniel Crenshaw, **R**
03 / Keith Self, **R**
04 / Pat Fallon, **R**
05 / Lance Gooden, **R**
06 / Jake Ellzey, **R**
07 / Lizzie Pannill Fletcher, **D**
08 / Morgan J. Luttrell, **R**
09 / Al Green, **D**
10 / Michael T. McCaul, **R**
11 / August L. Pfluger, **R**
12 / Kay N. Granger, **R**
13 / Ronny L. Jackson, **R**
14 / Randy Weber, **R**
15 / Monica De La Cruz, **R**
16 / Veronica Escobar, **D**
17 / Pete A. Sessions, **R**
18 / Sheila Jackson Lee, **D**
19 / Jodey Cook Arrington, **R**
20 / Joaquin Castro, **D**
21 / Chip Roy, **R**
22 / Troy E. Nehls, **R**
23 / Tony Gonzales, **R**
24 / Beth A. Van Duyne, **R**
25 / Roger Williams, **R**
26 / Michael C. Burgess, **R**
27 / Michael J. Cloud, **R**
28 / Henry R. Cuellar, **D**
29 / Sylvia R. Garcia, **D**
30 / Jasmine Crockett, **D**
31 / John R. Carter, **R**
32 / Colin Allred, **D**
33 / Marc A. Veasey, **D**
34 / Vicente Gonzalez, **D**
35 / Gregorio Casar, **D**
36 / Brian Babin, **R**
37 / Lloyd A. Doggett, **D**
38 / Wesley Hunt, **R**

TEXAS

♊ Sen. John Cornyn III (KOR-nuhn)　　　R-TX-Sr.　　p 202.224.2934

Rm. HSOB 517　**Web.** cornyn.senate.gov
Bio. 02/02/1952 • Houston • State Attorney General; State
Supreme Court Judge • Trinity Univ. (TX), B.A., 1973; St.
Mary's School of Law (TX), J.D., 1977; Univ. of Virginia,
LL.M., 1995 • Church of Christ • M. Sandra Hansen Cornyn,
2 ch　**Cmte.** Finance • Intelligence • Judiciary
CoS. Drew Brandewie
Sched. Emily Ziegler　　　**PS.** Natalie Yezbick
Dist. Off. Austin 512.469.6034 • Dallas 972.239.1310
• Harlingen 956.423.0162 • Houston 713.572.3337 •
Lubbock 806.472.7533 • San Antonio 210.224.7485 • Tyler
903.593.0902

R: 14　**T:** 4th 54%
Elected Year: 2002
Next Election: 2026

♊ Sen. Ted Cruz (krooz)　　　R-TX-Jr.　　p 202.224.5922

Rm. RSOB 127A　**Web.** cruz.senate.gov
Bio. 12/22/1970 • Calgary • Princeton Univ. (NJ), A.B., 1992;
Harvard Law School (MA), J.D., 1995 • Southern Baptist
• M. Heidi Nelson, 2 ch　**Cmte.** Commerce, Science &
Transportation • Foreign Relations • Judiciary • Rules &
Administration
CoS. Steve Chartan　　　**LD.** Chris Jaarda
Sched. Sara L. Sylvester　　**PS.** Darin Miller
Dist. Off. Austin 512.916.5834 • Dallas 214.599.8749
• Houston 713.718.3057 • McAllen 956.686.7339 • San
Antonio 210.340.2885 • Tyler 903.593.5130

R: 52　**T:** 2nd 51%
Elected Year: 2012
Next Election: 2024

⬥ Rep. Colin Allred (ALL-red)　　　D-TX-32　　p 202.225.2231

Rm. CHOB 348　**Web.** allred.house.gov
Bio. 04/15/1983 • Dallas • Baylor Univ. (TX), B.A.,
2005; Univ. of California, Berkeley, J.D., 2014 • M. Allred
Alexandra, 2 ch　**Cmte.** Foreign Affairs • Transportation &
Infrastructure
CoS. Paige Hutchinson　　　**LD.** Whitley O'Neal
Sched. Katie Payne　　　**PS.** Joshua Stewart
Dist. Off. Richardson 972.972.7949

R: 235　**T:** 3rd 65%
Elected Year: 2018

♊ Rep. Jodey Cook Arrington (AIR-ring-ten)　　R-TX-19　　p 202.225.4005

Rm. LHOB 1107　**Web.** arrington.house.gov　**f** 202.225.9615
Bio. 03/09/1972 • Kansas City • Texas Tech Univ., B.A.,
1994; Texas Tech Univ., M.P.A., 1997 • Presbyterian • M.
Anne Arrington, 3 ch　**Cmte.** Budget • Ways & Means
CoS. Elle Whitson　　　**LD.** Mason Champion
Sched. Lacey Wallace
Dist. Off. Abilene 325.675.9779 • Lubbock 806.763.1611

R: 194　**T:** 4th 80%
Elected Year: 2016

♊ Rep. Brian Babin (BA-bin)　　　R-TX-36　　p 202.225.1555

Rm. RHOB 2236　**Web.** babin.house.gov　**f** 202.226.0396
Bio. 03/23/1948 • Port Arthur • Lamar Univ., B.S., 1973;
Univ. of Texas-Houston, D.D.S., 1976 • Southern Baptist • M.
Roxanne Babin, 5 ch ; 16 gr-ch　**Cmte.** Science, Space &
Technology • Transportation & Infrastructure
CoS. Steve Janushkowsky　　**LD.** Lauren Ziegler
Sched. Avrie Hodges　　　**PS.** Sarah Reese
Dist. Off. Dayton 832.780.0966 • Deer Park 832.780.0966 •
Orange 409.883.8075 • Woodville 409.331.8066

R: 162　**T:** 5th 70%
Elected Year: 2014

⬛ Rep. Michael C. Burgess (BUR-juhs)   R-TX-26   p 202.225.7772

Rm. RHOB 2161 **Web.** burgess.house.gov   **f** 202.225.2919
Bio. 12/23/1950 • Rochester • Obstetrician • North Texas
State Univ., Dallas, B.S., 1972; North Texas State Univ., M.S.,
1976; Univ. of Texas-Houston, M.D., 1977; Univ. of Texas at
Dallas, M.S., 2000 • Anglican • M. Laura Burgess, 3 ch ; 2 gr-
ch   **Cmte.** Budget • Energy & Commerce • Rules
CoS. James A. Decker
Sched. Amanda Baldwin   **PS.** Sarah-Anne Voyles
Dist. Off. Lake Dallas 940.497.5031

R: 45 **T:** 11th 69%
Elected Year: 2002

⬛ Rep. John R. Carter (KAR-tur)   R-TX-31   p 202.225.3864

Rm. RHOB 2208 **Web.** carter.house.gov   **f** 202.225.5886
Bio. 11/06/1941 • Houston • Williamson County District
Judge; Attorney • Texas Technical Univ., B.A., 1964; Univ. of
Texas School of Law, J.D., 1969 • Lutheran • M. Erika Carter,
4 ch ; 6 gr-ch   **Cmte.** Appropriations
CoS. Jonas Miller (CD)   **LD.** Grady Bourn
                                    PS. Emily Dowdell (CD)
Dist. Off. Round Rock 512.246.1600 • Temple 254.933.1392

R: 46 **T:** 11th 100%
Elected Year: 2002

⬛ Rep. Gregorio Casar ()   D-TX-35   p 202.225.5645

Rm. LHOB 1339 **Web.** casarforcongress.com
Bio. 05/04/1989 • Houston • Univ. of Virginia, Bach. Deg, •
E.   **Cmte.** Oversight & Accountability
CoS. Stephanie Trinh   **LD.** Ann Olivelra
Dist. Off. Austin

R: 369 **T:** 1st 73%
Elected Year: 2022

⬛ Rep. Joaquin Castro (KAS-tro)   D-TX-20   p 202.225.3236

Rm. RHOB 2241 **Web.** castro.house.gov   **f** 202.225.1915
Bio. 09/16/1974 • San Antonio • Stanford Univ. (CA), A.B.,
1996; Harvard Univ. Law School (MA), J.D., 2000 • Roman
Catholic • M. Anna Flores, 2 ch   **Cmte.** Foreign Affairs •
Permanent Select on Intelligence
CoS. Ben Thomas   **LD.** Kaitlyn Montan
                             PS. Geneva Kropper
Dist. Off. San Antonio 210.348.8216

R: 130 **T:** 6th 68%
Elected Year: 2012

⬛ Rep. Michael J. Cloud ("cloud")   R-TX-27   p 202.225.7742

Rm. CHOB 171 **Web.** cloud.house.gov   **f** 202.226.1134
Bio. 05/13/1975 • Baton Rouge • Oral Roberts Univ.,
Bach. Deg. • M. Rosel Cloud, 3 ch   **Cmte.** Agriculture •
Appropriations
CoS. Ben Williamson   **LD.** Abby McHan
Sched. Shelby Boswell
Dist. Off. Corpus Christi 361.884.2222 • Victoria
361.894.6446

R: 228 **T:** 4th 64%
Elected Year: 2018

⬛ Rep. Daniel Crenshaw (KREN-shaw)   R-TX-02   p 202.225.6565

Rm. CHOB 413 **Web.** crenshaw.house.gov   **f** 202.225.5547
Bio. 03/14/1984 • Aberdeen • Tufts Univ. (MA), B.A., 2006;
Harvard Kennedy School of Government, M.P.A., 2017 •
Methodist • M. Tara Crenshaw   **Cmte.** Energy & Commerce
• Permanent Select on Intelligence
CoS. Justin Discigil   **LD.** Matt Hodge
Dist. Off. Houston 281.640.7720 • Kingwood 713.860.1330

R: 242 **T:** 3rd 66%
Elected Year: 2018

TEXAS

⚲ Rep. Jasmine Crockett ()　　　　　　D-TX-30　　p 202.225.8885

Rm. LHOB 1616 **Web.** jasmineforus.com
Bio. 03/29/1981 • St. Louis • Rhodes College, B.A., 2003;
Univ. of Houston Law Center, J.D., 2009 • NS. **Cmte.**
Oversight & Accountability
CoS. Jason Rodriguez
Sched. Caleb Tyler　　　　　　**PS.** Kendall Mitchell
Dist. Off. Dallas 469.527.4100

R: 374　**T:** 1st　75%
Elected Year: 2022

⚲ Rep. Henry R. Cuellar (KWAY-ar)　　　　D-TX-28　　p 202.225.1640

Rm. RHOB 2372 **Web.** cuellar.house.gov　　f 202.225.1641
Bio. 09/19/1955 • Laredo • State Representative; United
States Customs Broker • Laredo Community College (TX),
A.A., 1976; Georgetown Univ. (DC), B.S., 1978; Univ. of Texas
School of Law, J.D., 1981; Texas A and M International Univ.,
M.B.A., 1982; Univ. of Texas, Ph.D., 1998 • Roman Catholic •
M. Imelda Rios Cuellar, 2 ch **Cmte.** Appropriations
CoS. Jacob Hochberg
　　　　　　　　　　　PS. Arturo Olivarez
Dist. Off. Laredo 956.725.0639 • Mission 956.424.3942 •
Rio Grande City 956.487.5603 • San Antonio 210.271.2851

R: 58　**T:** 10th　57%
Elected Year: 2004

⚑ Rep. Monica De La Cruz ()　　　　　　R-TX-15　　p 202.225.9901

Rm. LHOB 1415 **Web.** delacruz.house.gov
Bio. 11/11/1974 • • Univ. of Texas at San Antonio, B.B.A. •
D., 2 ch **Cmte.** Financial Services
CoS. Karen Navarro
Sched. Paris Curry　　　　　　**PS.** Ryan Saylor
Dist. Off. Seguin 877.469.1210

R: 377　**T:** 1st　53%
Elected Year: 2022

⚲ Rep. Lloyd A. Doggett II (DAWG-eht)　　　D-TX-37　　p 202.225.4865

Rm. RHOB 2307 **Web.** doggett.house.gov　　f 202.225.3073
Bio. 10/06/1946 • Austin • State Supreme Court Justice;
Professor • Univ. of Texas, B.B.A., 1967; Univ. of Texas
School of Law, J.D., 1970 • Methodist • M. Libby Belk
Doggett, 2 ch ; 4 gr-ch **Cmte.** Budget • Ways & Means
CoS. Michael Mucchetti
Dist. Off. Austin 512.916.5921 • San Antonio 210.704.1080

R: 19　**T:** 15th　77%
Elected Year: 1994

⚑ Rep. Jake Ellzey ()　　　　　　　　R-TX-06　　p 202.225.2002

Rm. LHOB 1721 **Web.** ellzey.house.gov
Bio. 01/24/1970 • Potter County • U.S. Naval Academy
(MD), B.S., 1992 • M. Shelby Hoebeke, 2 ch **Cmte.**
Appropriations • Small Business
CoS. Robert Carretta　　　　**LD.** Don Barber
Sched. Molly Harris-Stevens　**PS.** Scott Gilfillan (CD)
Dist. Off. Arlington 817.775.0370 • Corsicana 903.602.7860
• Waxahachie 469.550.7150

R: 352　**T:** 2nd　100%
Elected Year: 2021

⚲ Rep. Veronica Escobar (ess-ko-BAR)　　　D-TX-16　　p 202.225.4831

Rm. RHOB 2448 **Web.** escobar.house.gov
Bio. 09/15/1969 • El Paso • Univ. of Texas, El Paso, B.A.,
1991; New York Univ., M.A., 1993 • Catholic • M. Michael
Pleters, 2 ch **Cmte.** Armed Services • Ethics • Judiciary
Dist. Off. El Paso 915.541.1400

R: 246　**T:** 3rd　64%
Elected Year: 2018

TEXAS

® Rep. Pat Fallon (FAH-luhn) R-TX-04 p 202.225.6673

Rm. RHOB 2416 **Web.** fallon.house.gov
Bio. 12/19/1967 • Pittsfield • Univ. of Notre Dame (IN), B.A.,
1990 • Roman Catholic • M. Susan Garner-Sherrill, 2 ch
Cmte. Armed Services • Oversight & Accountability
CoS. Shannan Sorrell **LD.** Shaun Taylor
  PS. Austin Higginbotham
Dist. Off. New Boston 903.716.7500 • Rockwall
972.771.0100 • Sherman 903.820.5170

R: 309 **T:** 2nd 67%
Elected Year: 2020

® Rep. Lizzie Pannill Fletcher (FLEH-chur) D-TX-07 p 202.225.2571

Web. fletcher.house.gov **f** 202.225.4381
Bio. 02/13/1975 • Houston • Kenyon College (OH),
B.A., 1997; William & Mary Law School (VA), J.D., 2006 •
Methodist • M. Scott Fletcher PE, 2 stepch **Cmte.** Energy &
Commerce
CoS. Sarah Kaplan **LD.** Ben Jackson (CD)
  Feinmann (CD)
Sched. Shannon McDermott **PS.** Clarissa Robles (CD)
  (CD)
Dist. Off. Houston 713.353.8680

R: 247 **T:** 3rd 64%
Elected Year: 2018

® Rep. Sylvia R. Garcia (gar-SEE-uh) D-TX-29 p 202.225.1688

Rm. RHOB 2419 **Web.** sylviagarcia.house.gov
Bio. 09/06/1950 • San Diego • Texas Woman's Univ., B.A.,
1972; Texas Southern Univ, Thurgood Marshall School of
Law, J.D., 1978 • Catholic • S. **Cmte.** Financial Services
Dist. Off. Houston 832.325.3150

R: 250 **T:** 3rd 71%
Elected Year: 2018

® Rep. Tony Gonzales II (gon-SAH-les) R-TX-23 p 202.225.4511

Rm. RHOB 2244 **Web.** gonzales.house.gov **f** 202.225.2237
Bio. 10/10/1980 • Fort McClellan • Chaminade Univ., A.A.,
2005; Excelsior College, B.S., 2009; American Public Univ.
System, M.A., 2014 • Catholic • M. Angel Gonzales, 6 ch
Cmte. Appropriations • Homeland Security
CoS. Cesar Prieto **LD.** Rachel Black
Dist. Off. Del Rio 830.308.6200 • Fort Stockton
432.299.6200 • San Antonio 210.806.9920 • Socorro
915.990.1500 • Uvalde 830.333.7410

R: 316 **T:** 2nd 56%
Elected Year: 2020

® Rep. Vicente Gonzalez (gon-SAH-les) D-TX-34 p 202.225.2531

Rm. CHOB 154 **Web.** gonzalez.house.gov **f** 202.225.5688
Bio. 09/04/1967 • Corpus Christi • Embry Riddle
Aeronautical Univ. (TX), B.A., 1992; Texas A & M Univ.
School of Law (formerly Texas Wesleyan School of Law),
J.D., 1996 • Catholic • M. Lorena Saenz **Cmte.** Financial
Services
CoS. Louise Colbath **LD.** Chandler K. Mills
  Bentsen
  PS. James Rivera

R: 209 **T:** 4th 53%
Elected Year: 2016

® Rep. Lance Gooden (GOOD-un) R-TX-05 p 202.225.3484

Rm. RHOB 2431 **Web.** gooden.house.gov **f** 202.225.2464
Bio. 12/01/1982 • Terrell • Univ. of Texas as Austin,
B.A., 2004 • Church of Christ • M. Alexa Calligas, 2 ch
Cmte. Financial Services • Judiciary • Transportation &
Infrastructure
Sched. Jackson Willis (CD)
Dist. Off. Canton 903.502.5300

R: 252 **T:** 3rd 64%
Elected Year: 2018

TEXAS

⚑ Rep. Kay N. Granger (GRAIN-jur)　　　　R-TX-12　　p 202.225.5071

Rm. RHOB 2308 **Web.** kaygranger.house.gov **f** 202.225.5683
Bio. 01/18/1943 • Greenville • Insurance Agent; Business
Owner; Mayor (Ft. Worth, TX) • Texas Wesleyan Univ., B.S.,
1965 • Methodist • D., 3 ch; 5 gr-ch **Cmte.** Appropriations
Sched. Joshua Key
Dist. Off. Fort Worth 817.338.0909

R: 26　**T:** 14th　64%
Elected Year: 1996

⚑ Rep. Al Green (green)　　　　D-TX-09　　p 202.225.7508

Rm. RHOB 2347 **Web.** algreen.house.gov **f** 202.225.2947
Bio. 09/01/1947 • New Orleans • Attorney • Tuskegee Univ.
(AL), Bach. Deg.; Texas Southern Univ., Thurgood Marshall
School of Law, J.D., 1973 • Baptist • NS. **Cmte.** Financial
Services

　　　　　　　　　　　　LD. Aaron Linfesty
　　　　　　　　　　　　PS. Lily Rodriguez (CD)
Dist. Off. Houston 713.383.9234

R: 60　**T:** 10th　77%
Elected Year: 2004

⚑ Rep. Wesley Hunt ()　　　　R-TX-38　　p 202.225.5646

Rm. LHOB 1520 **Web.** wesleyfortexas.com
Bio. 11/13/1981 • Houston • U.S. Military Academy (NY),
B.S., 2004; Cornell Univ. (NY), M.B.A., 2015; Cornell Univ.
(NY), M.P.A., 2015; Cornell Univ. (NY), Mast. Deg., 2016 • M.
Emily Hunt, 3 ch **Cmte.** Judiciary • Natural Resources •
Small Business
CoS. James D. Kyrkanides　　　**LD.** Jackie Modesett
Sched. Ellie Dick　　　**PS.** Matt Topolski
Dist. Off. Houston 832.357.0555 • Tomball 346.246.7355

R: 391　**T:** 1st　63%
Elected Year: 2022

⚑ Rep. Ronny L. Jackson (JAK-suhn)　　　　R-TX-13　　p 202.225.3706

Rm. CHOB 118 **Web.** jackson.house.gov **f** 202.225.3486
Bio. 05/04/1967 • Levelland • South Plains College (TX),
A.S., 1988; Texas A&M Univ., College Station, B.S., 1991; Univ.
of Texas Medical Branch, M.D., 1995 • Church of Christ • M.
Jane Ely, 3 ch **Cmte.** Armed Services • Foreign Affairs
CoS. Jeff Billman　　　**LD.** Bryan Brody
Sched. Kathy Zhu　　　**PS.** Thomas Carufel
Dist. Off. Amarillo 806.641.5600 • Wichita Falls
940.285.8000

R: 321　**T:** 2nd　75%
Elected Year: 2020

⚑ Rep. Sheila Jackson Lee (JAK-suhn-lee)　　　　D-TX-18　　p 202.225.3816

Rm. RHOB 2426 **Web.** jacksonlee.house.gov **f** 202.225.3317
Bio. 01/12/1950 • Jamaica • Judge; Attorney • Yale Univ.
(CT), B.A., 1972; Univ. of Virginia Law School, J.D., 1975
• Seventh-Day Adventist • M. Elwyn C. Lee, 2 ch ; 2 gr-ch
(twins) **Cmte.** Budget • Homeland Security • Judiciary
CoS. Lillie Coney
Sched. LaDedra
　Drummond
Dist. Off. Houston 713.227.7740 • Houston 713.655.0050 •
Houston 713.691.4882 • Houston 713.861.4070

R: 20　**T:** 15th　71%
Elected Year: 1994

⚑ Rep. Morgan J. Luttrell ()　　　　R-TX-08　　p 202.225.4901

Rm. LHOB 1320 **Web.** morganluttrell.com
Bio. 11/07/1975 • Houston • Sam Houston State Univ.,
Bach. Deg., 2000; Univ. of Texas at Dallas, M.S., 2016 • M.
Leslie Luttrell, 2 ch **Cmte.** Armed Services • Homeland
Security • Veterans' Affairs
CoS. Chrissi Lee　　　**LD.** Charles Truxal
Sched. Allie Faircloth　　　**PS.** Cally Perkins
Dist. Off. Magnolia

R: 407　**T:** 1st　68%
Elected Year: 2022

⌖ Rep. Michael T. McCaul (mih-KALL)　　R-TX-10　　p 202.225.2401

Rm. RHOB 2300　**Web.** mccaul.house.gov　**f** 202.225.5955
Bio. 01/14/1962 • Dallas • Attorney; Federal prosecutor •
Trinity Univ. (TX), B.A., 1984; St. Mary's Univ. School of Law
(TX), J.D., 1987 • Catholic • M. Linda McCaul, 5 ch (triplets)
Cmte. Foreign Affairs • Homeland Security
CoS. Chris Del Beccaro　　　**LD.** Zachary Isakowitz
Sched. Carrie Coxen
Dist. Off. Austin 512.473.2357

R: 62　**T:** 10th　63%
Elected Year: 2004

⌖ Rep. Nathaniel Moran ()　　R-TX-01　　p 202.225.3035

Rm. LHOB 1541　**Web.** nathanielmoran.com
Bio. 09/23/1974 • • Texas Tech Univ., B.A.; Texas Tech
Univ., M.B.A.; Texas Tech Univ., J.D. • Baptist • M. Kyna
Moran, 4 ch　**Cmte.** Education & Workforce • Foreign
Affairs • Judiciary
CoS. Joshua Bradley　　　**LD.** Delayne Hyatt
Sched. Chelsea Cohen　　　**PS.** Emily Hall
Dist. Off. Tyler 469.609.7917

R: 415　**T:** 1st　78%
Elected Year: 2022

⌖ Rep. Troy E. Nehls (nelz)　　R-TX-22　　p 202.225.5951

Rm. LHOB 1104　**Web.** nehls.house.gov　**f** 202.225.5241
Bio. 04/07/1968 • Beaver Dam • Liberty Univ. (VA), B.A.;
Univ. of Houston (TX), M.S., 2011 • Christian - Non-
Denominational • M. Jill Nehls, 3 ch　**Cmte.** Judiciary •
Transportation & Infrastructure
CoS. Robert Schroeder　　　**LD.** Evan Bender
Sched. Candace Aguirre
　(CD)
Dist. Off. Richmond 346.762.6600

R: 336　**T:** 2nd　62%
Elected Year: 2020

⌖ Rep. August L. Pfluger II (FLOO-gur)　　R-TX-11　　p 202.225.3605

Rm. LHOB 1124　**Web.** pfluger.house.gov　**f** 202.225.1783
Bio. 12/28/1977 • Harris County • United States Air Force
Academy, B.S., 2000; Embry-Riddle Aeronautical Univ., Mast.
Deg., 2007; United States Air Univ. (AL), Mast. Deg., 2012;
Georgetown Univerity School of Foreign Service, Mast. Deg.,
2020 • Christian - Non-Denominational • M. Camille Coley, 3
ch　**Cmte.** Energy & Commerce • Homeland Security
CoS. John Byers　　　**LD.** Preston Howey
Sched. Brooke Oliver　　　**PS.** Lyssa Bell
Dist. Off. Brownwood 325.646.1950 • Granbury
682.936.2577 • Llano 325.247.2826 • Midland 432.687.2390
• Odessa 432.331.9667 • San Angelo 325.659.4010

R: 339　**T:** 2nd　100%
Elected Year: 2020

⌖ Rep. Chip Roy (roy)　　R-TX-21　　p 202.225.4236

Web. roy.house.gov　**f** 202.225.8628
Bio. 08/07/1972 • Bethesda • Univ. of Virginia, B.S., 1994;
Univ. of Virginia, M.S., 1995; Univ. of Texas, J.D., 2003 •
Baptist • M. Carrah Roy, 2 ch　**Cmte.** Budget • Judiciary •
Rules

　　　　　　　　　　　　　　LD. Sabrina Hancock (CD)
Sched. Corinne Schillizzi　　　**PS.** Nate Madden (CD)
　(CD)
Dist. Off. Austin 512.871.5959 • Kerrville 830.896.0154 •
San Antonio 210.821.5024

R: 276　**T:** 3rd　63%
Elected Year: 2018

⌖ Rep. Keith Self ()　　R-TX-03　　p 202.225.4201

Rm. LHOB 1113　**Web.** selfforcongress.com
Bio. 03/20/1953 • Philadelphia • U.S. Military Academy
(NY), Bach. Deg.; Univ. of Southern California, M.A., 1981 •
M. Tracy Self　**Cmte.** Foreign Affairs • Veterans' Affairs
CoS. Hillary Parkinson　　　**LD.** Brad Decker
Sched. Brianna Garcia　　　**PS.** Michelle Myers
Dist. Off. McKinney 972.372.4851

R: 426　**T:** 1st　61%
Elected Year: 2022

TEXAS

⚑ Rep. Pete A. Sessions (SEH-shuhnz) R-TX-17 p 202.225.6105

Rm. RHOB 2204 **Web.** sessions.house.gov **f** 202.225.0350
Bio. 03/22/1955 • Waco • Telephone Company Executive
• Southwestern Univ. (TX), B.S., 1978 • Methodist • M.
Karen Sessions, 2 ch ; 3 stepch **Cmte.** Financial Services •
Oversight & Accountability
CoS. Robert McIntosh
Dist. Off. Huntsville 979.431.6340 • Lufkin •
Nacogdoches • Waco 254.633.4500

R: 38 **T:** 2nd 67%
Elected Year: 2020

⚑ Rep. Beth A. Van Duyne (van-DYN) R-TX-24 p 202.225.6605

Rm. LHOB 1725 **Web.** vanduyne.house.gov **f** 202.225.0074
Bio. 11/16/1970 • Ithaca • Cornell Univ. (NY), B.A., 1995 •
Episcopalian • D., 2 ch **Cmte.** Small Business • Ways &
Means
CoS. Jake Olson **LD.** Ryan Dilworth
Sched. Riley Bookout **PS.** Sam Denham
Dist. Off. Irving 972.966.5500

R: 347 **T:** 2nd 60%
Elected Year: 2020

⚑ Rep. Marc A. Veasey (VEE-zee) D-TX-33 p 202.225.9897

Rm. RHOB 2348 **Web.** veasey.house.gov **f** 202.225.9702
Bio. 01/03/1971 • Tarrant County • Texas Wesleyan Univ.,
B.S., 1995 • Christian Church • M. Tonya Veasey, 1 ch **Cmte.**
Energy & Commerce
CoS. Nicole Varner **LD.** Luke Dube
Sched. Jane Phipps **PS.** Emily Druckman
Dist. Off. Dallas 214.741.1387 • Fort Worth 817.920.9086

R: 149 **T:** 6th 72%
Elected Year: 2012

⚑ Rep. Randy Weber (WEH-bur) R-TX-14 p 202.225.2831

Rm. CHOB 107 **Web.** weber.house.gov **f** 202.225.0271
Bio. 07/02/1953 • Pearland • Alvin Community College
(TX), Assc. Deg., 1974; Univ. of Houston, Clear Lake (TX),
B.S., 1977 • Baptist • M. Brenda Weber, 3 ch ; 8 gr-ch **Cmte.**
Energy & Commerce • Science, Space & Technology
CoS. Jeanette Whitener **LD.** William Christian
Sched. Kendall Ivy **PS.** Laynee Buckels
Dist. Off. Beaumont 409.835.0108 • Lake Jackson
979.285.0231 • League City 281.316.0231

R: 151 **T:** 6th 70%
Elected Year: 2012

⚑ Rep. Roger Williams (WILL-yuhmz) R-TX-25 p 202.225.9896

Rm. RHOB 2336 **Web.** williams.house.gov **f** 202.225.9692
Bio. 09/13/1949 • Evanston • Texas Christian Univ., B.S.,
1972 • Disciples of Christ • M. Patty Williams, 2 ch **Cmte.**
Financial Services • Small Business
Dist. Off. Cleburne 817.774.2575

R: 153 **T:** 6th 100%
Elected Year: 2012

UTAH

⚑ Governor Spencer J. Cox (kahks) p 801.538.1000

Utah State Capitol Complex **C:** Salt Lake City
350 North State St., Suite 200 **P:** 3,161,105 (31)
Salt Lake City, UT 84114-2220 **A:** 82,169.46 mi² (12th)
Website utah.gov
Fax 801.538.1133
Term Ends 2025
Lt. Governor
Deidre Henderson, R

U.S. Senators
Mike Lee, **R**
Mitt Romney, **R**
U.S. Representatives
01 / Blake Moore, **R**
02 / Chris D. Stewart, **R**
03 / John R. Curtis, **R**
04 / Burgess Owens, **R**

UTAH

📧 Sen. Mike Lee (lee)   R-UT-Sr.   p 202.224.5444

Rm. RSOB 363 **Web.** lee.senate.gov   **f** 202.228.1168
Bio. 06/04/1971 • Mesa • Brigham Young Univ. (UT), B.A.,
1994; Brigham Young Univ. (UT), J.D., 1997 • Mormon •
M. Sharon Lee, 3 ch **Cmte.** Budget • Energy & Natural
Resources • Joint Economic • Judiciary
CoS. Allyson Bell   **LD.** Philip Reboli
                                     PS. Lee Lonsberry
Dist. Off. Ogden 801.392.9633 • Salt Lake City
801.524.5933 • St. George 435.628.5514

R: 43 **T:** 3rd 53%
Elected Year: 2010
Next Election: 2020

📧 Sen. Mitt Romney (RAHM-nee)   R-UT-Jr.   p 202.224.5251

Rm. RSOB 354 **Web.** romney.senate.gov   **f** 202.228.0836
Bio. 03/12/1947 • Detroit • Brigham Young Univ. (UT),
B.A., 1971; Harvard Univ. School of Business (MA), M.B.A.,
1975; Harvard Univ. Law School (MA), J.D., 1975 • Mormon
• M. Ann Davies, 5 ch; 16 gr-ch **Cmte.** Budget • Foreign
Relations • Health, Education, Labor & Pensions •
Homeland Security & Government Affairs
CoS. Liz Johnson
Sched. Meagan Shepherd   **PS.** Brianna W. Manzelli
Dist. Off. Ogden 385.264.7885 • Salt Lake City
801.524.4380 • Spanish Fork 801.515.7230 • St. George
435.522.7100

R: 79 **T:** 1st 63%
Elected Year: 2018
Next Election: 2024

📧 Rep. John R. Curtis (KUR-tiss)   R-UT-03   p 202.225.7751

Rm. RHOB 2323 **Web.** curtis.house.gov   **f** 202.225.5629
Bio. 05/10/1960 • Salt Lake City • Skyline High School, B.S.,
1978; Brigham Young Univ. (UT), B.S., 1985 • Mormon •
M. Sue Snarr, 6 ch ; 5 gr-ch **Cmte.** Energy & Commerce •
Natural Resources
CoS. Corey Norman   **LD.** Jake Bornstein
Sched. Sophie Draayer   **PS.** Adam Cloch
Dist. Off. Provo 801.922.5400

R: 226 **T:** 4th 64%
Elected Year: 2017

📧 Rep. Blake Moore (mor)   R-UT-01   p 202.225.0453

Rm. LHOB 1131 **Web.**   **f** 202.225.5857
blakemoore.house.gov
Bio. 06/22/1980 • Ogden • Univ. of Utah, Salt Lake City,
B.A.; Northwestern Univ., M.P.P.A., 2018 • Mormon • M. Jane
Moore, 3 ch **Cmte.** Budget • Ways & Means
CoS. Rachel Wagley   **LD.** Paul Johnson
Sched. Carol Kresse   **PS.** Caroline Tucker
Dist. Off. Ogden 801.625.0107

R: 334 **T:** 2nd 67%
Elected Year: 2020

UTAH

⚑ Rep. Burgess Owens (O-uhnz) R-UT-04 p 202.225.3011

Rm. LHOB 1039 **Web.** owens.house.gov
Bio. 08/02/1951 • Columbus • Univ. of Miami, B.S., 1974
• Mormon • D., 6 ch **Cmte.** Education & Workforce •
Transportation & Infrastructure
CoS. Keelie Broom **LD.** Miriam Harmer
Sched. Maxwell Malloy **PS.** Emma Hall
Dist. Off. West Jordan 801.999.9801

R: 338 **T:** 2nd 61%
Elected Year: 2020

⚑ Rep. Chris D. Stewart (STOO-urt) R-UT-02 p 202.225.9730

Rm. CHOB 166 **Web.** stewart.house.gov **f** 202.225.5629
Bio. 07/15/1960 • Logan • Utah State Univ., B.S., 1984 •
Mormon • M. Evie Stewart, 6 ch **Cmte.** Appropriations •
Permanent Select on Intelligence
CoS. Clay White **LD.** Cam Madsen
Sched. Mark Coffield **PS.** Liam Anderson
Dist. Off. Bountiful 801.364.5550 • St. George 435.627.1500

R: 145 **T:** 6th 60%
Elected Year: 2012

VERMONT

⚑ Governor Phil Scott (skaht) p 802.828.3333

109 State Street Pavilion
Montpelier, VT 05609-0101
Website vermont.gov
Fax 802.828.3339
Term Ends 2025
Lt. Governor
David E. Zuckerman, P

C: Montpelier
P: 626,299 (51)
A: 9,216.64 mi^2 (43rd)

U.S. Senators
Bernie Sanders, I
Peter F. Welch, D
U.S. Representatives
01 / Becca Balint, D

🐦 Sen. Bernie Sanders (SAN-durz) I-VT-Sr. p 202.224.5141

Caucuses with Democratic Party **f** 202.228.0776
Rm. DSOB 332 **Web.** sanders.senate.gov
Bio. 09/08/1941 • Brooklyn • U.S. Representative • Univ. of
Chicago (IL), B.A., 1964 • Jewish • M. Jane O'Meara Driscoll,
1 ch ; 3 stepch **Cmte.** Budget • Energy & Natural Resources
• Environment & Public Works • Health, Education, Labor &
Pensions • Veterans' Affairs
CoS. Misty Rebik **LD.** Billy Gendell
Sched. Jacob Gillison **PS.** Mike Casca
Dist. Off. Burlington 802.862.0697 • St. Johnsbury
802.332.6186

R: 20 **T:** 3rd 64%
Elected Year: 2006
Next Election: 2024

⚲ Sen. Peter F. Welch (welch)   D-VT-Jr.   p 202.224.4242

Rm. DSOB G12 **Web.** welchforcongress.com
Bio. 05/02/1947 • Springfield • Attorney • College of The
Holy Cross (MA), B.A., 1969; Univ. of California, Berkeley,
J.D., 1973 • Roman Catholic • M. Margaret Cheney, 5
ch ; 3 stepch   **Cmte.** Agriculture, Nutrition & Forestry •
Commerce, Science & Transportation • Judiciary • Rules &
Administration
CoS. Alexandra Golden   **LD.** Susannah Savage
Sched. Lindsay Wagner-   **PS.** Emily K. Becker
Oreson
Dist. Off. Burlington 802.264.9069 • Burlington
802.642.3193

R: 93   T: 1st 67%
Elected Year: 2022
Next Election: 2028

⚲ Rep. Becca Balint ()   D-VT-01   p 202.225.4115

Rm. LHOB 1408 **Web.** beccabalint.com
Bio. 05/04/1968 • Heidelberg • Smith College (MA), A.B.;
Harvard Univ. Graduate School of Education, M.Ed., 1995;
Univ. of Massachusetts Amherst, M.A., 2001 • M. Elizabeth R.
Wohl, 2 ch   **Cmte.** Budget • Oversight & Accountability
CoS. Megan Garcia
Dist. Off. Burlington

R: 363   T: 1st 61%
Elected Year: 2022

VIRGINIA

▣ Governor Glenn Youngkin ()   p 804.786.2211

P.O. Box 1475   **C:** Richmond
Richmond, VA 23218   **P:** 8,517,685 (12)
Website virginia.gov   **A:** 39,490.13 mi^2 (36th)
Fax 804.371.6351
Term Ends 2026
Lt. Governor
Winsome Sears, **R**

U.S. Senators
Mark R. Warner, **D**
Tim M. Kaine, **D**
U.S. Representatives
01 / Rob J. Wittman, **R**
02 / Jen A. Kiggans, **R**
03 / Bobby C. Scott, **D**
04 / Vacant
05 / Bob Good, **R**
06 / Ben L. Cline, **R**
07 / Abigail D. Spanberger, **D**
08 / Don S. Beyer, **D**
09 / Morgan M. Griffith, **R**
10 / Jennifer T. Wexton, **D**   11 / Gerry E. Connolly, **D**

⚲ Sen. Tim M. Kaine (kain)   D-VA-Jr.   p 202.224.4024

Rm. RSOB 231 **Web.** kaine.senate.gov   **f** 202.228.6363
Bio. 02/26/1958 • St. Paul • Mayor, City of Richmond; Mbr.,
Richmond City Council; Lt. Governor & President of the
Senate, VA; Governor, Commonwealth of Virginia • Univ.
of Missouri, A.B., 1979; Harvard Law School (MA), J.D., 1983
• Roman Catholic • M. Anne Bright Holton, 3 ch **Cmte.**
Armed Services • Budget • Foreign Relations • Health,
Education, Labor & Pensions
CoS. Mike Henry   **LD.** Nick Barbash
Sched. Kate McCarroll   **PS.** Katie Stuntz
Dist. Off. Abingdon 276.525.4790 • Fredericksburg
540.369.7667 • Manassas 703.361.3192 • Richmond
804.771.2221 • Roanoke 540.682.5693 • Virginia Beach
757.518.1674

R: 51   T: 2nd 57%
Elected Year: 2012
Next Election: 2024

VIRGINIA

➹ Sen. Mark R. Warner (WAR-nur) D-VA-Sr. p 202.224.2023

Rm. HSOB 703 **Web.** warner.senate.gov
Bio. 12/15/1954 • Indianapolis • Governor of Virginia •
George Washington Univ. (DC), B.A., 1977; Harvard Univ.
Law School (MA), J.D., 1980 • Presbyterian • M. Lisa Collis,
3 ch **Cmte.** Banking, Housing & Urban Affairs • Budget •
Finance • Intelligence • Rules & Administration
CoS. Elizabeth Falcone
Sched. Malcolm Fouhy **PS.** Rachel Cohen
Dist. Off. Abingdon 276.628.8158 • Norfolk 757.441.3079 •
Richmond 804.775.2314 • Roanoke 540.857.2676 • Vienna
703.442.0670

R: 29 **T:** 3rd 56%
Elected Year: 2008
Next Election: 2026

➹ Rep. Don S. Beyer Jr. (BY-ur) D-VA-08 p 202.225.4376

Rm. LHOB 1119 **Web.** beyer.house.gov **f** 202.225.0017
Bio. 06/20/1950 • Trieste • Williams College, B.A., 1972 •
Episcopalian • M. Megan Carroll, 4 ch ; 2 gr-ch **Cmte.** Ways
& Means
CoS. Zachary Cafritz **LD.** Kate Schisler
PS. Aaron Fritschner
Dist. Off. Arlington 703.658.5403

R: 163 **T:** 5th 74%
Elected Year: 2014

➹ Rep. Ben L. Cline (kline) R-VA-06 p 202.225.5431

Rm. RHOB 2443 **Web.** cline.house.gov **f** 202.225.9681
Bio. 02/29/1972 • Stillwater • Lexington High School, B.A.;
Bates College (ME), B.A., 1994; Univ. of Richmond School of
Law, J.D., 2007 • Roman Catholic • M. Elizabeth Rocovich, 2
ch **Cmte.** Appropriations • Budget • Judiciary
CoS. Matt M. Miller
Sched. Meagan Jennings
Dist. Off. Harrisonburg 540.432.2391 • Roanoke
540.857.2672 • Staunton 540.885.3861 • Winchester
540.546.0876

R: 240 **T:** 3rd 64%
Elected Year: 2018

➹ Rep. Gerry E. Connolly (KAH-nuh-lee) D-VA-11 p 202.225.1492

Rm. RHOB 2265 **Web.** connolly.house.gov **f** 202.225.3071
Bio. 03/30/1950 • Boston • Transportation Commissioner;
US Senate Committee Staffer • Maryknoll College (IL), B.A.,
1971; Harvard Univ., M.P.A., 1979 • Roman Catholic • M.
Cathy Connolly, 1 ch **Cmte.** Foreign Affairs • Oversight &
Accountability
CoS. Jamie Smith **LD.** Collin Davenport
Sched. Lauren Covington
Dist. Off. Annandale 703.256.3071 • Fairfax •
Woodbridge 571.408.4407

R: 84 **T:** 8th 67%
Elected Year: 2008

➹ Rep. Bob Good (good) R-VA-05 p 202.225.4711

Rm. CHOB 461 **Web.** good.house.gov **f** 202.225.5681
Bio. 09/11/1965 • Wilkes Barre • Liberty Univ. (VA), B.S.,
1988; Liberty Univ. (VA), M.B.A., 2010 • Christian Church
• M. Tracey Good, 3 ch **Cmte.** Budget • Education &
Workforce
CoS. Mark Kelly **LD.** Peter Holland
Sched. Victoria White **PS.** Marjorie W. Jackson
Dist. Off. Lynchburg 434.791.2596

R: 317 **T:** 2nd 58%
Elected Year: 2020

➹ Rep. Morgan M. Griffith (GRIH-fith) R-VA-09 p 202.225.3861

Rm. RHOB 2202 **Web.** **f** 202.225.0076
morgangriffith.house.gov
Bio. 03/15/1958 • Philadelphia • Emory and Henry College
(VA), B.A., 1980; Washington and Lee Univ. School of Law
(VA), J.D., 1983 • Episcopalian • M. Hilary Davis, 3 ch **Cmte.**
Administration • Energy & Commerce
CoS. Kelly Lungren **LD.** Emily Michael
McCollum
Dist. Off. Abingdon 276.525.1405 • Christiansburg
540.381.5671

R: 106 **T:** 7th 73%
Elected Year: 2010

VIRGINIA

⚑ Rep. Jen A. Kiggans ()　　　　　R-VA-02　　p 202.225.4215

Rm. LHOB 1037　**Web.** jenforcongress.com
Bio. 06/18/1971 • Tampa • Boston Univ. (MA), B.A., 1993;
Old Dominion Univ. (VA), B.S.N., 2011; Vanderbilt Univ.
School of Nursing (TN), M.Nurs., 2012 • Catholic • M. Steve
Kiggans, 4 ch　**Cmte.** Armed Services • Natural Resources
• Veterans' Affairs
CoS. Katherine Sears
Dist. Off. Onley • Virginia Beach 757.990.3080

R: 398　**T:** 1st 52%
Elected Year: 2022

⚑ Rep. Bobby C. Scott (skaht)　　　　D-VA-03　　p 202.225.8351

Rm. RHOB 2328　**Web.** bobbyscott.house.gov　**f** 202.225.8354
Bio. 04/30/1947 • Washington • State Legislator • Army
Reserve 1970-74; Massachusetts National Guard 1974-76 •
Harvard Univ., B.A., 1969; Boston College Law School (MA),
J.D., 1973 • Episcopalian • D.　**Cmte.** Budget • Education &
Workforce
CoS. David Dailey　　　　　**LD.** Paige Schwartz
Sched. Randi Petty　　　　　**PS.** Austin Barbera
Dist. Off. Newport News 757.380.1000

R: 15　**T:** 16th 67%
Elected Year: 1992

⚑ Rep. Abigail D. Spanberger (SPAN-bur-gur)　D-VA-07　p 202.225.2815

Rm. CHOB 562　**Web.** spanberger.house.gov　**f** 202.225.0011
Bio. 08/07/1979 • Red Bank • Univ. of Virginia, B.A., 2001
Purdue Univ. (Germany), M.B.A., 2002 • Christian Church •
M. Adam Spanberger, 3 ch　**Cmte.** Agriculture • Permanent
Select on Intelligence
Dist. Off. Glen Allen 804.401.4110 • Spotsylvania
540.321.6130

R: 280　**T:** 3rd 52%
Elected Year: 2018

⚑ Rep. Jennifer T. Wexton (WEHK-stuhn)　D-VA-10　p 202.225.5136

Rm. LHOB 1210　**Web.** wexton.house.gov　**f** 202.225.0437
Bio. 05/27/1968 • Washington • Univ. of Maryland - College
Park, B.A., 1991; College of William and Mary - Marshall-
Wythe Law School (VA), J.D., 1995 • Unspecified/Other • M.
Andrew Wexton, 2 ch　**Cmte.** Appropriations • Budget
CoS. Abby M. Carter　　　　**LD.** Chris Gibson
　　　　　　　　　　　　　　　PS. Justin McCartney
Dist. Off. Leesburg 703.234.3800 • Winchester
703.236.1300

R: 293　**T:** 3rd 53%
Elected Year: 2018

⚑ Rep. Rob J. Wittman (WIT-muhn)　　R-VA-01　　p 202.225.4261

Rm. RHOB 2055　**Web.** wittman.house.gov　**f** 202.225.4382
Bio. 02/03/1959 • Washington • Mayor (Montrose Town,
VA); State Legislator • Virginia Polytechnic Institute, B.S.,
1981; Univ. of North Carolina Chapel Hill (UNC), M.PH, 1990;
Virginia Commonwealth Univ., Ph.D., 2002 • Episcopalian
• M. Kathryn Jane Sisson Wittman, 2 ch ; 4 gr-ch　**Cmte.**
Armed Services • Natural Resources • Select China
Committee
CoS. Carolyn King
　　　　　　　　　　　　　　　PS. Sarah Newsome
Dist. Off. Glen Allen 804.401.4120 • Tappahannock
804.443.0668

R: 81　**T:** 9th 56%
Elected Year: 2007

WASHINGTON

⚑ Governor Jay Inslee (INZ-lee)　　　　　　p 360.902.4111

PO Box 40002　　　　　　　**C:** Olympia
Olympia, WA 98404-0002　　　**P:** 7,535,591 (13)
Website wa.gov　　　　　　　**A:** 66,455.49 mi² (20th)
Fax 360.753.4110
Term Ends 2025
Lt. Governor
Denny Heck, **D**

WASHINGTON

WASHINGTON

U.S. Senators
Patty Murray, **D**
Maria Cantwell, **D**
U.S. Representatives
01 / Suzan DelBene, **D**
02 / Rick R. Larsen, **D**
03 / Marie Gluesenkamp Perez, **D**
04 / Dan M. Newhouse, **R**
05 / Cathy A. McMorris Rodgers, **R**
06 / Derek Kilmer, **D**
07 / Pramila Jayapal, **D**
08 / Kim Schrier, **D**
09 / Adam Smith, **D**
10 / Marilyn Strickland, **D**

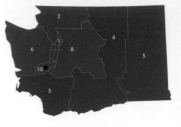

⚑ Sen. Maria Cantwell (KANT-wel)　　　　D-WA-Jr.　 p 202.224.3441

Rm. HSOB 511 **Web.** cantwell.senate.gov　 **f** 202.228.0514
Bio. 10/13/1958 • Indianapolis • Representative • Miami
Univ. of Ohio, B.A., 1980 • Roman Catholic • S. **Cmte.**
Commerce, Science & Transportation • Energy & Natural
Resources • Finance • Indian Affairs • Joint Economic •
Joint Taxation • Small Business & Entrepreneurship
CoS. Jami Burgess
Sched. Grant Friedman　　　　**PS.** Ansley Lacitis
　(CD)
Dist. Off. Everett 425.303.0114 • Richland 509.946.8106
• Seattle 206.220.6400 • Spokane 509.353.2507 • Tacoma
253.572.2281 • Vancouver 360.696.7838

R: 13　**T:** 4th　58%
Elected Year: 2000
Next Election: 2024

⚑ Sen. Patty Murray (MUR-ree)　　　　D-WA-Sr.　 p 202.224.2621

Rm. RSOB 154 **Web.** murray.senate.gov　 **f** 202.224.0238
Bio. 10/11/1950 • Bothell • State Senator; Teacher •
Washington State Univ., B.A., 1972 • Roman Catholic • M.
Robert Randall Murray, 2 ch **Cmte.** Appropriations • Budget
• Health, Education, Labor & Pensions • Veterans' Affairs
CoS. Mindi Linquist　　　　**LD.** Benjamin Merkel
Sched. Rachel Skeirik　　　　**PS.** Amir Avin
Dist. Off. Everett 425.259.6515 • Seattle 206.553.5545 •
Spokane 509.624.9515 • Tacoma 253.572.3636 • Vancouver
360.696.7797 • Yakima 509.453.7462

R: 4　**T:** 6th　57%
Elected Year: 1992
Next Election: 2028

⚑ Rep. Suzan DelBene (del-BEH-nay)　　　　D-WA-01　 p 202.225.6311

Rm. RHOB 2330 **Web.** delbene.house.gov　 **f** 202.226.1606
Bio. 02/17/1962 • Selma • Reed College (OR), B.A., 1983;
Univ. of Washington, M.B.A., 1990 • Episcopalian • M. Kurt
Delbene, 2 ch **Cmte.** Ways & Means
CoS. Aaron Schmidt　　　　**LD.** Victoria Honard
Sched. Kelly Schulz　　　　**PS.** Nick Martin
Dist. Off. Kirkland 425.485.0085

R: 120　**T:** 7th　64%
Elected Year: 2012

⚑ Rep. Marie Gluesenkamp Perez ()　　　　D-WA-03　 p 202.225.3536

Rm. LHOB 1431 **Web.** marieforcongress.com
Bio. 06/04/1988 • • Reed College (OR), Bach. Deg., 2012 •
M. Dean Gluesenkamp, 1 ch **Cmte.** Small Business
Dist. Off. Vancouver 360.695.6292

R: 386　**T:** 1st　50%
Elected Year: 2022

🐦 Rep. Pramila Jayapal (JIE-ah-pall)　　　D-WA-07　　p 202.225.3106

Rm. RHOB 2346　　　　　　　　　　　　　　　　**f** 202.225.6197
Bio. 09/21/1965 • Chennai • Georgetown Univ. (DC), A.B., 1986; Northwestern Univ. Kellogg School Management (IL), M.B.A., 1990 • Hinduism • M. Steve Williamson, 1 ch ; 1 stepch　**Cmte.** Education & Workforce • Judiciary
Dist. Off.　Seattle 206.674.0040

R: 212　**T:** 4th　85%
Elected Year: 2016

🐦 Rep. Derek Kilmer (KILL-mur)　　　　D-WA-06　　p 202.225.5916

Rm. LHOB 1226　**Web.** kilmer.house.gov　　**f** 202.226.3575
Bio. 01/01/1974 • Port Angeles • Princeton Univ. (NJ), A.B., 1996; Univ. of Oxford (UK), Ph.D., 2003 • Methodist • M. Jennifer Kilmer, 2 ch　**Cmte.** Administration • Appropriations
CoS. Andrea Roper (CD)
Sched. Cameron Seib (CD)
Dist. Off.　Bremerton 360.373.9725 • Port Angeles 360.797.3623 • Tacoma 253.272.3515

R: 137　**T:** 6th　60%
Elected Year: 2012

🐦 Rep. Rick R. Larsen (LAR-suhn)　　　D-WA-02　　p 202.225.2605

Rm. RHOB 2163　**Web.** larsen.house.gov　　**f** 202.225.4420
Bio. 06/15/1965 • Arlington • Economic Development official; Member, Snohomish County Council • Pacific Lutheran Univ. (WA), B.A., 1987; Univ. of Minnesota, M.P.A., 1990 • Methodist • M. Tiia Karlen Larsen, 2 ch　**Cmte.** Transportation & Infrastructure
CoS. Robin Chand　　　　**LD.** Jonathan Z. Golden
Sched. Per Bergstrom　　　**PS.** Joseph Tutino
Dist. Off.　Bellingham 360.733.4500 • Everett 425.252.3188

R: 40　**T:** 12th　60%
Elected Year: 2000

🐦 Rep. Cathy A. McMorris Rodgers (mik-MOR-iss R-WA-05
RAH-jurz)　　　　　　　　　　　　　　　　　　p 202.225.2006

Rm. RHOB 2188　**Web.** mcmorris.house.gov　**f** 202.225.3392
Bio. 05/22/1969 • Salem • State Legislator • Pensacola Christian College (FL), B.A., 1990; Univ. of Washington, M.B.A., 2002 • Evangelical • M. Brian Rodgers, 3 ch　**Cmte.** Energy & Commerce
CoS. Patrick Bell (CD)
Sched. Caitlin O'Dell (CD)
Dist. Off.　Colville 509.684.3481 • Spokane 509.353.2374 • Walla Walla 509.529.9358

R: 64　**T:** 10th　60%
Elected Year: 2004

🐦 Rep. Dan M. Newhouse (NOO-hous)　　　R-WA-04　　p 202.225.5816

Rm. CHOB 504　**Web.** newhouse.house.gov　**f** 202.225.3251
Bio. 07/10/1955 • Sunnyside • Washington State Univ., B.S., 1977 • Presbyterian • M. Carol Newhouse, 2 ch　**Cmte.** Appropriations • Select China Committee
CoS. Ashley Stubbs (CD)
　　　　　　　　　　　　　　　PS. Amanda Fitzmorris
Dist. Off.　Grand Coulee 509.433.7760 • Richland 509.713.7374 • Yakima 509.452.3243

R: 180　**T:** 5th　67%
Elected Year: 2014

🐦 Rep. Kim Schrier (SHRY-uhr)　　　　D-WA-08　　p 202.225.7761

Rm. LHOB 1110　**Web.** schrier.house.gov　　**f** 202.225.4282
Bio. 08/23/1968 • Los Angeles • Univ. of California, Berkeley, B.A., 1991; Univ. of California, Davis School of Medicine, M.D., 1997 • Jewish • M. David Gowing, 1 ch
Cmte. Agriculture • Energy & Commerce
CoS. Erin O'Quinn　　　　**LD.** Jennifer E. Cash
Sched. Emilee Milborn　　**PS.** Elizabeth Carlson
Dist. Off.　Issaquah 425.657.1001 • Wenatchee 509.850.5340

R: 277　**T:** 3rd　53%
Elected Year: 2018

WASHINGTON

⚑ Rep. Adam Smith (smith)   D-WA-09   p 202.225.8901

Rm. RHOB 2264 **Web.** adamsmith.house.gov
Bio. 06/15/1965 • Washington • Attorney • Fordham Univ.
(NY), B.A., 1987; Univ. of Washington, J.D., 1990 • Christian
Church • M. Sara Bickle-Eldridge Smith, 2 ch **Cmte.** Armed
Services
CoS. Sarah Servin   **LD.** Connor Stubbs
Sched. Josette Wicker (CD)   **PS.** Jaelin O'Halloran
Dist. Off. Renton 425.793.5180

R: 30   **T:** 14th 72%
Elected Year: 1996

⚑ Rep. Marilyn Strickland (STRIK-luhnd)   D-WA-10   p 202.225.9740

Rm. LHOB 1708 **Web.** strickland.house.gov
Bio. 09/25/1962 • Seoul • Univ. of Washington, B.A.,
1984; Clark Atlanta Univ., M.B.A., 1992 • M. Pactrick Erwin,
2 stepch **Cmte.** Armed Services • Transportation &
Infrastructure
CoS. Andrew Noh   **LD.** Hector Colon
Sched. Jesse Mayer
Dist. Off. Lacey 360.459.8514

R: 345   **T:** 2nd 57%
Elected Year: 2020

WEST VIRGINIA

WEST VIRGINIA

⚑ Governor Jim Justice (JUHS-tiss)   p 304.558.2000

State Capitol   **C:** Charleston
1900 Kanawha Blvd., East   **P:** 1,805,832 (39)
Charleston, WV 25305   **A:** 24,038.32 mi^2 (41st)
Website wv.gov
Fax 304.342.7025
Term Ends 2025
Lt. Governor
Craig Blair, **R**

U.S. Senators
Joe Manchin, **D**
Shelley Moore Capito, **R**
U.S. Representatives
01 / Carol D. Miller, **R**
02 / Alex X. Mooney, **R**

⚑ Sen. Shelley Moore Capito (KA-pih-toe)   R-WV-Jr.   p 202.224.6472

Rm. RSOB 172 **Web.** capito.senate.gov   **f** 202.224.7665
Bio. 11/26/1953 • Glen Dale • State Legislator • Duke Univ.
(NC), B.S., 1975; Univ. of Virginia, M.Ed., 1976 • Presbyterian
• M. Dr. Charles Lewis Capito, 3 ch ; 4 gr-ch **Cmte.**
Appropriations • Commerce, Science & Transportation •
Environment & Public Works • Rules & Administration
CoS. Joel Brubaker   **LD.** Jeffrey T. Jezierski
Sched. Lauren Allen   **PS.** Kelley Moore
Dist. Off. Charleston 304.347.5372 • Martinsburg
304.262.9285 • Morgantown 304.292.2310

R: 57   **T:** 2nd 70%
Elected Year: 2014
Next Election: 2026

Sen. Joe Manchin III (MAN-shin)   D-WV-Sr.   p 202.224.3954

Rm. HSOB 306 **Web.** manchin.senate.gov   **f** 202.228.0002
Bio. 08/24/1947 • Farmington • Candidate, Governor of
West Virginia; President, Marion County Rescue Squad;
Secretary of State, West Virginia; Mbr., WV House of
Delegates; Mbr., WV Senate; Mbr., Marion County Airport
Authority • West Virginia Univ., B.S., 1970 • Catholic •
M. Gayle Conelly, 3 ch ; 8 gr-ch   **Cmte.** Appropriations •
Armed Services • Energy & Natural Resources • Veterans'
Affairs
CoS. Wes Kungel
Sched. Anne Raffaelli   **PS.** Sam Runyon
Dist. Off. Charleston 304.342.5855 • Fairmont 304.368.0567
• Martinsburg 304.264.4626

R: 34   **T:** 3rd   50%
Elected Year: 2010
Next Election: 2024

Rep. Carol D. Miller (MIH-lur)   R-WV-01   p 202.225.3452

Rm. CHOB 465 **Web.** miller.house.gov
Bio. 11/04/1950 • Columbus • Columbia College, B.S., 1972
• Baptist • M. Matt Miller, 2 ch   **Cmte.** Ways & Means
CoS. Matthew Donnellan   **LD.** Max Pedrotti
Dist. Off. Beckley 304.250.6177 • Bluefield 304.325.6800 •
Huntington 304.522.2201

R: 265   **T:** 3rd   67%
Elected Year: 2018

Rep. Alex X. Mooney (MOON-ee)   R-WV-02   p 202.225.2711

Rm. RHOB 2228 **Web.** mooney.house.gov   **f** 202.225.7856
Bio. 06/07/1971 • Washington • Dartmouth College, A.B.,
1993 • Roman Catholic • M. Grace Gonzalez, 3 ch   **Cmte.**
Financial Services
CoS. Michael J. Hough
Sched. Steven Clark   **PS.** Ryan Kelly
Dist. Off. Charleston 304.925.5964 • Martinsburg
304.264.8810

R: 178   **T:** 5th   66%
Elected Year: 2014

WISCONSIN

Governor Tony Evers (EV-urz)   p 608.266.1212

115 E. Capitol
Madison, WI 53702
Website wisconsin.gov
Fax 608.267.8983
Term Ends 2027
Lt. Governor
Sara Rodriguez, **D**

C: Madison
P: 5,813,568 (20)
A: 54,157.76 mi^2 (25th)

U.S. Senators
Ron H. Johnson, **R**
Tammy Baldwin, **D**
U.S. Representatives
01 / Bryan G. Steil, **R**
02 / Mark Pocan, **D**
03 / Derrick F. Van Orden, **R**
04 / Gwen S. Moore, **D**
05 / Scott L. Fitzgerald, **R**
06 / Glenn S. Grothman, **R**
07 / Tom Tiffany, **R**
08 / Mike J. Gallagher, **R**

WISCONSIN

⌁ Sen. Tammy Baldwin (BALLD-win)　　　D-WI-Jr.　　p 202.224.5653

Rm. HSOB 709　**Web.** baldwin.senate.gov　**f** 202.224.9787
Bio. 02/11/1962 • Madison • City Council Member; Member,
State Assembly • Smith College (MA), A.B., 1984; Univ.
of Wisconsin Law School, J.D., 1989 • Unspecified/Other
• S. **Cmte.** Appropriations • Commerce, Science &
Transportation • Health, Education, Labor & Pensions
CoS. Ken B. Reidy　　　　**LD.** Meghan E. Ladwig
Sched. Carolyn D. Walser　　**PS.** Eli Rosen
Dist. Off. Eau Claire 715.832.8424 • Green Bay
920.498.2668 • La Crosse 608.796.0045 • Madison
608.264.5338 • Milwaukee 414.297.4451

R: 46　**T:** 2nd　55%
Elected Year: 2012
Next Election: 2024

⌁ Sen. Ron H. Johnson (JAHN-suhn)　　　R-WI-Sr.　　p 202.224.5323

Rm. HSOB 328　**Web.** ronjohnson.senate.gov　**f** 202.228.6965
Bio. 04/08/1955 • Mankato • Univ. of Minnesota, B.S.,
1977 • Lutheran • M. Jane Johnson, 3 ch ; 2 gr-ch　**Cmte.**
Budget • Finance • Foreign Relations • Homeland Security
& Government Affairs
CoS. Sean Riley　　　　　**LD.** Courtney Rutland
Sched. Chloe Pickle　　　**PS.** Corinne Day
Dist. Off. Madison 608.240.9629 • Milwaukee 414.276.7282
• Oshkosh 920.230.7250

R: 40　**T:** 3rd　50%
Elected Year: 2010
Next Election: 2028

⌁ Rep. Scott L. Fitzgerald (fits-JAIR-uld)　　R-WI-05　　p 202.225.5101

Rm. LHOB 1507　**Web.** fitzgerald.house.gov
Bio. 11/16/1963 • Chicago • Univ. of Wisconsin - Oshkosh,
B.S., 1985 • Catholic • M. Lisa Fitzgerald, 3 ch　**Cmte.**
Financial Services • Judiciary
CoS. Ryan McCormack　　　**LD.** Robert N. Wagener
　　　　　　　　　　　　　　PS. Alexander Crane
Dist. Off. Brookfield 262.784.1111

R: 312　**T:** 2nd　64%
Elected Year: 2020

⌁ Rep. Mike J. Gallagher (GA-luh-gur)　　R-WI-08　　p 202.225.5665

Rm. LHOB 1211　**Web.** gallagher.house.gov　**f** 202.225.5729
Bio. 03/03/1984 • Green Bay • Princeton Univ. Woodrow
Wilson School of Public and International Affairs (NJ),
B.A., 2006; National Intelligence Univ. (DC), M.S., 2010;
Georgetown Univ. (DC), M.A., 2012; Georgetown Univ. (DC),
M.A., 2013; Georgetown Univ. (DC), Ph.D., 2015 • Catholic
• M. Holli A. Horak MD, 1 ch　**Cmte.** Armed Services •
Permanent Select on Intelligence • Select China Committee
CoS. Taylor Andreae
　　　　　　　　　　PS. Jordan Dunn
Dist. Off. De Pere 920.301.4500

R: 208　**T:** 4th　72%
Elected Year: 2016

⌁ Rep. Glenn S. Grothman ("GROWTH"-muhn)　R-WI-06　　p 202.225.2476

Rm. LHOB 1511　**Web.** grothman.house.gov　**f** 202.225.2356
Bio. 07/03/1955 • Milwaukee • Univ. of Wisconsin -
Madison, B.B.A., 1977; Univ. of Wisconsin Law School,
J.D., 1983 • Lutheran • S. Growth Muhn　**Cmte.** Budget •
Education & Workforce • Oversight & Accountability
CoS. Alan Ott (CD)
Sched. Kayla Robson　　　**PS.** Timothy Svoboda
Dist. Off. Fond du Lac 920.907.0624

R: 173　**T:** 5th　95%
Elected Year: 2014

Rep. Gwen S. Moore (mor)　　　D-WI-04　　p 202.225.4572

Rm. RHOB 2252 **Web.**　　　　　　　　　**f** 202.225.8135
gwenmoore.house.gov
Bio. 04/18/1951 • Racine • State Senator; Member, State
Assembly • Marquette Univ. (WI), B.A., 1978 • Baptist • S., 3
ch ; 3 gr-ch　**Cmte.** Ways & Means
Sched. Jonathan McCray　　　**PS.** Samara Sheff
Jones (CD)
Dist. Off.　Milwaukee 414.297.1140

R: 65　**T:** 10th　75%
Elected Year: 2004

 **Rep. Mark Pocan** (po-KAN)　　　D-WI-02　　p 202.225.2906

Rm. LHOB 1026 **Web.** pocan.house.gov
Bio. 08/14/1964 • Kenosha • Univ. of Wisconsin - Madison,
B.A., 1986 • Unspecified/Other • M. Philip Frank　**Cmte.**
Appropriations
CoS. Glenn Wavrunek
　　　　　　　　　　　　　　　PS. Matthew Handverger
Dist. Off.　Madison 608.258.9800

R: 143　**T:** 6th　71%
Elected Year: 2012

 Rep. Bryan G. Steil ("style")　　　R-WI-01　　p 202.225.3031

Rm. LHOB 1526 **Web.** steil.house.gov
Bio. 03/03/1981 • Janesville • Georgetown Univ. (DC), B.A.,
2003, Univ. of Wisconsin, J.D., 2007 • Catholic • S.　**Cmte.**
Administration • Financial Services
CoS. Ryan Carney　　　　　**LD.** David Goldfarb
Sched. Matt Holsen (CD)　　**PS.** Grace White
Dist. Off.　Janesville 608.752.4050

R: 283　**T:** 3rd　54%
Elected Year: 2018

 Rep. Tom Tiffany (TIF-uh-nee)　　　R-WI-07　　p 202.225.3365

Rm. CHOB 451 **Web.** tiffany.house.gov
Bio. 12/30/1957 • Wabasha • Univ. of Wisconsin, River
Falls, B.S., 1980 • M. Christine Sully, 3 ch　**Cmte.** Judiciary •
Natural Resources
Sched. Maggie Cronin (CD)
Dist. Off.　Wausau 715.298.9344

R: 297　**T:** 3rd　62%
Elected Year: 2020

 Rep. Derrick F. Van Orden ()　　　R-WI-03　　p 202.225.5506

Rm. LHOB 1513 **Web.**
vanordenforcongress.com
Bio. 09/15/1969 •　• Excelsior College, B.S. • M. Sara Jane
Cmte. Transportation & Infrastructure • Veterans' Affairs
Dist. Off.　Eau Claire　•Lacrosse

R: 432　**T:** 1st　52%
Elected Year: 2022

WYOMING

 Governor Mark Gordon (GOR-duhn)　　　　　p 307.777.7434

State Capitol　　　　　　　　**C:** Cheyenne
200 W. 24th St.　　　　　　　**P:** 577,737 (52)
Cheyenne, WY 82002-0010　　**A:** 97,093.07 mi^2 (9th)
Website wyoming.gov
Fax 307.632.3909
Term Ends 2027

WYOMING

U.S. Senators
John A. Barrasso, **R**
Cynthia M. Lummis, **R**
U.S. Representatives
01 / Harriet M. Hageman, **R**

♠ Sen. John A. Barrasso (bah-RAH-so)　　　R-WY-Sr.　　p 202.224.6441

Rm. DSOB 307 **Web.** barrasso.senate.gov　　**f** 202.224.1724
Bio. 07/21/1952 • Reading • State Legislator; Orthopedic
Surgeon • Georgetown Univ. (DC), B.S., 1974; Georgetown
Univ. School of Medicine (DC), M.D., 1978 • Presbyterian •
M. Bobbi Brown, 3 ch (2 from previous marriage) **Cmte.**
Energy & Natural Resources • Finance • Foreign Relations
CoS. Dan Kunsman　　　　**LD.** Amber Bland
Sched. Kathi Wise　　　　**PS.** Laura Mengelkamp
Dist. Off. Casper 307.261.6413 • Cheyenne 307.772.2451
• Riverton 307.856.6642 • Rock Springs 307.362.5012 •
Sheridan 307.672.6456

R: 26　**T:** 4th　67%
Elected Year: 2007
Next Election: 2024

♠ Sen. Cynthia M. Lummis (LUH-muhs)　　　R-WY-Jr.　　p 202.224.3424

Web. lummis.senate.gov　　　　　　**f** 202.224.3265
Bio. 09/10/1954 • Cheyenne • State Legislator; Attorney •
Univ. of Wyoming (WY), B.S., 1976; Univ. of Wyoming (WY),
B.S., 1978; Univ. of Wyoming College of Law, J.D., 1985 •
Lutheran • W., 1 ch ; 1 gr-ch **Cmte.** Banking, Housing &
Urban Affairs • Commerce, Science & Transportation •
Environment & Public Works
CoS. Kristin Walker (CD)　　**LD.** Darrin Munoz (CD)
Sched. Mikalah Skates (CD)　**PS.** Stacey Daniels (CD)
Dist. Off. Afton 307.248.1736 • Casper 307.261.6572 •
Cheyenne 307.772.2477 • Cody 307.527.9444 • Sheridan
307.439.7783 • Sundance 307.283.3461

R: 85　**T:** 1st　73%
Elected Year: 2020
Next Election: 2026

♠ Rep. Harriet M. Hageman ()　　　　R-WY-01　　p 202.225.2311

Rm. LHOB 1531 **Web.**
  hagemanforwyoming.com
Bio. 10/18/1962 • • Univ. of Wyoming (WY), B.S., 1986;
Univ. of Wyoming College of Law, J.D., 1989 • M. John
Sundahl **Cmte.** Judiciary • Natural Resources
Dist. Off. Casper 307.441.6328 • Cheyenne 307.829.3299 •
Gillette 307.228.6399

R: 388　**T:** 1st　68%
Elected Year: 2022

AMERICAN SAMOA

🕊 Governor　Lemanu Palepoi Mauga ()　　　　　　p 684.633.4116

Executive Office Building, Third　　**C:** Pago Pago
Floor, Utulei　　　　　　　　　　**P:** 55,689 (55)
Pago Pago, AS 96799　　　　　　　**A:** 76.45 mi^2 (55th)
Website americansamoa.gov
Fax 684.633.2269
Term Ends 2025
Lt. Governor
Talauega Eleasalo Vaalele Ale, **D**

Delegate

🔴 **Del. Amata Coleman Radewagen** (RAD-eh-wag-R-AS-01 uhn)　　　　　　　　　　　　　　　　p 202.225.8577

Rm. RHOB 2001 **Web.** radewagen.house.gov **f** 202.225.8757
Bio. 12/29/1947 • Pago Pago • Univ. of Guam, B.S., 1975 • Roman Catholic • M. Fred Radewagen, 3 ch ; 1 gr-ch **Cmte.** Foreign Affairs • Natural Resources • Veterans' Affairs
CoS. Leafaina Yahn　　　　**LD.** Richard Stanton
Sched. Nancy Dehlinger　　**PS.** Joel Hannahs
Dist. Off. Fagatogo 684.633.3601

R: 438　**T:** 5th 100%
Elected Year: 2014

DISTRICT OF COLUMBIA

🔰 **Mayor Muriel Bowser** (BOU-zur)　　　　　　p 202.727.2643

Executive Office of the Mayor　　**C:** Washington
1350 Pennsylvania Avenue NW,　**P:** 702,455 (50)
Suite 316　　　　　　　　　　　**A:** 61.00 mi^2 (56th)
Washington, DC 20004
Website dc.gov
Fax 202.727.0505
Term Ends 2027

Delegate

🔰 **Del. Eleanor Holmes Norton** (NOR-tuhn)　　D-DC-01　　p 202.225.8050

Rm. RHOB 2136 **Web.** norton.house.gov　　**f** 202.225.3002
Bio. 06/13/1937 • Washington • Professor; Employment Commission Chair • Antioch College (OH), B.A., 1960; Yale Univ. (CT), M.A., 1963; Yale Univ. Law School (CT), J.D., 1964 • Episcopalian • D., 2 ch **Cmte.** Oversight & Accountability • Transportation & Infrastructure
CoS. Raven Reeder　　　　　**LD.** Bradley Truding
Sched. Try Onaghise-　　　　**PS.** Sharon Eliza Nichols
Coburn
Dist. Off. Washington 202.408.9041 • Washington
202.678.8900

R: 435　**T:** 17th 87%
Elected Year: 1990

GUAM

🔰 **Governor Lou Leon Guerrero** (guh-RAIR-o)　　p 671.472.8931

Richard J. Bordallo Governor's　**C:** Hagatna
Complex　　　　　　　　　　　**P:** 164,229 (53)
Adelup, GU 96910　　　　　　　**A:** 209.65 mi^2 (52nd)
Website guam.gov
Fax 671.477.4826
Term Ends 2027
Lt. Governor
Josh Tenorio, **D**

Delegate

🔴 **Del. James C. Moylan** ()　　　　R-GU-01　　p 202.225.1188

Rm. LHOB 1628 **Web.** jamesmoylan.com
Bio. • Univ. of Guam, Bach. Deg. • NS. **Cmte.** Armed Services • Natural Resources
CoS. Bobby Shringi
　　　　　　　　　　　　PS. Hannah D'avanzo
Dist. Off. Hagatna 671.922.6673

R: 440　**T:** 1st 52%
Elected Year: 2022

Governor Arnold Indalecio Palacios () p 670.664.2280

Juan Atalig Memorial Building
Isla Dr., Capitol Hill, Caller Box 10007
Saipan, MP 96950
Website gov.mp
Fax 670.664.2211
Term Ends 2027
Lt. Governor
David Mundo Apatang, I

C: Saipan
P: 52,263 (56)
A: 182.24 mi^2 (53rd)

Delegate

Del. Gregorio Kilili Camacho Sablan (sah-BLAHN) D-MP-01 p 202.225.2646

Rm. RHOB 2267 **Web.** sablan.house.gov **f** 202.226.4249
Bio. 01/19/1955 • Saipan • Public Administrator • Army
• Roman Catholic • M. Andrea C. Sablan, 6 ch **Cmte.**
Education & Workforce • Natural Resources
CoS. Robert Schwalbach **LD.** Herb Yamada
Sched. John R.P. Del Rosario
Dist. Off. Rota 670.532.2647 • Saipan 670.323.2647 • Tinian 670.433.2647

R: 436 **T:** 7th 100%
Elected Year: 2008

Governor Pedro R. Pierluisi (pee-air-loo-EE-see) p 787.721.7000

PO Box 9023431
San Juan, PR 00902-0082
Website pr.gov
Fax 787.729.5072
Term Ends 2025

C: San Juan
P: 3,195,153 (30)
A: 3,423.95 mi^2 (49th)

Delegate

Del. Jenniffer A. González-Colón (gon-SAH-les ko-LOAN) R-PR-01 p 202.225.2615

Rm. RHOB 2338 **Web.** gonzalez-colon.house.gov **f** 202.225.2154
Bio. 08/05/1976 • San Juan, PR • Univ. of Puerto Rico, Bach. Deg.; Inter-American Univ. of Puerto Rico, J.D.; Inter-American Univ. of Puerto Rico, LL.M. • Unspecified/Other • S. **Cmte.** Natural Resources • Transportation & Infrastructure
CoS. Gabriella Boffelli **LD.** Natalia Gandia
Sched. Juan C. Ruiz **PS.** Linoshka Luna
Dist. Off. San Juan 787.723.6333

R: 439 **T:** 2nd 41%
Elected Year: 2016

Governor Albert Bryan (BRY-uhn) p 340.774.0001

Government House
21-22 Kongens Gade, Charlotte Amalie
St. Thomas, VI 00802
Website vi.gov
Fax 340.774.1361
Term Ends 2027
Lt. Governor
Tregenza Roach, **D**

C: Charlotte Amalie
P: 104,901 (54)
A: 134.36 mi^2 (54th)

VIRGIN ISLANDS

Delegate

⋈ Del. Stacey E. Plaskett (PLAS-ket) D-VI-01 p 202.225.1790

Rm. RHOB 2059 **Web.** plaskett.house.gov **f** 202.225.5517
Bio. 05/13/1964 • New York • Georgetown Univ. Foreign
Service School (DC), B.S., 1984; American Univ., Washington
College of Law, J.D., 1994 • Lutheran • M. Jeremy Buckney
Small, 5 ch **Cmte.** Permanent Select on Intelligence
CoS. Angeline Jabbar **LD.** Jeffrey M. Nowill
  PS. Tionee Scotland (CD)
Dist. Off. Frederiksted 340.778.5900 • St. Thomas
340.774.4408

R: 437 **T:** 5th 99%
Elected Year: 2014

INDEX OF COMMITTEES AND SUBCOMMITTEES

Below is an alphabetical listing of all committees and subcommittees by name. Bold type indicates committee, non-bold type indicates subcommittee. Entries are grouped by Senate, Joint and House.

SENATE

JOINT

HOUSE

SENATE COMMITTEES

SENATE COMMITTEES

Committee rosters are listed in order of ranking membership with the Chairman and Ranking Member indicated with "C" and "RM" respectively. The chairman and ranking member of each committee usually have membership status on all subcommittees of which they are not members. This is referred to as ex officio membership. These memberships are subject to the rules of the individual committees.

AGRICULTURE, NUTRITION & FORESTRY

Room: RSOB 328A
Website: www.agriculture.senate.gov
Phone: 202.224.2035
Ratio: 12 Democrats/11 Republicans
Subcommittees: 5

Majority:		Minority:	
C: Debbie Stabenow, MI	HSOB 731	**RM: John Boozman, AR**	HSOB 141
Sherrod Brown, OH	HSOB 503	Mitch McConnell, KY	RSOB 317
Amy Klobuchar, MN	DSOB 425	John Hoeven, ND	RSOB 338
Michael Bennet, CO	RSOB 261	Joni Ernst, IA	HSOB 730
Kirsten Gillibrand, NY	RSOB 478	Cindy Hyde-Smith, MS	HSOB 702
Tina Smith, MN	HSOB 720	Roger Marshall, KS	RSOB 479A
Dick Durbin, IL	HSOB 711	Tommy Tuberville, AL	RSOB 142
Cory Booker, NJ	HSOB 717	Mike Braun, IN	RSOB 404
Ben Ray Luján, NM	RSOB 498	Chuck Grassley, IA	HSOB 135
Raphael Warnock, GA	RSOB 388	John Thune, SD	DSOB 511
Peter Welch, VT	DSOB G12	Deb Fischer, NE	RSOB 454
John Fetterman, PA	DSOB B40B		

Majority CoS: Erica Chabot   **Minority CoS:** Fitzhugh Elder IV

———————————— Subcommittees ————————————

COMMODITIES, RISK MANAGEMENT & TRADE
Room: RSOB 328A
Phone: 202.224.2035

Majority:		Minority:	
C: Raphael Warnock, GA	RSOB 388	**RM: John Hoeven, ND**	RSOB 338
Dick Durbin, IL	HSOB 711	Mitch McConnell, KY	RSOB 317
Kirsten Gillibrand, NY	RSOB 478	John Thune, SD	DSOB 511
Ben Ray Luján, NM	RSOB 498	Chuck Grassley, IA	HSOB 135
Sherrod Brown, OH	HSOB 503	Cindy Hyde-Smith, MS	HSOB 702
Tina Smith, MN	HSOB 720	Tommy Tuberville, AL	RSOB 142

CONSERVATION, CLIMATE, FORESTRY & NATURAL RESOURCES
Room: RSOB 328A
Phone: 202.224.2035

Majority:		Minority:	
C: Michael Bennet, CO	RSOB 261	**RM: Roger Marshall, KS**	RSOB 479A
Peter Welch, VT	DSOB G12	John Thune, SD	DSOB 511
Amy Klobuchar, MN	DSOB 425	John Hoeven, ND	RSOB 338
Ben Ray Luján, NM	RSOB 498	Cindy Hyde-Smith, MS	HSOB 702
Sherrod Brown, OH	HSOB 503	Mike Braun, IN	RSOB 404
Cory Booker, NJ	HSOB 717	Tommy Tuberville, AL	RSOB 142

FOOD & NUTRITION, SPECIALTY CROPS, ORGANICS & RESEARCH
Room: RSOB 328A
Phone: 202.224.2035

Majority:		Minority:	
C: Cory Booker, NJ	HSOB 717	**RM: Mike Braun, IN**	RSOB 404
Michael Bennet, CO	RSOB 261	Mitch McConnell, KY	RSOB 317
Kirsten Gillibrand, NY	RSOB 478	John Hoeven, ND	RSOB 338
Peter Welch, VT	DSOB G12	Deb Fischer, NE	RSOB 454
Amy Klobuchar, MN	DSOB 425	Joni Ernst, IA	HSOB 730
Raphael Warnock, GA	RSOB 388	Roger Marshall, KS	RSOB 479A

LIVESTOCK, DAIRY, POULTRY, LOCAL FOOD SYS & FOOD SAFETY & SEC
Room: RSOB 328A
Phone: 202.224.2035

Majority:		Minority:	
C: Kirsten Gillibrand, NY	RSOB 478	**RM: Cindy Hyde-Smith, MS**	HSOB 702
Dick Durbin, IL	HSOB 711		
Peter Welch, VT	DSOB G12	John Thune, SD	DSOB 511
Cory Booker, NJ	HSOB 717	Chuck Grassley, IA	HSOB 135
Tina Smith, MN	HSOB 720	Deb Fischer, NE	RSOB 454
Raphael Warnock, GA	RSOB 388	Joni Ernst, IA	HSOB 730
		Roger Marshall, KS	RSOB 479A

RURAL DEVELOPMENT & ENERGY
Room: RSOB 328A
Phone: 202.224.2035

Majority:		Minority:	
C: Tina Smith, MN	HSOB 720	**RM: Joni Ernst, IA**	HSOB 730
Dick Durbin, IL	HSOB 711	Mitch McConnell, KY	RSOB 317
Michael Bennet, CO	RSOB 261	Chuck Grassley, IA	HSOB 135
Amy Klobuchar, MN	DSOB 425	Deb Fischer, NE	RSOB 454
Ben Ray Luján, NM	RSOB 498	Mike Braun, IN	RSOB 404
Sherrod Brown, OH	HSOB 503	Tommy Tuberville, AL	RSOB 142

APPROPRIATIONS
Room: The Capitol S-128
Website: www.appropriations.senate.gov
Phone: 202.224.7363
Ratio: 15 Democrats/14 Republicans
Subcommittees: 12

Majority:		Minority:	
C: Patty Murray, WA	RSOB 154	**RM: Susan Collins, ME**	DSOB 413
Dianne Feinstein, CA	HSOB 331	Mitch McConnell, KY	RSOB 317
Dick Durbin, IL	HSOB 711	Lisa Murkowski, AK	HSOB 522
Jack Reed, RI	HSOB 728	Lindsey Graham, SC	RSOB 290
Jon Tester, MT	HSOB 311	Jerry Moran, KS	DSOB 521
Jeanne Shaheen, NH	HSOB 506	John Hoeven, ND	RSOB 338
Jeff Merkley, OR	HSOB 531	John Boozman, AR	HSOB 141
Chris Coons, DE	RSOB 218	Shelley Capito, WV	RSOB 172
Brian Schatz, HI	HSOB 722	John Kennedy, LA	RSOB 416
Tammy Baldwin, WI	HSOB 709	Cindy Hyde-Smith, MS	HSOB 702
Chris Murphy, CT	HSOB 136	Bill Hagerty, TN	RSOB 248
Joe Manchin, WV	HSOB 306	Katie Britt, AL	DSOB B40A
Chris Van Hollen, MD	HSOB 110	Marco Rubio, FL	RSOB 284
Martin Heinrich, NM	HSOB 303	Deb Fischer, NE	RSOB 454
Gary Peters, MI	HSOB 724		

Majority CoS: Charles E. Kieffer   **Minority CoS:** William D. Duhnke III

—————————— Subcommittees ——————————

AGRICULTURE, RURAL DEVELOPMENT, FDA & RELATED AGENCIES
Room: DSOB 129
Phone: 202.224.8090

Majority:		Minority:	
C: Martin Heinrich, NM	HSOB 303	**RM: John Hoeven, ND**	RSOB 338
Gary Peters, MI	HSOB 724	Susan Collins, ME	DSOB 413
Dianne Feinstein, CA	HSOB 331	Jerry Moran, KS	DSOB 521
Tammy Baldwin, WI	HSOB 709	Mitch McConnell, KY	RSOB 317
Jon Tester, MT	HSOB 311	Deb Fischer, NE	RSOB 454
Jeff Merkley, OR	HSOB 531	Cindy Hyde-Smith, MS	HSOB 702
Joe Manchin, WV	HSOB 306		

COMMERCE, JUSTICE, SCIENCE & RELATED AGENCIES
Room: DSOB 142
Phone: 202.224.5202

Majority:		Minority:	
C: Jeanne Shaheen, NH	HSOB 506	**RM: Jerry Moran, KS**	DSOB 521
Jack Reed, RI	HSOB 728	Shelley Capito, WV	RSOB 172
Gary Peters, MI	HSOB 724	Lisa Murkowski, AK	HSOB 522
Dianne Feinstein, CA	HSOB 331	Deb Fischer, NE	RSOB 454
Jeff Merkley, OR	HSOB 531	Katie Britt, AL	DSOB B40A
Chris Van Hollen, MD	HSOB 110	John Kennedy, LA	RSOB 416
Joe Manchin, WV	HSOB 306	Bill Hagerty, TN	RSOB 248
Chris Coons, DE	RSOB 218		
Brian Schatz, HI	HSOB 722		

DEPARTMENT OF DEFENSE
Room: DSOB 122
Phone: 202.224.6688

Majority:		Minority:	
C: Jon Tester, MT	HSOB 311	**RM: Susan Collins, ME**	DSOB 413
Jack Reed, RI	HSOB 728	Jerry Moran, KS	DSOB 521
Dianne Feinstein, CA	HSOB 331	Mitch McConnell, KY	RSOB 317
Tammy Baldwin, WI	HSOB 709	Shelley Capito, WV	RSOB 172
Dick Durbin, IL	HSOB 711	John Boozman, AR	HSOB 141
Chris Murphy, CT	HSOB 136	Lisa Murkowski, AK	HSOB 522
Jeanne Shaheen, NH	HSOB 506	Lindsey Graham, SC	RSOB 290
Patty Murray, WA	RSOB 154	John Hoeven, ND	RSOB 338
Brian Schatz, HI	HSOB 722		

DEPARTMENT OF HOMELAND SECURITY
Room: DSOB 131
Phone: 202.224.8244

Majority:		Minority:	
C: Chris Murphy, CT	HSOB 136	RM: Katie Britt, AL	DSOB B40A
Gary Peters, MI	HSOB 724	Shelley Capito, WV	RSOB 172
Tammy Baldwin, WI	HSOB 709	Lisa Murkowski, AK	HSOB 522
Jon Tester, MT	HSOB 311	John Kennedy, LA	RSOB 416
Jeanne Shaheen, NH	HSOB 506	Cindy Hyde-Smith, MS	HSOB 702
Patty Murray, WA	RSOB 154		

DEPARTMENT OF THE INTERIOR, ENVIRONMENT & RELATED AGENCIES
Room: DSOB 142
Phone: 202.224.0774

Majority:		Minority:	
C: Jeff Merkley, OR	HSOB 531	RM: Lisa Murkowski, AK	HSOB 522
Jack Reed, RI	HSOB 728	Mitch McConnell, KY	RSOB 317
Gary Peters, MI	HSOB 724	Shelley Capito, WV	RSOB 172
Dianne Feinstein, CA	HSOB 331	John Hoeven, ND	RSOB 338
Jon Tester, MT	HSOB 311	Deb Fischer, NE	RSOB 454
Chris Van Hollen, MD	HSOB 110	Katie Britt, AL	DSOB B40A
Martin Heinrich, NM	HSOB 303		

DOL, HHS & EDUCATION & RELATED AGENCIES
Room: DSOB 136
Phone: 202.224.9145

Majority:		Minority:	
C: Tammy Baldwin, WI	HSOB 709	RM: Shelley Capito, WV	RSOB 172
Jack Reed, RI	HSOB 728	Jerry Moran, KS	DSOB 521
Dick Durbin, IL	HSOB 711	John Boozman, AR	HSOB 141
Jeff Merkley, OR	HSOB 531	Lindsey Graham, SC	RSOB 290
Chris Murphy, CT	HSOB 136	Marco Rubio, FL	RSOB 284
Jeanne Shaheen, NH	HSOB 506	Katie Britt, AL	DSOB B40A
Patty Murray, WA	RSOB 154	John Kennedy, LA	RSOB 416
Joe Manchin, WV	HSOB 306	Cindy Hyde-Smith, MS	HSOB 702
Brian Schatz, HI	HSOB 722		

ENERGY & WATER DEVELOPMENT
Room: DSOB 131
Phone: 202.224.8119

Majority:		Minority:	
C: Dianne Feinstein, CA	HSOB 331	RM: John Kennedy, LA	RSOB 416
Tammy Baldwin, WI	HSOB 709	Mitch McConnell, KY	RSOB 317
Dick Durbin, IL	HSOB 711	Lisa Murkowski, AK	HSOB 522
Jon Tester, MT	HSOB 311	Lindsey Graham, SC	RSOB 290
Jeff Merkley, OR	HSOB 531	John Hoeven, ND	RSOB 338
Martin Heinrich, NM	HSOB 303	Katie Britt, AL	DSOB B40A
Jeanne Shaheen, NH	HSOB 506	Cindy Hyde-Smith, MS	HSOB 702
Patty Murray, WA	RSOB 154	Bill Hagerty, TN	RSOB 248
Chris Coons, DE	RSOB 218		

FINANCIAL SERVICES & GENERAL GOVERNMENT
Room: DSOB 133
Phone: 202.224.1133

Majority:		Minority:	
C: Chris Van Hollen, MD	HSOB 110	RM: Bill Hagerty, TN	RSOB 248
Dick Durbin, IL	HSOB 711	John Boozman, AR	HSOB 141
Martin Heinrich, NM	HSOB 303	Marco Rubio, FL	RSOB 284
Joe Manchin, WV	HSOB 306	John Kennedy, LA	RSOB 416
Chris Coons, DE	RSOB 218		

LEGISLATIVE BRANCH
Room: The Capitol S-128
Phone: 202.224.7264

Majority:		Minority:	
C: Jack Reed, RI	HSOB 728	RM: Deb Fischer, NE	RSOB 454
Chris Van Hollen, MD	HSOB 110	Marco Rubio, FL	RSOB 284
Chris Murphy, CT	HSOB 136		

MILITARY CONSTRUCTION & VETERAN AFFAIRS & RELATED AGENCIES
Room: DSOB 125
Phone: 202.224.8224

Majority:		Minority:	
C: Patty Murray, WA	RSOB 154	Susan Collins, ME	DSOB 413
Jack Reed, RI	HSOB 728	Mitch McConnell, KY	RSOB 317
Gary Peters, MI	HSOB 724	John Boozman, AR	HSOB 141

Tammy Baldwin, WI	HSOB 709	Lisa Murkowski, AK	HSOB 522
Jon Tester, MT	HSOB 311	John Hoeven, ND	RSOB 338
Martin Heinrich, NM	HSOB 303	Marco Rubio, FL	RSOB 284
Joe Manchin, WV	HSOB 306	Deb Fischer, NE	RSOB 454
Chris Coons, DE	RSOB 218	Bill Hagerty, TN	RSOB 248
Brian Schatz, HI	HSOB 722		

STATE, FOREIGN OPERATIONS & RELATED PROGRAMS
Room: DSOB 127
Phone: 202.224.7284

Majority:		Minority:	
C: Chris Coons, DE	RSOB 218	**RM: Lindsey Graham, SC**	RSOB 290
Dick Durbin, IL	HSOB 711	Jerry Moran, KS	DSOB 521
Jeff Merkley, OR	HSOB 531	Mitch McConnell, KY	RSOB 317
Chris Van Hollen, MD	HSOB 110	John Boozman, AR	HSOB 141
Chris Murphy, CT	HSOB 136	Marco Rubio, FL	RSOB 284
Jeanne Shaheen, NH	HSOB 506	Bill Hagerty, TN	RSOB 248
Brian Schatz, HI	HSOB 722		

TRANSPORTATION, HUD & RELATED AGENCIES
Room: DSOB 184
Phone: 202.224.7281

Majority:		Minority:	
C: Brian Schatz, HI	HSOB 722	**RM: Cindy Hyde-Smith, MS**	HSOB 702
Jack Reed, RI	HSOB 728		
Dianne Feinstein, CA	HSOB 331	Susan Collins, ME	DSOB 413
Dick Durbin, IL	HSOB 711	Jerry Moran, KS	DSOB 521
Chris Van Hollen, MD	HSOB 110	Shelley Capito, WV	RSOB 172
Chris Murphy, CT	HSOB 136	John Boozman, AR	HSOB 141
Patty Murray, WA	RSOB 154	Lindsey Graham, SC	RSOB 290
Joe Manchin, WV	HSOB 306	John Hoeven, ND	RSOB 338
Chris Coons, DE	RSOB 218	John Kennedy, LA	RSOB 416

ARMED SERVICES
Room: RSOB 228
Website: www.armed-services.senate.gov
Phone: 202.224.3871
Ratio: 12 Democrats/12 Republicans
Subcommittees: 7

Majority:		Minority:	
C: Jack Reed, RI	HSOB 728	**RM: Roger Wicker, MS**	DSOB 555
Angus King, ME	HSOB 133	Deb Fischer, NE	RSOB 454
Jeanne Shaheen, NH	HSOB 506	Tom Cotton, AR	RSOB 326
Kirsten Gillibrand, NY	RSOB 478	Mike Rounds, SD	HSOB 716
Richard Blumenthal, CT	HSOB 706	Joni Ernst, IA	HSOB 730
Mazie Hirono, HI	HSOB 109	Dan Sullivan, AK	HSOB 302
Tim Kaine, VA	RSOB 231	Kevin Cramer, ND	HSOB 330
Elizabeth Warren, MA	HSOB 309	Rick Scott, FL	HSOB 502
Gary Peters, MI	HSOB 724	Tommy Tuberville, AL	RSOB 142
Joe Manchin, WV	HSOB 306	Markwayne Mullin, OK	RSOB B33
Tammy Duckworth, IL	HSOB 524	Ted Budd, NC	RSOB B85
Jacky Rosen, NV		Eric Schmitt, MO	RSOB B11
Mark Kelly, AZ	HSOB 516		

Majority CoS: Hon. Elizabeth L. King

──────── Subcommittees ────────

AIRLAND
Room: RSOB 228
Phone: 202.224.3871

Majority:		Minority:	
C: Mark Kelly, AZ	HSOB 516	**RM: Tom Cotton, AR**	RSOB 326
Richard Blumenthal, CT	HSOB 706	Deb Fischer, NE	RSOB 454
Gary Peters, MI	HSOB 724	Joni Ernst, IA	HSOB 730
Joe Manchin, WV	HSOB 306	Rick Scott, FL	HSOB 502
Tammy Duckworth, IL	HSOB 524	Markwayne Mullin, OK	RSOB B33
Jack Reed, RI	HSOB 728	Roger Wicker, MS	DSOB 555

CYBERSECURITY
Room: RSOB 228
Phone: 202.224.3871

Majority:		Minority:	
C: Joe Manchin, WV	HSOB 306	**RM: Mike Rounds, SD**	HSOB 716
Kirsten Gillibrand, NY	RSOB 478	Joni Ernst, IA	HSOB 730
Jacky Rosen, NV		Ted Budd, NC	RSOB B85
Gary Peters, MI	HSOB 724	Eric Schmitt, MO	RSOB B11
Tammy Duckworth, IL	HSOB 524	Roger Wicker, MS	DSOB 555
Jack Reed, RI	HSOB 728		

SENATE COMMITTEES

EMERGING THREATS & CAPABILITIES
Room: RSOB 228
Phone: 202.224.3871

Majority:		Minority:	
C: Kirsten Gillibrand, NY	RSOB 478	**RM: Joni Ernst, IA**	HSOB 730
Jeanne Shaheen, NH	HSOB 506	Tom Cotton, AR	RSOB 326
Elizabeth Warren, MA	HSOB 309	Markwayne Mullin, OK	RSOB B33
Gary Peters, MI	HSOB 724	Ted Budd, NC	RSOB B85
Jacky Rosen, NV		Eric Schmitt, MO	RSOB B11
Mark Kelly, AZ	HSOB 516	Roger Wicker, MS	DSOB 555
Jack Reed, RI	HSOB 728		

PERSONNEL
Room: RSOB 228
Phone: 202.224.3871

Majority:		Minority:	
C: Elizabeth Warren, MA	HSOB 309	**RM: Rick Scott, FL**	HSOB 502
Richard Blumenthal, CT	HSOB 706	Mike Rounds, SD	HSOB 716
Mazie Hirono, HI	HSOB 109	Dan Sullivan, AK	HSOB 302
Tim Kaine, VA	RSOB 231	Ted Budd, NC	RSOB B85
Tammy Duckworth, IL	HSOB 524	Roger Wicker, MS	DSOB 555
Jack Reed, RI	HSOB 728		

READINESS & MANAGEMENT SUPPORT
Room: RSOB 228
Phone: 202.224.3871

Majority:		Minority:	
C: Mazie Hirono, HI	HSOB 109	**RM: Dan Sullivan, AK**	HSOB 302
Jeanne Shaheen, NH	HSOB 506	Deb Fischer, NE	RSOB 454
Richard Blumenthal, CT	HSOB 706	Kevin Cramer, ND	HSOB 330
Tim Kaine, VA	RSOB 231	Tommy Tuberville, AL	RSOB 142
Tammy Duckworth, IL	HSOB 524	Markwayne Mullin, OK	RSOB B33
Mark Kelly, AZ	HSOB 516	Roger Wicker, MS	DSOB 555
Jack Reed, RI	HSOB 728		

SEAPOWER
Room: RSOB 228
Phone: 202.224.3871

Majority:		Minority:	
C: Tim Kaine, VA	RSOB 231	**RM: Kevin Cramer, ND**	HSOB 330
Jeanne Shaheen, NH	HSOB 506	Dan Sullivan, AK	HSOB 302
Richard Blumenthal, CT	HSOB 706	Rick Scott, FL	HSOB 502
Mazie Hirono, HI	HSOB 109	Tommy Tuberville, AL	RSOB 142
Gary Peters, MI	HSOB 724	Eric Schmitt, MO	RSOB B11
Jack Reed, RI	HSOB 728	Roger Wicker, MS	DSOB 555

STRATEGIC FORCES
Room: RSOB 228
Phone: 202.224.3871

Majority:		Minority:	
Kirsten Gillibrand, NY	RSOB 478	**RM: Deb Fischer, NE**	RSOB 454
Elizabeth Warren, MA	HSOB 309	Tom Cotton, AR	RSOB 326
Joe Manchin, WV	HSOB 306	Mike Rounds, SD	HSOB 716
Jacky Rosen, NV		Kevin Cramer, ND	HSOB 330
Mark Kelly, AZ	HSOB 516	Tommy Tuberville, AL	RSOB 142
Jack Reed, RI	HSOB 728	Roger Wicker, MS	DSOB 555

BANKING, HOUSING & URBAN AFFAIRS

Room: DSOB 534
Website: www.banking.senate.gov
Phone: 202.224.7391
Ratio: 12 Democrats/11 Republicans
Subcommittees: 5

Majority:		Minority:	
C: Sherrod Brown, OH	HSOB 503	**RM: Tim Scott, SC**	HSOB 104
Jack Reed, RI	HSOB 728	Mike Crapo, ID	DSOB 239
Bob Menendez, NJ	HSOB 528	Mike Rounds, SD	HSOB 716
Jon Tester, MT	HSOB 311	Thom Tillis, NC	DSOB 113
Mark Warner, VA	HSOB 703	John Kennedy, LA	RSOB 416
Elizabeth Warren, MA	HSOB 309	Bill Hagerty, TN	RSOB 248
Chris Van Hollen, MD	HSOB 110	Cynthia Lummis, WY	RSOB 124
Catherine Cortez Masto, NV	HSOB 313	J.D. Vance, OH	DSOB B40
		Katie Britt, AL	DSOB B40
Tina Smith, MN	HSOB 720	Kevin Cramer, ND	HSOB 3
Kyrsten Sinema, AZ	HSOB 317	Steve Daines, MT	HSOB
Raphael Warnock, GA	RSOB 388		
John Fetterman, PA	DSOB B40B		

Majority CoS: Laura Swanson   **Minority CoS:** Lila Nieves-Lee
——————————— Subcommittees ———————————

ECONOMIC POLICY
Room: RSOB 124
Phone: 202.224.2353

Majority:		Minority:	
C: Elizabeth Warren, MA	HSOB 309	**RM: John Kennedy, LA**	RSOB 416
Jack Reed, RI	HSOB 728	Mike Rounds, SD	HSOB 716
Bob Menendez, NJ	HSOB 528	Thom Tillis, NC	DSOB 113
Chris Van Hollen, MD	HSOB 110	Cynthia Lummis, WY	RSOB 124
Tina Smith, MN	HSOB 720	Steve Daines, MT	HSOB 320
John Fetterman, PA	DSOB B40B	Tim Scott, SC	HSOB 104
Sherrod Brown, OH	HSOB 503		

FINANCIAL INSTITUTIONS & CONSUMER PROTECTION
Room: HSOB 104
Phone: 202.224.6121

Majority:		Minority:	
C: Raphael Warnock, GA	RSOB 388	**RM: Thom Tillis, NC**	DSOB 113
Mark Warner, VA	HSOB 703	Mike Crapo, ID	DSOB 239
Chris Van Hollen, MD	HSOB 110	Cynthia Lummis, WY	RSOB 124
Catherine Cortez Masto, NV	HSOB 313	J.D. Vance, OH	DSOB B40C
		Katie Britt, AL	DSOB B40A
Tina Smith, MN	HSOB 720	Kevin Cramer, ND	HSOB 330
John Fetterman, PA	DSOB B40B	Tim Scott, SC	HSOB 104
Sherrod Brown, OH	HSOB 503		

HOUSING, TRANSPORTATION & COMMUNITY DEVELOPMENT
Room: RSOB 455
Phone: 202.224.3521

Majority:		Minority:	
C: Tina Smith, MN	HSOB 720	**RM: Cynthia Lummis, WY**	RSOB 124
Jack Reed, RI	HSOB 728	Mike Crapo, ID	DSOB 239
Bob Menendez, NJ	HSOB 528	Mike Rounds, SD	HSOB 716
Jon Tester, MT	HSOB 311	John Kennedy, LA	RSOB 416
Catherine Cortez Masto, NV	HSOB 313	Bill Hagerty, TN	RSOB 248
		J.D. Vance, OH	DSOB B40C
Kyrsten Sinema, AZ	HSOB 317	Katie Britt, AL	DSOB B40A
Raphael Warnock, GA	RSOB 388	Tim Scott, SC	HSOB 104
John Fetterman, PA	DSOB B40B		
Sherrod Brown, OH	HSOB 503		

NATIONAL SECURITY & INTERNATIONAL TRADE & FINANCE
Room: RSOB 136
Phone: 202.224.4224

Majority:		Minority:	
C: Mark Warner, VA	HSOB 703	**RM: Bill Hagerty, TN**	RSOB 248
Jon Tester, MT	HSOB 311	Katie Britt, AL	DSOB B40A
Chris Van Hollen, MD	HSOB 110	Kevin Cramer, ND	HSOB 330
Catherine Cortez Masto, NV	HSOB 313	Steve Daines, MT	HSOB 320
		Tim Scott, SC	HSOB 104
Kyrsten Sinema, AZ	HSOB 317		
Sherrod Brown, OH	HSOB 503		

SECURITIES, INSURANCE & INVESTMENT
Room: RSOB 248
Phone: 202.224.4254

Majority:		Minority:	
C: Bob Menendez, NJ	HSOB 528	**RM: Mike Rounds, SD**	HSOB 716
Jack Reed, RI	HSOB 728	Mike Crapo, ID	DSOB 239
Jon Tester, MT	HSOB 311	Thom Tillis, NC	DSOB 113
Mark Warner, VA	HSOB 703	John Kennedy, LA	RSOB 416
Elizabeth Warren, MA	HSOB 309	Bill Hagerty, TN	RSOB 248
Kyrsten Sinema, AZ	HSOB 317	J.D. Vance, OH	DSOB B40C
Raphael Warnock, GA	RSOB 388	Tim Scott, SC	HSOB 104
Sherrod Brown, OH	HSOB 503		

BUDGET

Room: DSOB 624
Website: www.budget.senate.gov
Phone: 202.224.0642
10 Democrats/10 Republicans
Subcommittees: 0

Majority:		Minority:	
C: Sheldon Whitehouse,	HSOB 530	**RM: Chuck Grassley, IA**	HSOB 135
		Mike Crapo, ID	DSOB 239
Bernie Sanders, VT	DSOB 332	Lindsey Graham, SC	RSOB 290

SENATE CO...

Patty Murray, WA	RSOB 154	Ron Johnson, WI	HSOB 328
Ron Wyden, OR	DSOB 221	Mitt Romney, UT	RSOB 354
Debbie Stabenow, MI	HSOB 731	Roger Marshall, KS	RSOB 479A
Mark Warner, VA	HSOB 703	Mike Braun, IN	RSOB 404
Jeff Merkley, OR	HSOB 531	John Kennedy, LA	RSOB 416
Tim Kaine, VA	RSOB 231	Rick Scott, FL	HSOB 502
Chris Van Hollen, MD	HSOB 110	Mike Lee, UT	RSOB 363
Ben Ray Luján, NM	RSOB 498		
Alex Padilla, CA	HSOB 112		

Majority CoS: Mike Jones   **Minority CoS:** Matthew Giroux

COMMERCE, SCIENCE & TRANSPORTATION

Room: RSOB 253
Website: www.commerce.senate.gov
Phone: 202.224.0411
Ratio: 14 Democrats/13 Republicans
Subcommittees: 7

Majority:		Minority:	
C: Maria Cantwell, WA	HSOB 511	**RM: Ted Cruz, TX**	RSOB 127A
Amy Klobuchar, MN	DSOB 425	John Thune, SD	DSOB 511
Brian Schatz, HI	HSOB 722	Roger Wicker, MS	DSOB 555
Ed Markey, MA	DSOB 255	Deb Fischer, NE	RSOB 454
Gary Peters, MI	HSOB 724	Jerry Moran, KS	DSOB 521
Tammy Baldwin, WI	HSOB 709	Dan Sullivan, AK	HSOB 302
Tammy Duckworth, IL	HSOB 524	Marsha Blackburn, TN	DSOB 357
Jon Tester, MT	HSOB 311	Todd Young, IN	DSOB 185
Kyrsten Sinema, AZ	HSOB 317	Ted Budd, NC	RSOB B85
Jacky Rosen, NV		Eric Schmitt, MO	RSOB B11
Ben Ray Luján, NM	RSOB 498	J.D. Vance, OH	DSOB B40C
John Hickenlooper, CO	RSOB 374	Shelley Capito, WV	RSOB 172
Raphael Warnock, GA	RSOB 388	Cynthia Lummis, WY	RSOB 124
Peter Welch, VT	DSOB G12		

Majority CoS: Lila H. Helms   **Minority CoS:** Brad Grantz

———————— Subcommittees ————————

AVIATION SAFETY, OPERATIONS & INNOVATIONS
Room: RSOB 253
Phone: 202.224.0411

Majority:		Minority:	
C: Tammy Duckworth, IL	HSOB 524	**RM: John Thune, SD**	DSOB 511
Jon Tester, MT	HSOB 311	Jerry Moran, KS	DSOB 521
Jacky Rosen, NV		Shelley Capito, WV	RSOB 172
John Hickenlooper, CO	RSOB 374		
Raphael Warnock, GA	RSOB 388		

COMMUNICATIONS, MEDIA & BROADBAND
Room: RSOB 253
Phone: 202.224.0411

Majority:		Minority:	
C: Ben Ray Luján, NM	RSOB 498	**RM: John Thune, SD**	DSOB 511
Ed Markey, MA	DSOB 255	Jerry Moran, KS	DSOB 521
Gary Peters, MI	HSOB 724	Cynthia Lummis, WY	RSOB 124
Tammy Baldwin, WI	HSOB 709	Marsha Blackburn, TN	DSOB 357
Jon Tester, MT	HSOB 311	Todd Young, IN	DSOB 185
Amy Klobuchar, MN	DSOB 425	Deb Fischer, NE	RSOB 454
Brian Schatz, HI	HSOB 722	Dan Sullivan, AK	HSOB 302
Tammy Duckworth, IL	HSOB 524		
Kyrsten Sinema, AZ	HSOB 317		
Jacky Rosen, NV			
John Hickenlooper, CO	RSOB 374		
Raphael Warnock, GA	RSOB 388		

CONSUMER PROTECTION, PRODUCT SAFETY & DATA SECURITY
Room: RSOB 253
Phone: 202.224.0411

Majority:		Minority:	
C: John Hickenlooper, CO	RSOB 374	**RM: Marsha Blackburn,**	DSOB 35
Ed Markey, MA	DSOB 255	**TN**	
Tammy Baldwin, WI	HSOB 709	Jerry Moran, KS	DSOB
Amy Klobuchar, MN	DSOB 425	John Thune, SD	DSOB
Ben Ray Luján, NM	RSOB 498	Todd Young, IN	DSO
Brian Schatz, HI	HSOB 722		

OCEANS, FISHERIES, CLIMATE CHANGE & MANUFACTURING
Room: RSOB 253
Phone: 202.224.0411

Majority:		Minority:	
C: Tammy Baldwin, WI	HSOB 709	**RM: Dan Sullivan, AK**	

Ed Markey, MA	DSOB 255	Marsha Blackburn, TN	DSOB 357
Gary Peters, MI	HSOB 724	Todd Young, IN	DSOB 185
Ben Ray Luján, NM	RSOB 498	Deb Fischer, NE	RSOB 454
Brian Schatz, HI	HSOB 722		

SPACE & SCIENCE
Room: RSOB 253
Phone: 202.224.0411

Majority:		Minority:	
C: Kyrsten Sinema, AZ	HSOB 317	**RM: Eric Schmitt, MO**	RSOB B11
Ed Markey, MA	DSOB 255	Jerry Moran, KS	DSOB 521
Gary Peters, MI	HSOB 724	Todd Young, IN	DSOB 185
Ben Ray Luján, NM	RSOB 498	Deb Fischer, NE	RSOB 454
Raphael Warnock, GA	RSOB 388		

SURFACE TRANSPORTATION, MARITIME FREIGHT & PORTS
Room: RSOB 253
Phone: 202.224.0411

Majority:		Minority:	
Todd Young, IN	DSOB 185	Gary Peters, MI	HSOB 724
Cynthia Lummis, WY	RSOB 124	Ed Markey, MA	DSOB 255
Shelley Capito, WV	RSOB 172	Tammy Baldwin, WI	HSOB 709
John Thune, SD	DSOB 511	Jon Tester, MT	HSOB 311
Dan Sullivan, AK	HSOB 302	Amy Klobuchar, MN	DSOB 425
		Brian Schatz, HI	HSOB 722
		Tammy Duckworth, IL	HSOB 524
		Raphael Warnock, GA	RSOB 388

TOURISM, TRADE & EXPORT PROMOTION
Room: RSOB 253
Phone: 202.224.0411

Majority:		Minority:	
C: Jacky Rosen, NV		**RM: Ted Budd, NC**	RSOB B85
Jon Tester, MT	HSOB 311	Cynthia Lummis, WY	RSOB 124
Amy Klobuchar, MN	DSOB 425	Shelley Capito, WV	RSOB 172
Tammy Duckworth, IL	HSOB 524	Marsha Blackburn, TN	DSOB 357
Kyrsten Sinema, AZ	HSOB 317	Dan Sullivan, AK	HSOB 302
John Hickenlooper, CO	RSOB 374		

ENERGY & NATURAL RESOURCES

Room: DSOB 304
Website: www.energy.senate.gov
Phone: 202.224.4971
Ratio: 8 Democrats/9 Republicans
Subcommittees: 4

Majority:		Minority:	
C: Joe Manchin, WV	HSOB 306	**RM: John Barrasso, WY**	DSOB 307
Bernie Sanders, VT	DSOB 332	James Risch, ID	RSOB 483
Angus King, ME	HSOB 133	Mike Lee, UT	RSOB 363
Ron Wyden, OR	DSOB 221	Steve Daines, MT	HSOB 320
Maria Cantwell, WA	HSOB 511	Lisa Murkowski, AK	HSOB 522
Martin Heinrich, NM	HSOB 303	John Hoeven, ND	RSOB 338
Mazie Hirono, HI	HSOB 109	Bill Cassidy, LA	HSOB 520
Catherine Cortez Masto, NV	HSOB 313	Cindy Hyde-Smith, MS	HSOB 702
Mark Kelly, AZ	HSOB 516	Josh Hawley, MO	RSOB 115
John Hickenlooper, CO	RSOB 374		

Majority CoS: Renae Black

Minority CoS: Richard Russell

———————————— Subcommittees ————————————

ENERGY
Room: DSOB 304
Phone: 202.224.4971

Majority:		Minority:	
C: Mazie Hirono, HI	HSOB 109	**RM: John Hoeven, ND**	RSOB 338
Bernie Sanders, VT	DSOB 332	James Risch, ID	RSOB 483
Ron Wyden, OR	DSOB 221	Bill Cassidy, LA	HSOB 520
Martin Heinrich, NM	HSOB 303	Lisa Murkowski, AK	HSOB 522
Angus King, ME	HSOB 133	Cindy Hyde-Smith, MS	HSOB 702
Catherine Cortez Masto, NV	HSOB 313		
John Hickenlooper, CO	RSOB 374		

NATIONAL PARKS
Room: DSOB 304
Phone: 202.224.4971

Majority:		Minority:	
Angus King, ME	HSOB 133	**RM: Steve Daines, MT**	HSOB 320

Mazie Hirono, HI	HSOB 109	Lisa Murkowski, AK	HSOB 522
Martin Heinrich, NM	HSOB 303	John Hoeven, ND	RSOB 338
		Mike Lee, UT	RSOB 363

PUBLIC LANDS, FORESTS & MINING
Room: DSOB 304
Phone: 202.224.4971

Majority:		Minority:	
C: Catherine Cortez Masto, NV	HSOB 313	**RM: Mike Lee, UT**	RSOB 363
		James Risch, ID	RSOB 483
Mazie Hirono, HI	HSOB 109	Bill Cassidy, LA	HSOB 520
Ron Wyden, OR	DSOB 221	Lisa Murkowski, AK	HSOB 522
Martin Heinrich, NM	HSOB 303	Steve Daines, MT	HSOB 320
Angus King, ME	HSOB 133	Cindy Hyde-Smith, MS	HSOB 702
John Hickenlooper, CO	RSOB 374		

WATER & POWER
Room: DSOB 304
Phone: 202.224.4971

Majority:		Minority:	
C: Ron Wyden, OR	DSOB 221	**RM: Cindy Hyde-Smith, MS**	HSOB 702
John Hickenlooper, CO	RSOB 374		
Catherine Cortez Masto, NV	HSOB 313	James Risch, ID	RSOB 483
		John Hoeven, ND	RSOB 338
		Mike Lee, UT	RSOB 363

ENVIRONMENT & PUBLIC WORKS
Room: DSOB 410
Website: www.epw.senate.gov
Phone: 202.224.8832
Ratio: 9 Democrats/9 Republicans
Subcommittees: 4

Majority:		Minority:	
C: Tom Carper, DE	HSOB 513	**RM: Shelley Capito, WV**	RSOB 172
Bernie Sanders, VT	DSOB 332	Kevin Cramer, ND	HSOB 330
Ben Cardin, MD	HSOB 509	Cynthia Lummis, WY	RSOB 124
Sheldon Whitehouse, RI	HSOB 530	Markwayne Mullin, OK	RSOB B33
Jeff Merkley, OR	HSOB 531	Pete Ricketts, NE	DSOB 40D
Ed Markey, MA	DSOB 255	John Boozman, AR	HSOB 141
Debbie Stabenow, MI	HSOB 731	Roger Wicker, MS	DSOB 555
Mark Kelly, AZ	HSOB 516	Dan Sullivan, AK	HSOB 302
Alex Padilla, CA	HSOB 112	Lindsey Graham, SC	RSOB 290
John Fetterman, PA	DSOB B40B		

Majority CoS: Courtney O'Hara Taylor   **Minority CoS:** Adam Tomlinson

———————————— Subcommittees ————————————

CHEM SAFETY, WASTE MNGMNT, ENVIRO JUSTICE & REG OVERSIGHT
Room: HSOB Suite 502
Phone: 202.224.5842

Majority:		Minority:	
C: Jeff Merkley, OR	HSOB 531	**RM: Markwayne Mullin, OK**	RSOB B33
Sheldon Whitehouse, RI	HSOB 530		
Ed Markey, MA	DSOB 255	John Boozman, AR	HSOB 141
John Fetterman, PA	DSOB B40B	Roger Wicker, MS	DSOB 555
		Dan Sullivan, AK	HSOB 302

CLEAN AIR, CLIMATE & NUCLEAR SAFETY
Room: RSOB B-85
Phone: 202.224.4814

Majority:		Minority:	
C: Ed Markey, MA	DSOB 255	**RM: Pete Ricketts, NE**	DSOB 40D
Ben Cardin, MD	HSOB 509	Kevin Cramer, ND	HSOB 330
Sheldon Whitehouse, RI	HSOB 530	Cynthia Lummis, WY	RSOB 124
Jeff Merkley, OR	HSOB 531	Markwayne Mullin, OK	RSOB B33
Debbie Stabenow, MI	HSOB 731	Roger Wicker, MS	DSOB 555
Mark Kelly, AZ	HSOB 516	Dan Sullivan, AK	HSOB 302
Alex Padilla, CA	HSOB 112	Lindsey Graham, SC	RSOB 290

FISHERIES, WATER, AND WILDLIFE
Room: DSOB B40C
Phone: 202.224.2043

Majority:		Minority:	
C: Alex Padilla, CA	HSOB 112	**RM: Cynthia Lummis, WY**	RSOB 124
Ben Cardin, MD	HSOB 509	Kevin Cramer, ND	HSOB 330
Sheldon Whitehouse, RI	HSOB 530	Pete Ricketts, NE	DSOB 40D
Ed Markey, MA	DSOB 255	John Boozman, AR	HSOB 141
Debbie Stabenow, MI	HSOB 731	Dan Sullivan, AK	HSOB 302

Mark Kelly, AZ	HSOB 516		

TRANSPORTATION & INFRASTRUCTURE
Room: RSOB 172
Phone: 202.224.6472

Majority:		Minority:	
C: Mark Kelly, AZ	HSOB 516	**RM: Kevin Cramer, ND**	HSOB 330
Ben Cardin, MD	HSOB 509	Cynthia Lummis, WY	RSOB 124
Jeff Merkley, OR	HSOB 531	Markwayne Mullin, OK	RSOB B33
Ed Markey, MA	DSOB 255	Pete Ricketts, NE	DSOB 40D
Debbie Stabenow, MI	HSOB 731	John Boozman, AR	HSOB 141
Alex Padilla, CA	HSOB 112	Roger Wicker, MS	DSOB 555
John Fetterman, PA	DSOB B40B	Lindsey Graham, SC	RSOB 290

FINANCE

Room: DSOB 219
Website: finance.senate.gov
Phone: 202.224.4515
Ratio: 14 Democrats/13 Republicans
Subcommittees: 6

Majority:		Minority:	
C: Ron Wyden, OR	DSOB 221	**RM: Mike Crapo, ID**	DSOB 239
Debbie Stabenow, MI	HSOB 731	Chuck Grassley, IA	HSOB 135
Maria Cantwell, WA	HSOB 511	John Cornyn, TX	HSOB 517
Bob Menendez, NJ	HSOB 528	John Thune, SD	DSOB 511
Tom Carper, DE	HSOB 513	Tim Scott, SC	HSOB 104
Ben Cardin, MD	HSOB 509	Bill Cassidy, LA	HSOB 520
Sherrod Brown, OH	HSOB 503	James Lankford, OK	HSOB 316
Michael Bennet, CO	RSOB 261	Steve Daines, MT	HSOB 320
Bob Casey, PA	RSOB 393	Todd Young, IN	DSOB 185
Mark Warner, VA	HSOB 703	John Barrasso, WY	DSOB 307
Sheldon Whitehouse, RI	HSOB 530	Thom Tillis, NC	DSOB 113
Maggie Hassan, NH	HSOB 324	Ron Johnson, WI	HSOB 328
Catherine Cortez Masto, NV	HSOB 313	Marsha Blackburn, TN	DSOB 357
Elizabeth Warren, MA	HSOB 309		

Majority CoS: Joshua L. Sheinkman   **Minority CoS:** Gregg Richard
——————————————— Subcommittees ———————————————

ENERGY, NATURAL RESOURCES & INFRASTRUCTURE
Room: DSOB 219
Phone: 202.224.4515

Majority:		Minority:	
C: Debbie Stabenow, MI	HSOB 731	**RM: James Lankford, OK**	HSOB 316
Ron Wyden, OR	DSOB 221	John Cornyn, TX	HSOB 517
Tom Carper, DE	HSOB 513	Tim Scott, SC	HSOB 104
Michael Bennet, CO	RSOB 261	Steve Daines, MT	HSOB 320
Sheldon Whitehouse, RI	HSOB 530	John Barrasso, WY	DSOB 307
Catherine Cortez Masto, NV	HSOB 313	Mike Crapo, ID	DSOB 239

FISCAL RESPONSIBILITY & ECONOMIC GROWTH
Room: DSOB 219
Phone: 202.224.4515

Majority:		Minority:	
C: Maggie Hassan, NH	HSOB 324	**RM: Chuck Grassley, IA**	HSOB 135
Ron Wyden, OR	DSOB 221	Mike Crapo, ID	DSOB 239

HEALTH CARE
Room: DSOB 219
Phone: 202.224.4515

Majority:		Minority:	
C: Ben Cardin, MD	HSOB 509	**RM: Steve Daines, MT**	HSOB 320
Ron Wyden, OR	DSOB 221	Chuck Grassley, IA	HSOB 135
Debbie Stabenow, MI	HSOB 731	John Thune, SD	DSOB 511
Bob Menendez, NJ	HSOB 528	Tim Scott, SC	HSOB 104
Tom Carper, DE	HSOB 513	Bill Cassidy, LA	HSOB 520
Bob Casey, PA	RSOB 393	James Lankford, OK	HSOB 316
Mark Warner, VA	HSOB 703	Todd Young, IN	DSOB 185
Sheldon Whitehouse, RI	HSOB 530	John Barrasso, WY	DSOB 307
Maggie Hassan, NH	HSOB 324	Ron Johnson, WI	HSOB 328
Catherine Cortez Masto, NV	HSOB 313	Marsha Blackburn, TN	DSOB 357
		Mike Crapo, ID	DSOB 239
Elizabeth Warren, MA	HSOB 309		

INTERNATIONAL TRADE, CUSTOMS & GLOBAL COMPETITIVENESS
Room: DSOB 219
Phone: 202.224.4515

Majority:		Minority:	
C: Tom Carper, DE	HSOB 513	**RM: John Cornyn, TX**	HSOB 517
Ron Wyden, OR	DSOB 221	John Thune, SD	DSOB 511
Debbie Stabenow, MI	HSOB 731	Tim Scott, SC	HSOB 104
Bob Menendez, NJ	HSOB 528	Bill Cassidy, LA	HSOB 520
Ben Cardin, MD	HSOB 509	Steve Daines, MT	HSOB 320
Sherrod Brown, OH	HSOB 503	Todd Young, IN	DSOB 185
Michael Bennet, CO	RSOB 261	John Barrasso, WY	DSOB 307
Bob Casey, PA	RSOB 393	Ron Johnson, WI	HSOB 328
Mark Warner, VA	HSOB 703	Thom Tillis, NC	DSOB 113
Catherine Cortez Masto, NV	HSOB 313	Mike Crapo, ID	DSOB 239

SOCIAL SECURITY, PENSIONS & FAMILY POLICY
Room: DSOB 219
Phone: 202.224.4515

Majority:		Minority:	
C: Sherrod Brown, OH	HSOB 503	**RM: Thom Tillis, NC**	DSOB 113
Ron Wyden, OR	DSOB 221	Bill Cassidy, LA	HSOB 520
Bob Casey, PA	RSOB 393	Todd Young, IN	DSOB 185
Maggie Hassan, NH	HSOB 324	Marsha Blackburn, TN	DSOB 357
Elizabeth Warren, MA	HSOB 309	Mike Crapo, ID	DSOB 239

TAXATION & IRS OVERSIGHT
Room: DSOB 219
Phone: 202.224.4515

Majority:		Minority:	
C: Michael Bennet, CO	RSOB 261	**RM: John Thune, SD**	DSOB 511
Ron Wyden, OR	DSOB 221	Chuck Grassley, IA	HSOB 135
Bob Menendez, NJ	HSOB 528	John Cornyn, TX	HSOB 517
Ben Cardin, MD	HSOB 509	James Lankford, OK	HSOB 316
Mark Warner, VA	HSOB 703	Ron Johnson, WI	HSOB 328
Sheldon Whitehouse, RI	HSOB 530	Marsha Blackburn, TN	DSOB 357
Elizabeth Warren, MA	HSOB 309	Mike Crapo, ID	DSOB 239

FOREIGN RELATIONS

Room: DSOB 423
Website: www.foreign.senate.gov
Phone: 202.224.4651
Ratio: 11 Democrats/11 Republicans
Subcommittees: 7

Majority:		Minority:	
C: Bob Menendez, NJ	HSOB 528	**RM: James Risch, ID**	RSOB 483
Ben Cardin, MD	HSOB 509	Mike Rounds, SD	HSOB 716
Jeanne Shaheen, NH	HSOB 506	Ron Johnson, WI	HSOB 328
Chris Coons, DE	RSOB 218	J.D. Vance, OH	DSOB B40C
Chris Murphy, CT	HSOB 136	Marco Rubio, FL	RSOB 284
Tim Kaine, VA	RSOB 231	Mitt Romney, UT	RSOB 354
Ed Markey, MA	DSOB 255	Rand Paul, KY	RSOB 167
Jeff Merkley, OR	HSOB 531	Todd Young, IN	DSOB 185
Cory Booker, NJ	HSOB 717	John Barrasso, WY	DSOB 307
Brian Schatz, HI	HSOB 722	Ted Cruz, TX	RSOB 127A
Chris Van Hollen, MD	HSOB 110	Bill Hagerty, TN	RSOB 248

Majority CoS: Damian Murphy   **Minority CoS:** Chris Socha

──────── Subcommittees ────────

AFRICA & GLOBAL HEALTH POLICY
Room: DSOB 423
Phone: 202.224.4651

Majority:		Minority:	
Mike Rounds, SD	HSOB 716	Chris Van Hollen, MD	HSOB 110
John Barrasso, WY	DSOB 307	Jeff Merkley, OR	HSOB 531
Todd Young, IN	DSOB 185	Tim Kaine, VA	RSOB 231
Marco Rubio, FL	RSOB 284	Chris Coons, DE	RSOB 218
Rand Paul, KY	RSOB 167	Cory Booker, NJ	HSOB 717

EAST ASIA, THE PACIFIC & INTERNATIONAL CYBERSECURITY POLICY
Room: DSOB 423
Phone: 202.224.4651

Majority:		Minority:	
Mitt Romney, UT	RSOB 354	Ed Markey, MA	DSOB 255
Mike Rounds, SD	HSOB 716	Jeff Merkley, OR	HSOB 531
Ron Johnson, WI	HSOB 328	Chris Murphy, CT	HSOB 136
Ted Cruz, TX	RSOB 127A	Chris Coons, DE	RSOB 218
Bill Hagerty, TN	RSOB 248	Brian Schatz, HI	HSOB 722

EUROPE & REGIONAL SECURITY COOPERATION
Room: DSOB 423
Phone: 202.224.4651

Majority:		Minority:	
Ron Johnson, WI	HSOB 328	Jeanne Shaheen, NH	HSOB 506
John Barrasso, WY	DSOB 307	Ben Cardin, MD	HSOB 509
Todd Young, IN	DSOB 185	Chris Van Hollen, MD	HSOB 110
Mitt Romney, UT	RSOB 354	Chris Murphy, CT	HSOB 136
J.D. Vance, OH	DSOB B40C	Chris Coons, DE	RSOB 218

INTERNAT'L DEV INSTIT & INTERNAT'L ECON, ENERGY & ENVIRON POLICY
Room: DSOB 423
Phone: 202.224.4651

Majority:		Minority:	
C: Chris Coons, DE	RSOB 218	**RM: J.D. Vance, OH**	DSOB B40C
Ben Cardin, MD	HSOB 509	Todd Young, IN	DSOB 185
Jeanne Shaheen, NH	HSOB 506	Rand Paul, KY	RSOB 167
Brian Schatz, HI	HSOB 722	John Barrasso, WY	DSOB 307
Cory Booker, NJ	HSOB 717	Mike Rounds, SD	HSOB 716

NEAR EAST, SOUTH ASIA, CENTRAL ASIA & COUNTERTERRORISM
Room: DSOB 423
Phone: 202.224.4651

Majority:		Minority:	
C: Chris Murphy, CT	HSOB 136	**RM: Todd Young, IN**	DSOB 185
Ed Markey, MA	DSOB 255	Rand Paul, KY	RSOB 167
Chris Van Hollen, MD	HSOB 110	Ted Cruz, TX	RSOB 127A
Jeanne Shaheen, NH	HSOB 506	Mitt Romney, UT	HSOB 354
Cory Booker, NJ	HSOB 717	Bill Hagerty, TN	RSOB 248

STATE DEPT & USAID MNGMNT, INTERNAT'L OPS & INTERNAT'L DEV
Room: DSOB 423
Phone: 202.224.4651

Majority:		Minority:	
C: Ben Cardin, MD	HSOB 509	**RM: Bill Hagerty, TN**	RSOB 248
Tim Kaine, VA	RSOB 231	Marco Rubio, FL	RSOB 284
Brian Schatz, HI	HSOB 722	Rand Paul, KY	RSOB 167
Chris Murphy, CT	HSOB 136	Ron Johnson, WI	HSOB 328
Ed Markey, MA	DSOB 255	Ted Cruz, TX	RSOB 127A

WEST HEM CRIME CIV SEC DEM RIGHTS & WOMEN'S ISSUES
Room: DSOB 423
Phone: 202.224.4651

Majority:		Minority:	
C: Tim Kaine, VA	RSOB 231	**RM: Marco Rubio, FL**	RSOB 284
Ed Markey, MA	DSOB 255	John Barrasso, WY	DSOB 307
Ben Cardin, MD	HSOB 509	Ted Cruz, TX	RSOB 127A
Jeff Merkley, OR	HSOB 531	Bill Hagerty, TN	RSOB 248
Jeanne Shaheen, NH	HSOB 506	J.D. Vance, OH	DSOB B40C

HEALTH, EDUCATION, LABOR & PENSIONS

Room: DSOB 428
Website: help.senate.gov
Phone: 202.224.0767
Ratio: 10 Democrats/10 Republicans
Subcommittees: 3

Majority:		Minority:	
C: Bernie Sanders, VT	DSOB 332	**RM: Bill Cassidy, LA**	HSOB 520
Patty Murray, WA	RSOB 154	Rand Paul, KY	RSOB 167
Bob Casey, PA	RSOB 393	Susan Collins, ME	DSOB 413
Tammy Baldwin, WI	HSOB 709	Lisa Murkowski, AK	HSOB 522
Chris Murphy, CT	HSOB 136	Mike Braun, IN	RSOB 404
Tim Kaine, VA	RSOB 231	Roger Marshall, KS	RSOB 479A
Maggie Hassan, NH	HSOB 324	Mitt Romney, UT	RSOB 354
Tina Smith, MN	HSOB 720	Tommy Tuberville, AL	RSOB 142
Ben Ray Luján, NM	RSOB 498	Markwayne Mullin, OK	RSOB B33
John Hickenlooper, CO	RSOB 374	Ted Budd, NC	RSOB B85
Ed Markey, MA	DSOB 255		

Majority CoS: Warren Scott Gunnels   **Minority CoS:** David P. Cleary

———————— Subcommittees ————————

CHILDREN & FAMILIES
Room: DSOB 428
Phone: 202.224.5375

Majority:	Minority:

C: Bob Casey, PA	RSOB 393	**RM: Tommy Tuberville, AL**	RSOB 142
Bernie Sanders, VT	DSOB 332	Bill Cassidy, LA	HSOB 520
Chris Murphy, CT	HSOB 136	Lisa Murkowski, AK	HSOB 522
Patty Murray, WA	RSOB 154	Rand Paul, KY	RSOB 167
Tim Kaine, VA	RSOB 231	Markwayne Mullin, OK	RSOB B33
Maggie Hassan, NH	HSOB 324		
Tina Smith, MN	HSOB 720		

EMPLOYMENT & WORKPLACE SAFETY
Room: DSOB 428
Phone: 202.224.5375

Majority:		**Minority:**	
C: John Hickenlooper, CO	RSOB 374	**RM: Mike Braun, IN**	RSOB 404
Tammy Baldwin, WI	HSOB 709	Roger Marshall, KS	RSOB 479A
Bob Casey, PA	RSOB 393	Ted Budd, NC	RSOB B85
Ben Ray Luján, NM	RSOB 498	Mitt Romney, UT	RSOB 354
Bernie Sanders, VT	DSOB 332		

PRIMARY HEALTH & RETIREMENT SECURITY
Room: DSOB 428
Phone: 202.224.5375

Majority:		**Minority:**	
C: Ed Markey, MA	DSOB 255	**RM: Roger Marshall, KS**	RSOB 479A
Tammy Baldwin, WI	HSOB 709	Susan Collins, ME	DSOB 413
Ben Ray Luján, NM	RSOB 498	Rand Paul, KY	RSOB 167
Patty Murray, WA	RSOB 154	Markwayne Mullin, OK	RSOB B33
Maggie Hassan, NH	HSOB 324	Mike Braun, IN	RSOB 404
Bernie Sanders, VT	DSOB 332	Bill Cassidy, LA	HSOB 520

HOMELAND SECURITY & GOVERNMENT AFFAIRS

Room: DSOB 340
Website: www.hsgac.senate.gov
Phone: 202.224.2627
Ratio: 8 Democrats/7 Republicans
Subcommittees: 3

Majority:		**Minority:**	
C: Gary Peters, MI	HSOB 724	**RM: Rand Paul, KY**	RSOB 167
Tom Carper, DE	HSOB 513	Ron Johnson, WI	HSOB 328
Maggie Hassan, NH	HSOB 324	James Lankford, OK	HSOB 316
Kyrsten Sinema, AZ	HSOB 317	Mitt Romney, UT	RSOB 354
Jacky Rosen, NV		Rick Scott, FL	HSOB 502
Alex Padilla, CA	HSOB 112	Josh Hawley, MO	RSOB 115
Jon Ossoff, GA	RSOB 455	Roger Marshall, KS	RSOB 479A
Richard Blumenthal, CT	HSOB 706		

Majority CoS: David Weinberg   **Minority CoS:** Pam Thiessen
Majority Sched: April Beasley

———————————— Subcommittees ————————————

EMERGING THREATS & SPENDING OVERSIGHT
Room: DSOB 348
Phone: 202.224.7155

Majority:		**Minority:**	
Mitt Romney, UT	RSOB 354	Maggie Hassan, NH	HSOB 324
James Lankford, OK	HSOB 316	Kyrsten Sinema, AZ	HSOB 317
Rick Scott, FL	HSOB 502	Jacky Rosen, NV	
Rand Paul, KY	RSOB 167	Jon Ossoff, GA	RSOB 455
		Gary Peters, MI	HSOB 724

GOVERNMENT OPERATIONS & BORDER MANAGEMENT
Room: HSOB 601
Phone: 202.224.4551

Majority:		**Minority:**	
James Lankford, OK	HSOB 316	Kyrsten Sinema, AZ	HSOB 317
Ron Johnson, WI	HSOB 328	Tom Carper, DE	HSOB 513
Mitt Romney, UT	RSOB 354	Alex Padilla, CA	HSOB 112
Rand Paul, KY	RSOB 167	Richard Blumenthal, CT	HSOB 706
		Gary Peters, MI	HSOB 724

INVESTIGATIONS
Room: RSOB 199
Phone: 202.224.3721

Majority:		**Minority:**	
C: Richard Blumenthal, CT	HSOB 706	**RM: Ron Johnson, WI**	HSOB 328
		Rick Scott, FL	HSOB 502
Tom Carper, DE	HSOB 513	Josh Hawley, MO	RSOB 115
Maggie Hassan, NH	HSOB 324	Roger Marshall, KS	RSOB 479A
Alex Padilla, CA	HSOB 112	Rand Paul, KY	RSOB 167
Jon Ossoff, GA	RSOB 455		

| Gary Peters, MI | HSOB 724 |

INDIAN AFFAIRS

Room: HSOB 838
Website: indian.senate.gov
Phone: 202.224.2251
Ratio: 6 Democrats/5 Republicans
Subcommittees: 0

Majority:		Minority:	
C: Brian Schatz, HI	HSOB 722	RM: Lisa Murkowski, AK	HSOB 522
Maria Cantwell, WA	HSOB 511	John Hoeven, ND	RSOB 338
Jon Tester, MT	HSOB 311	Steve Daines, MT	HSOB 320
Catherine Cortez Masto, NV	HSOB 313	Markwayne Mullin, OK	RSOB B33
		Mike Rounds, SD	HSOB 716
Tina Smith, MN	HSOB 720		
Ben Ray Luján, NM	RSOB 498		

Majority CoS: Jennifer Romero   **Minority CoS:** Amber Ebarb

JUDICIARY

Room: DSOB 224
Website: judiciary.senate.gov
Phone: 202.224.7703
Ratio: 11 Democrats/11 Republicans
Subcommittees: 8

Majority:		Minority:	
C: Dick Durbin, IL	HSOB 711	RM: Chuck Grassley, IA	HSOB 135
Dianne Feinstein, CA	HSOB 331	John Cornyn, TX	HSOB 517
Sheldon Whitehouse, RI	HSOB 530	Lindsey Graham, SC	RSOB 290
Amy Klobuchar, MN	DSOB 105	Mike Lee, UT	RSOB 363
Chris Coons, DE	RSOB 218	Ted Cruz, TX	RSOB 127A
Richard Blumenthal, CT	HSOB 706	Josh Hawley, MO	RSOB 115
Mazie Hirono, HI	HSOB 109	Tom Cotton, AR	RSOB 326
Cory Booker, NJ	HSOB 717	Pete Ricketts, NE	DSOB 40D
Alex Padilla, CA	HSOB 112	John Kennedy, LA	RSOB 416
Jon Ossoff, GA	RSOB 455	Thom Tillis, NC	DSOB 113
Peter Welch, VT	DSOB G12	Marsha Blackburn, TN	DSOB 357

Majority CoS: Joseph R. Zogby   **Minority CoS:** Kolan L. Davis

——————— Subcommittees ———————

COMPETITION POLICY, ANTITRUST & CONSUMER RIGHTS
Room: DSOB 425
Phone: 202.224.3244

Majority:		Minority:	
C: Amy Klobuchar, MN	DSOB 425	RM: Mike Lee, UT	RSOB 363
Jon Ossoff, GA	RSOB 455	Marsha Blackburn, TN	DSOB 357
Peter Welch, VT	DSOB G12	Tom Cotton, AR	RSOB 326
Richard Blumenthal, CT	HSOB 706	Thom Tillis, NC	DSOB 113
Cory Booker, NJ	HSOB 717	Josh Hawley, MO	RSOB 115

CONSTITUTION
Room: HSOB 713
Phone: 202.224.6361

Majority:		Minority:	
C: Richard Blumenthal, CT	HSOB 706	RM: Ted Cruz, TX	RSOB 127A
		John Cornyn, TX	HSOB 517
Jon Ossoff, GA	RSOB 455	Mike Lee, UT	RSOB 363
Sheldon Whitehouse, RI	HSOB 530	Pete Ricketts, NE	DSOB 40D
Dianne Feinstein, CA	HSOB 331		

CRIMINAL JUSTICE & COUNTERTERRORISM
Room: DSOB 152
Phone: 202.224.2921

Majority:		Minority:	
C: Cory Booker, NJ	HSOB 717	RM: Tom Cotton, AR	RSOB 326
Jon Ossoff, GA	RSOB 455	John Cornyn, TX	HSOB 517
Sheldon Whitehouse, RI	HSOB 530	Lindsey Graham, SC	RSOB 290
Dianne Feinstein, CA	HSOB 331	Mike Lee, UT	RSOB 363
Peter Welch, VT	DSOB G12	Ted Cruz, TX	RSOB 127A
Amy Klobuchar, MN	DSOB 425	John Kennedy, LA	RSOB 416
Alex Padilla, CA	HSOB 112	Josh Hawley, MO	RSOB 115

FEDERAL COURTS, OVERSIGHT, AGENCY ACTION & FEDERAL RIGHTS
Room: HSOB 706
Phone: 202.224.2823

Majority:		Minority:	
		RM: John Kennedy, LA	RSOB 416

C: Sheldon Whitehouse, RI	HSOB 530	Lindsey Graham, SC	RSOB 290
		Mike Lee, UT	RSOB 363
Jon Ossoff, GA	RSOB 455	Ted Cruz, TX	RSOB 127A
Mazie Hirono, HI	HSOB 109	Thom Tillis, NC	DSOB 113
Peter Welch, VT	DSOB G12	Pete Ricketts, NE	DSOB 40D
Cory Booker, NJ	HSOB 717		
Alex Padilla, CA	HSOB 112		

HUMAN RIGHTS & THE LAW
Room: DSOB 224
Phone: 202.224.3841

Majority:		Minority:	
C: Dianne Feinstein, CA	HSOB 331	**RM: Josh Hawley, MO**	RSOB 115
Chris Coons, DE	RSOB 218	John Kennedy, LA	RSOB 416
Richard Blumenthal, CT	HSOB 706	Pete Ricketts, NE	DSOB 40D

IMMIGRATION, CITIZENSHIP & BORDER SECURITY
Room: DSOB 224
Phone: 202.224.6991

Majority:		Minority:	
C: Alex Padilla, CA	HSOB 112	**RM: John Cornyn, TX**	HSOB 517
Dianne Feinstein, CA	HSOB 331	Marsha Blackburn, TN	DSOB 357
Mazie Hirono, HI	HSOB 109	Lindsey Graham, SC	RSOB 290
Amy Klobuchar, MN	DSOB 425	Tom Cotton, AR	RSOB 326
Chris Coons, DE	RSOB 218	Ted Cruz, TX	RSOB 127A
Richard Blumenthal, CT	HSOB 706	Thom Tillis, NC	DSOB 113
Cory Booker, NJ	HSOB 717	John Kennedy, LA	RSOB 416

PRIVACY, TECHNOLOGY & THE LAW
Room: DSOB 224
Phone: 202.224.5042

Majority:		Minority:	
C: Chris Coons, DE	RSOB 218	**RM: Pete Ricketts, NE**	DSOB 40D
Jon Ossoff, GA	RSOB 455	Marsha Blackburn, TN	DSOB 357
Sheldon Whitehouse, RI	HSOB 530	Lindsey Graham, SC	RSOB 290
Mazie Hirono, HI	HSOB 109	John Kennedy, LA	RSOB 416
Amy Klobuchar, MN	DSOB 425	Josh Hawley, MO	RSOB 115

SUBCOMMITTEE ON INTELLECTUAL PROPERTY
Room: RSOB 127A
Phone: 202.224.5042

Majority:		Minority:	
C: Peter Welch, VT	DSOB G12	**RM: Thom Tillis, NC**	DSOB 113
Mazie Hirono, HI	HSOB 109	Marsha Blackburn, TN	DSOB 357
Chris Coons, DE	RSOB 218	John Cornyn, TX	HSOB 517
Alex Padilla, CA	HSOB 112	Tom Cotton, AR	RSOB 326

RULES & ADMINISTRATION
Room: RSOB 305
Website: www.rules.senate.gov
Phone: 202.224.6352
Ratio: 9 Democrats/8 Republicans
Subcommittees: 0

Majority:		Minority:	
C: Amy Klobuchar, MN	DSOB 425	**RM: Deb Fischer, NE**	RSOB 454
Dianne Feinstein, CA	HSOB 331	Mitch McConnell, KY	RSOB 317
Chuck Schumer, NY	HSOB 322	Ted Cruz, TX	RSOB 127A
Mark Warner, VA	HSOB 703	Shelley Capito, WV	RSOB 172
Jeff Merkley, OR	HSOB 531	Roger Wicker, MS	DSOB 555
Alex Padilla, CA	HSOB 112	Cindy Hyde-Smith, MS	HSOB 702
Jon Ossoff, GA	RSOB 455	Bill Hagerty, TN	RSOB 248
Michael Bennet, CO	RSOB 261	Katie Britt, AL	DSOB B40A
Peter Welch, VT	DSOB G12		

Majority CoS: Elizabeth Peluso   **Minority CoS:** Rachelle G. Schroeder

SMALL BUSINESS & ENTREPRENEURSHIP
Room: RSOB 428A
Website: www.sbc.senate.gov
Phone: 202.224.5175
Ratio: 10 Democrats/9 Republicans
Subcommittees: 0

Majority:		Minority:	
C: Ben Cardin, MD	HSOB 509	**RM: Joni Ernst, IA**	HSOB 730
Maria Cantwell, WA	HSOB 511	Marco Rubio, FL	RSOB 284
Jeanne Shaheen, NH	HSOB 506	James Risch, ID	RSOB 483
Ed Markey, MA	DSOB 255	Rand Paul, KY	RSOB 167
Cory Booker, NJ	HSOB 717	Tim Scott, SC	HSOB 104

Chris Coons, DE	RSOB 218	Todd Young, IN	DSOB 185
Mazie Hirono, HI	HSOB 109	John Kennedy, LA	RSOB 416
Tammy Duckworth, IL	HSOB 524	Josh Hawley, MO	RSOB 115
Jacky Rosen, NV		Ted Budd, NC	RSOB B85
John Hickenlooper, CO	RSOB 374		

Majority CoS: Sean Moore   **Minority CoS:** Meredith D. West

VETERANS' AFFAIRS

Room: RSOB 412
Website: veterans.senate.gov
Phone: 202.224.9126
Ratio: 8 Democrats/9 Republicans
Subcommittees: 0

Majority:		**Minority:**	
C: Jon Tester, MT	HSOB 311	RM: Jerry Moran, KS	DSOB 521
Bernie Sanders, VT	DSOB 332	John Boozman, AR	HSOB 141
Angus King, ME	HSOB 133	Bill Cassidy, LA	HSOB 520
Patty Murray, WA	RSOB 154	Mike Rounds, SD	HSOB 716
Sherrod Brown, OH	HSOB 503	Thom Tillis, NC	DSOB 113
Richard Blumenthal, CT	HSOB 706	Dan Sullivan, AK	HSOB 302
Mazie Hirono, HI	HSOB 109	Marsha Blackburn, TN	DSOB 357
Joe Manchin, WV	HSOB 306	Kevin Cramer, ND	HSOB 330
Kyrsten Sinema, AZ	HSOB 317	Tommy Tuberville, AL	RSOB 142
Maggie Hassan, NH	HSOB 324		

Majority CoS: Tony McClain   **Minority CoS:** Jonathan A. Towers

SELECT AND SPECIAL COMMITTEES

AGING

Room: DSOB G-41
Website: www.aging.senate.gov
Phone: 202.224.0185
Ratio: 7 Democrats/6 Republicans
Subcommittees: 0

Majority:		Minority:	
C: Bob Casey, PA	RSOB 393	**RM: Mike Braun, IN**	RSOB 404
Kirsten Gillibrand, NY	RSOB 478	Tim Scott, SC	HSOB 104
Richard Blumenthal, CT	HSOB 706	Marco Rubio, FL	RSOB 284
Elizabeth Warren, MA	HSOB 309	Rick Scott, FL	HSOB 502
Mark Kelly, AZ	HSOB 516	J.D. Vance, OH	DSOB B40C
Raphael Warnock, GA	RSOB 388	Pete Ricketts, NE	DSOB 40D
John Fetterman, PA	DSOB B40B		

Majority CoS: Elizabeth Letter   **Minority CoS:** Neri A. Martinez

ETHICS

Room: HSOB 220
Website: ethics.senate.gov
Phone: 202.224.2981
Ratio: 3 Democrats/3 Republicans
Subcommittees: 0

Majority:		Minority:	
C: Chris Coons, DE	RSOB 218	**RM: James Lankford, OK**	HSOB 316
Brian Schatz, HI	HSOB 722	James Risch, ID	RSOB 483
Jeanne Shaheen, NH	HSOB 506	Deb Fischer, NE	RSOB 454

INTELLIGENCE

Room: HSOB 211
Website: www.intelligence.senate.gov
Phone: 202.224.1700
Ratio: 10 Democrats/8 Republicans
Subcommittees: 0

Majority:		Minority:	
C: Mark Warner, VA	HSOB 703	**RM: Marco Rubio, FL**	RSOB 284
Angus King, ME	HSOB 133	James Risch, ID	RSOB 483
Dianne Feinstein, CA	HSOB 331	Susan Collins, ME	DSOB 413
Ron Wyden, OR	DSOB 221	Tom Cotton, AR	RSOB 326
Martin Heinrich, NM	HSOB 303	John Cornyn, TX	HSOB 517
Michael Bennet, CO	RSOB 261	Jerry Moran, KS	DSOB 521
Bob Casey, PA	RSOB 393	James Lankford, OK	HSOB 316
Kirsten Gillibrand, NY	RSOB 478	Mike Rounds, SD	HSOB 716
Jon Ossoff, GA	RSOB 455		
Jack Reed, RI	HSOB 728		
Chuck Schumer, NY	HSOB 322		

Majority CoS: William Wu   **Minority CoS:** Michael Colin Casey

JOINT COMMITTEES

JOINT CONGRESSIONAL COMMITTEE ON INAUGURAL CEREMONIES

Room: RSOB 260
Website: www.inaugural.senate.gov
Phone: 202.224.5721
Information for this committee, including membership, was not finalized as of the publication date and is therefore subject to change.

JOINT CONGRESSIONAL-EXECUTIVE COMMISSION ON CHINA

Room: FHOB 243
Website: www.cecc.gov
Phone: 202.226.3766

Majority U.S. Senate:		Minority U.S. Senate:	
Co-C: Jeff Merkley, OR	HSOB 531	Information not available as of press time.	
Majority U.S. House:		Minority U.S. House:	
C: Chris Smith, NJ-04	RHOB 2373	RM: Jim McGovern, MA-02	CHOB 370

JOINT CONGRESSIONAL OVERSIGHT COMMISSION

Room: The Capitol ST-76
Website: www.coc.senate.gov
Phone: 202.224.5050
Information for this committee, including membership, was not finalized as of the publication date and is therefore subject to change.

JOINT ECONOMIC

Room: DSOB G-01
Website: www.jec.senate.gov
Phone: 202.224.5171

Majority U.S. Senate:		Minority U.S. Senate:	
C: Martin Heinrich, NM	HSOB 303	Mike Lee, UT	RSOB 363
Amy Klobuchar, MN	DSOB 425	Tom Cotton, AR	RSOB 326
Maggie Hassan, NH	HSOB 324	Eric Schmitt, MO	RSOB B11
Mark Kelly, AZ	HSOB 516	J.D. Vance, OH	DSOB B40C
John Fetterman, PA	DSOB B40B	Mike Crapo, ID	DSOB 239
Ron Wyden, OR	DSOB 221	Chuck Grassley, IA	HSOB 135
Debbie Stabenow, MI	HSOB 731		
Maria Cantwell, WA	HSOB 511		
Majority U.S. House:		**Minority U.S. House:**	
Information not available as of press time.		Information not available as of press time.	
		Minority CoS: Dr. Kevin C. Corinth	

JOINT LIBRARY

Room: LHOB 1309
Website: cha.house.gov
Phone: 202.225.2061
Information for this committee, including membership, was not finalized as of the publication date and is therefore subject to change.

JOINT PRINTING

Room: LHOB 1309
Website: cha.house.gov
Phone: 202.225.2061
Information for this committee, including membership, was not finalized as of the publication date and is therefore subject to change.

JOINT SECURITY & COOPERATION IN EUROPE

Room: FHOB 234
Website: www.csce.gov
Phone: 202.225.1901

Majority U.S. Senate:		Minority U.S. Senate:
Co-C: Ben Cardin, MD	HSOB 509	Information not available as of press time.
Majority U.S. House:		Minority U.S. House:
C: Joe Wilson, SC-02	LHOB 1436	Information not available as of press time.

JOINT TAXATION

Room: FHOB H2-502
Website: www.jct.gov
Phone: 202.225.3621

Majority U.S. Senate:		Minority U.S. Senate:	
Debbie Stabenow, MI	HSOB 731	Mike Crapo, ID	DSOB 239
Ron Wyden, OR	DSOB 221	Chuck Grassley, IA	HSOB 135
Maria Cantwell, WA	HSOB 511		
Majority U.S. House:		**Minority U.S. House:**	
Information not available as of press time.		Information not available as of press time.	

HOUSE COMMITTEES

Committee rosters are listed in order of ranking membership with the Chairman and Ranking Member indicated with "C" and "RM" respectively. The chairman and ranking member of each committee usually have membership status on all subcommittees of which they are not members. This is referred to as ex officio membership. These memberships are subject to the rules of the individual committees.

ADMINISTRATION

Room: LHOB 1216
Website: cha.house.gov
Phone: 202.225.8281
Ratio: 8 Republicans/4 Democrats
Subcommittees: 4

Majority:		Minority:	
C: Bryan Steil, WI-01	LHOB 1526	**RM: Joseph Morelle,**	CHOB 570
Barry Loudermilk, GA-11	RHOB 2133	**NY-25**	
Morgan Griffith, VA-09	RHOB 2202	Terri Sewell, AL-07	LHOB 1035
Gregory Murphy, NC-03	CHOB 407	Derek Kilmer, WA-06	LHOB 1226
Stephanie Bice, OK-05	RHOB 2437	Norma Torres, CA-35	RHOB 2227
Mike Carey, OH-15	LHOB 1433		
Laurel Lee, FL-15	LHOB 1118		
Anthony D'Esposito, NY-04	LHOB 1508		

Majority CoS: Tim Monahan   **Minority CoS:** Jamie Fleet
Majority Sched: Janet G. Schwalb

――――――――――――― Subcommittees ―――――――――――――

COMMUNICATIONS STANDARDS COMMISSION
Room: LHOB 1216
Phone: 202.226.0647

Information for this committee, including membership, was not finalized as of the publication date and is therefore subject to change.

ELECTIONS
Room: LHOB 1216
Phone: 202.225.8281

Majority:		Minority:	
C: Laurel Lee, FL-15	LHOB 1118	**RM: Terri Sewell, AL-07**	LHOB 1035
Barry Loudermilk, GA-11	RHOB 2133	Norma Torres, CA-35	RHOB 2227
Stephanie Bice, OK-05	RHOB 2437		
Anthony D'Esposito, NY-04	LHOB 1508		

MODERNIZATION
Room: LHOB 1216
Phone: 202.225.8281

Majority:		Minority:	
C: Stephanie Bice, OK-05	RHOB 2437	**RM: Derek Kilmer, WA-06**	LHOB 1226
Mike Carey, OH-15	LHOB 1433	Joseph Morelle, NY-25	CHOB 570

OVERSIGHT
Room: LHOB 1216
Phone: 202.225.8281

Majority:		Minority:	
C: Barry Loudermilk,	RHOB 2133	**RM: Norma Torres, CA-35**	RHOB 2227
GA-11		Derek Kilmer, WA-06	LHOB 1226
Morgan Griffith, VA-09	RHOB 2202		
Gregory Murphy, NC-03	CHOB 407		
Anthony D'Esposito, NY-04	LHOB 1508		

AGRICULTURE

Room: LHOB 1301
Website: agriculture.house.gov
Phone: 202.225.2171
Ratio: 18 Republicans/18 Democrats
Subcommittees: 6

Majority:		Minority:	
C: Glenn Thompson,	CHOB 400	**RM: David Scott, GA-13**	CHOB 468
PA-05		Sanford Bishop, GA-02	RHOB 2407
Michael Cloud, TX-27	CHOB 171	Marcy Kaptur, OH-09	RHOB 2186
Troy Balderson, OH-12	RHOB 2429	Ann Kuster, NH-02	RHOB 2201
Michelle Fischbach, MN-07	LHOB 1004	Jimmy Panetta, CA-19	CHOB 304
Austin Scott, GA-08	RHOB 2185	Lou Correa, CA-46	RHOB 2301
Rick Crawford, AR-01	RHOB 2422	Ro Khanna, CA-17	CHOB 306
Scott DesJarlais, TN-04	RHOB 2304	Kim Schrier, WA-08	LHOB 1110
Doug LaMalfa, CA-01	CHOB 408	Jim Costa, CA-21	RHOB 2081

David Rouzer, NC-07	RHOB 2333	Jim McGovern, MA-02	CHOB 370
Trent Kelly, MS-01	RHOB 2243	Alma Adams, NC-12	RHOB 2436
Don Bacon, NE-02	RHOB 2104	Abigail Spanberger, VA-07	CHOB 562
Dusty Johnson, SD-01	LHOB 1714	Jahana Hayes, CT-05	RHOB 2458
Jim Baird, IN-04	RHOB 2303	Shontel Brown, OH-11	CHOB 449
Tracey Mann, KS-01	CHOB 344	Sharice Davids, KS-03	RHOB 2435
Randy Feenstra, IA-04	LHOB 1440	Salud Carbajal, CA-24	RHOB 2331
Mary Miller, IL-15	LHOB 1740	Angie Craig, MN-02	RHOB 2442
Barry Moore, AL-02	LHOB 1504	Chellie Pingree, ME-01	RHOB 2354
Kat Cammack, FL-03	RHOB 2421		

Majority CoS: Parish M. Braden   **Minority CoS:** Anne L. Simmons

───────────── Subcommittees ─────────────

BIOTECHNOLOGY, HORTICULTURE & RESEARCH
Room: LHOB 1301

Majority:		Minority:	
C: Jim Baird, IN-04	RHOB 2303	**RM: Lou Correa, CA-46**	RHOB 2301
Austin Scott, GA-08	RHOB 2185	Salud Carbajal, CA-24	RHOB 2331
Rick Crawford, AR-01	RHOB 2422	Chellie Pingree, ME-01	RHOB 2354
Don Bacon, NE-02	RHOB 2104	Jimmy Panetta, CA-19	CHOB 304
Troy Balderson, OH-12	RHOB 2429	Kim Schrier, WA-08	LHOB 1110
Michelle Fischbach, MN-07	LHOB 1004	Shontel Brown, OH-11	CHOB 449

COMMODITY EXCHANGES, ENERGY & CREDIT
Room: LHOB 1301

Majority:		Minority:	
C: Michelle Fischbach, MN-07	LHOB 1004	**RM: Ro Khanna, CA-17**	CHOB 306
		Ann Kuster, NH-02	RHOB 2201
Austin Scott, GA-08	RHOB 2185	Angie Craig, MN-02	RHOB 2442
Doug LaMalfa, CA-01	CHOB 408		
Michael Cloud, TX-27	CHOB 171		
Troy Balderson, OH-12	RHOB 2429		
Randy Feenstra, IA-04	LHOB 1440		

CONSERVATION & FORESTRY
Room: LHOB 1301

Majority:		Minority:	
C: Doug LaMalfa, CA-01	CHOB 408	**RM: Abigail Spanberger, VA-07**	CHOB 562
Scott DesJarlais, TN-04	RHOB 2304		
Trent Kelly, MS-01	RHOB 2243	Chellie Pingree, ME-01	RHOB 2354
Dusty Johnson, SD-01	LHOB 1714	Ann Kuster, NH-02	RHOB 2201
Barry Moore, AL-02	LHOB 1504	Jimmy Panetta, CA-19	CHOB 304
Mary Miller, IL-15	LHOB 1740	Lou Correa, CA-46	RHOB 2301
		Kim Schrier, WA-08	LHOB 1110

GENERAL FARM COMMODITIES & RISK MANAGEMENT
Room: LHOB 1301

Majority:		Minority:	
C: Austin Scott, GA-08	RHOB 2185	**RM: Sanford Bishop, GA-02**	RHOB 2407
Rick Crawford, AR-01	RHOB 2422		
Tracey Mann, KS-01	CHOB 344	Salud Carbajal, CA-24	RHOB 2331
Mary Miller, IL-15	LHOB 1740	Angie Craig, MN-02	RHOB 2442

LIVESTOCK & FOREIGN AGRICULTURE
Room: LHOB 1301
Phone: 202.225.2171

Majority:		Minority:	
C: Dusty Johnson, SD-01	LHOB 1714	**RM: Jim Costa, CA-21**	RHOB 2081
Scott DesJarlais, TN-04	RHOB 2304	Abigail Spanberger, VA-07	CHOB 562
David Rouzer, NC-07	RHOB 2333	Jahana Hayes, CT-05	RHOB 2458
Trent Kelly, MS-01	RHOB 2243	Lou Correa, CA-46	RHOB 2301
Don Bacon, NE-02	RHOB 2104	Ro Khanna, CA-17	CHOB 306
Jim Baird, IN-04	RHOB 2303	Angie Craig, MN-02	RHOB 2442
Tracey Mann, KS-01	CHOB 344	Sanford Bishop, GA-02	RHOB 2407
Randy Feenstra, IA-04	LHOB 1440		
Barry Moore, AL-02	LHOB 1504		

NUTRITION, OVERSIGHT & DEPARTMENT OPERATIONS
Room: LHOB 1301
Phone: 202.225.2171

Majority:		Minority:	
C: Don Bacon, NE-02	RHOB 2104	**RM: Jahana Hayes, CT-05**	RHOB 2458
Rick Crawford, AR-01	RHOB 2422	Jim McGovern, MA-02	CHOB 370
Scott DesJarlais, TN-04	RHOB 2304	Ann Kuster, NH-02	RHOB 2201
Kat Cammack, FL-03	RHOB 2421	Alma Adams, NC-12	RHOB 2436
Michael Cloud, TX-27	CHOB 171	Jimmy Panetta, CA-19	CHOB 304
Jim Baird, IN-04	RHOB 2303	Salud Carbajal, CA-24	RHOB 2331
		Shontel Brown, OH-11	CHOB 449

APPROPRIATIONS

Room: The Capitol H-307
Website: appropriations.house.gov
Phone: 202.225.2771
Ratio: 34 Republicans/27 Democrats
Subcommittees: 12

Majority:		Minority:	
C: Kay Granger, TX-12	RHOB 2308	**RM: Rosa DeLauro, CT-03**	RHOB 2413
Tom Cole, OK-04	RHOB 2207	Grace Meng, NY-06	RHOB 2209
Hal Rogers, KY-05	RHOB 2406	Steny Hoyer, MD-05	LHOB 1705
Robert Aderholt, AL-04	CHOB 266	Marcy Kaptur, OH-09	RHOB 2186
Mike Simpson, ID-02	RHOB 2084	Sanford Bishop, GA-02	RHOB 2407
John Carter, TX-31	RHOB 2208	Barbara Lee, CA-12	RHOB 2470
Ken Calvert, CA-41	RHOB 2205	Betty McCollum, MN-04	RHOB 2426
Mario Diaz-Balart, FL-26	CHOB 374	Dutch Ruppersberger,	RHOB 2206
Steve Womack, AR-03	RHOB 2412	MD-02	
Chuck Fleischmann, TN-03	RHOB 2187	Debbie Wasserman	CHOB 270
Dave Joyce, OH-14	RHOB 2065	Schultz, FL-25	
Andy Harris, MD-01	LHOB 1536	Henry Cuellar, TX-28	RHOB 2372
Mark Amodei, NV-02	CHOB 104	Chellie Pingree, ME-01	RHOB 2354
Chris Stewart, UT-02	CHOB 166	Mike Quigley, IL-05	RHOB 2083
David Valadao, CA-22	RHOB 2465	Derek Kilmer, WA-06	LHOB 1226
Dan Newhouse, WA-04	CHOB 504	Matt Cartwright, PA-08	RHOB 2102
John Moolenaar, MI-02	CHOB 246	Mark Pocan, WI-02	LHOB 1026
John Rutherford, FL-05	LHOB 1711	Pete Aguilar, CA-33	CHOB 108
Ben Cline, VA-06	RHOB 2443	Lois Frankel, FL-22	RHOB 2305
Guy Reschenthaler, PA-14	CHOB 409	Bonnie Watson Coleman,	CHOB 168
Mike Garcia, CA-27	CHOB 144	NJ-12	
Ashley Hinson, IA-02	LHOB 1717	Norma Torres, CA-35	RHOB 2227
Tony Gonzales, TX-23	RHOB 2244	Ed Case, HI-01	RHOB 2210
Julia Letlow, LA-05	CHOB 142	Adriano Espaillat, NY-13	RHOB 2332
Michael Cloud, TX-27	CHOB 171	Josh Harder, CA-09	CHOB 209
Michael Guest, MS-03	CHOB 450	Jennifer Wexton, VA-10	LHOB 1210
Ryan Zinke, MT-01	CHOB 512	David Trone, MD-06	RHOB 2404
Andrew Clyde, GA-09	CHOB 445	Lauren Underwood, IL-14	LHOB 1410
Jake LaTurner, KS-02	RHOB 2441	Susie Lee, NV-03	CHOB 365
Jerry Carl, AL-01	LHOB 1330	Joseph Morelle, NY-25	CHOB 570
Stephanie Bice, OK-05	RHOB 2437		
Scott Franklin, FL-18	CHOB 249		
Jake Ellzey, TX-06	LHOB 1721		
Juan Ciscomani, AZ-06	LHOB 1429		

Majority CoS: Anne Marie Chotvacs   **Minority CoS:** Robin Juliano

—————————————— Subcommittees ——————————————

AGRICULTURE, RURAL DEVELOPMENT, FDA & RELATED AGENCIES
Room: LHOB 1036
Phone: 202.225.3481

Majority:		Minority:	
C: Andy Harris, MD-01	LHOB 1536	**RM: Sanford Bishop,**	RHOB 2407
David Valadao, CA-22	RHOB 2465	**GA-02**	
John Moolenaar, MI-02	CHOB 246	Chellie Pingree, ME-01	RHOB 2354
Dan Newhouse, WA-04	CHOB 504	Lauren Underwood, IL-14	LHOB 1410
Julia Letlow, LA-05	CHOB 142	Marcy Kaptur, OH-09	RHOB 2186
Ben Cline, VA-06	RHOB 2443	Barbara Lee, CA-12	RHOB 2470
Ashley Hinson, IA-02	LHOB 1717	Debbie Wasserman	CHOB 270
Jerry Carl, AL-01	LHOB 1330	Schultz, FL-25	
Scott Franklin, FL-18	CHOB 249	Rosa DeLauro, CT-03	RHOB 2413
Kay Granger, TX-12	RHOB 2308		

COMMERCE, JUSTICE, SCIENCE & RELATED AGENCIES
Room: LHOB 1036
Phone: 202.225.3481

Majority:		Minority:	
C: Hal Rogers, KY-05	RHOB 2406	**RM: Matt Cartwright,**	RHOB 2102
Robert Aderholt, AL-04	CHOB 266	**PA-08**	
John Carter, TX-31	RHOB 2208	Grace Meng, NY-06	RHOB 2209
Ben Cline, VA-06	RHOB 2443	Dutch Ruppersberger,	RHOB 2206
Mike Garcia, CA-27	CHOB 144	MD-02	
Tony Gonzales, TX-23	RHOB 2244	David Trone, MD-06	RHOB 2404
Andrew Clyde, GA-09	CHOB 445	Joseph Morelle, NY-25	CHOB 570
Jake Ellzey, TX-06	LHOB 1721	Rosa DeLauro, CT-03	RHOB 2413
Kay Granger, TX-12	RHOB 2308		

DEFENSE
Room: LHOB 1036
Phone: 202.225.3481

Majority:	Minority:

C: Ken Calvert, CA-41	RHOB 2205	RM: Betty McCollum,	RHOB 2426
Hal Rogers, KY-05	RHOB 2406	MN-04	
Tom Cole, OK-04	RHOB 2207	Dutch Ruppersberger,	RHOB 2206
Steve Womack, AR-03	RHOB 2412	MD-02	
Robert Aderholt, AL-04	CHOB 266	Marcy Kaptur, OH-09	RHOB 2186
John Carter, TX-31	RHOB 2208	Henry Cuellar, TX-28	RHOB 2372
Mario Diaz-Balart, FL-26	CHOB 374	Derek Kilmer, WA-06	LHOB 1226
Dave Joyce, OH-14	RHOB 2065	Pete Aguilar, CA-33	CHOB 108
Chris Stewart, UT-02	CHOB 166	Ed Case, HI-01	RHOB 2210
Mike Garcia, CA-27	CHOB 144	Rosa DeLauro, CT-03	RHOB 2413
Kay Granger, TX-12	RHOB 2308		

ENERGY & WATER DEVELOPMENT & RELATED AGENCIES
Room: LHOB 1036
Phone: 202.225.3481

Majority:		Minority:	
Chuck Fleischmann, TN-03	RHOB 2187	Marcy Kaptur, OH-09	RHOB 2186
Mike Simpson, ID-02	RHOB 2084	Debbie Wasserman	CHOB 270
Ken Calvert, CA-41	RHOB 2205	Schultz, FL-25	
Dan Newhouse, WA-04	CHOB 504	Susie Lee, NV-03	CHOB 365
Guy Reschenthaler, PA-14	CHOB 409	Mike Quigley, IL-05	RHOB 2083
Mike Garcia, CA-27	CHOB 144	Joseph Morelle, NY-25	CHOB 570
Julia Letlow, LA-05	CHOB 142	Derek Kilmer, WA-06	LHOB 1226
Michael Guest, MS-03	CHOB 450	Rosa DeLauro, CT-03	RHOB 2413
Stephanie Bice, OK-05	RHOB 2437		
Kay Granger, TX-12	RHOB 2308		

FINANCIAL SERVICES & GENERAL GOVERNMENT
Room: LHOB 1036
Phone: 202.225.3481

Majority:		Minority:	
C: Steve Womack, AR-03	RHOB 2412	RM: Steny Hoyer, MD-05	LHOB 1705
Mark Amodei, NV-02	CHOB 104	Matt Cartwright, PA-08	RHOB 2102
Dave Joyce, OH-14	RHOB 2065	Mark Pocan, WI-02	LHOB 1026
John Moolenaar, MI-02	CHOB 246	Sanford Bishop, GA-02	RHOB 2407
Ashley Hinson, IA-02	LHOB 1717	Norma Torres, CA-35	RHOB 2227
Michael Cloud, TX-27	CHOB 171	Rosa DeLauro, CT-03	RHOB 2413
Jerry Carl, AL-01	LHOB 1330		
Juan Ciscomani, AZ-06	LHOB 1429		
Kay Granger, TX-12	RHOB 2308		

HOMELAND SECURITY
Room: LHOB 1036
Phone: 202.225.3481

Majority:		Minority:	
C: Dave Joyce, OH-14	RHOB 2065	RM: Henry Cuellar, TX-28	RHOB 2372
John Rutherford, FL-05	LHOB 1711	Lauren Underwood, IL-14	LHOB 1410
Andy Harris, MD-01	LHOB 1536	Ed Case, HI-01	RHOB 2210
Dan Newhouse, WA-04	CHOB 504	David Trone, MD-06	RHOB 2404
Ashley Hinson, IA-02	LHOB 1717	Rosa DeLauro, CT-03	RHOB 2413
Michael Cloud, TX-27	CHOB 171		
Michael Guest, MS-03	CHOB 450		
Kay Granger, TX-12	RHOB 2308		

INTERIOR, ENVIRONMENT & RELATED AGENCIES
Room: LHOB 1036
Phone: 202.225.3481

Majority:		Minority:	
C: Mike Simpson, ID-02	RHOB 2084	RM: Chellie Pingree,	RHOB 2354
Chris Stewart, UT-02	CHOB 166	ME-01	
Mark Amodei, NV-02	CHOB 104	Betty McCollum, MN-04	RHOB 2420
Guy Reschenthaler, PA-14	CHOB 409	Derek Kilmer, WA-06	LHOB 1226
Michael Cloud, TX-27	CHOB 171	Josh Harder, CA-09	CHOB 209
Ryan Zinke, MT-01	CHOB 512	Rosa DeLauro, CT-03	RHOB 2413
Jake Ellzey, TX-06	LHOB 1721		
Kay Granger, TX-12	RHOB 2308		

LABOR, HEALTH & HUMAN SERVICES, EDUCATION & RELATED AGENCIES
Room: LHOB 1036
Phone: 202.225.3481

Majority:		Minority:	
C: Robert Aderholt, AL-04	CHOB 266	RM: Rosa DeLauro, CT-03	RHOB 2413
Mike Simpson, ID-02	RHOB 2084	Steny Hoyer, MD-05	LHOB 1705
Andy Harris, MD-01	LHOB 1536	Barbara Lee, CA-12	RHOB 2470
Chuck Fleischmann, TN-03	RHOB 2187	Mark Pocan, WI-02	LHOB 1026
John Moolenaar, MI-02	CHOB 246	Lois Frankel, FL-22	RHOB 2305
Julia Letlow, LA-05	CHOB 142		

Andrew Clyde, GA-09	CHOB 445	Bonnie Watson Coleman,	CHOB 168
Jake LaTurner, KS-02	RHOB 2441	NJ-12	
Jake Ellzey, TX-06	LHOB 1721	Josh Harder, CA-09	CHOB 209
Juan Ciscomani, AZ-06	LHOB 1429		
Kay Granger, TX-12	RHOB 2308		

LEGISLATIVE BRANCH
Room: LHOB 1036
Phone: 202.225.3481

Majority:		Minority:	
C: Mark Amodei, NV-02	CHOB 104	RM: Adriano Espaillat,	RHOB 2332
Andrew Clyde, GA-09	CHOB 445	NY-13	
Jake LaTurner, KS-02	RHOB 2441	Jennifer Wexton, VA-10	LHOB 1210
Stephanie Bice, OK-05	RHOB 2437	Mike Quigley, IL-05	RHOB 2083
Scott Franklin, FL-18	CHOB 249	Rosa DeLauro, CT-03	RHOB 2413
Kay Granger, TX-12	RHOB 2308		

MILITARY CONSTRUCTION, VETERANS AFFAIRS & RELATED AGENCIES
Room: LHOB 1036
Phone: 202.225.3481

Majority:		Minority:	
C: John Carter, TX-31	RHOB 2208	RM: Debbie Wasserman	CHOB 270
David Valadao, CA-22	RHOB 2465	Schultz, FL-25	
John Rutherford, FL-05	LHOB 1711	Sanford Bishop, GA-02	RHOB 2407
Tony Gonzales, TX-23	RHOB 2244	Susie Lee, NV-03	CHOB 365
Michael Guest, MS-03	CHOB 450	Henry Cuellar, TX-28	RHOB 2372
Ryan Zinke, MT-01	CHOB 512	Chellie Pingree, ME-01	RHOB 2354
Stephanie Bice, OK-05	RHOB 2437	Rosa DeLauro, CT-03	RHOB 2413
Scott Franklin, FL-18	CHOB 249		
Kay Granger, TX-12	RHOB 2308		

STATE, FOREIGN OPERATIONS & RELATED PROGRAMS
Room: LHOB 1036
Phone: 202.225.3481

Majority:		Minority:	
C: Mario Diaz-Balart,	CHOB 374	RM: Barbara Lee, CA-12	RHOB 2470
FL-26		Grace Meng, NY-06	RHOB 2209
Hal Rogers, KY-05	RHOB 2406	Lois Frankel, FL-22	RHOB 2305
Chris Stewart, UT-02	CHOB 166	Norma Torres, CA-35	RHOB 2227
Guy Reschenthaler, PA-14	CHOB 409	Rosa DeLauro, CT-03	RHOB 2413
Chuck Fleischmann, TN-03	RHOB 2187		
Jake LaTurner, KS-02	RHOB 2441		
Jerry Carl, AL-01	LHOB 1330		
Kay Granger, TX-12	RHOB 2308		

TRANSPORTATION, HUD & RELATED AGENCIES
Room: LHOB 1036
Phone: 202.225.3481

Majority:		Minority:	
C: Tom Cole, OK-04	RHOB 2207	RM: Mike Quigley, IL-05	RHOB 2083
Mario Diaz-Balart, FL-26	CHOB 374	Bonnie Watson Coleman,	CHOB 168
Steve Womack, AR-03	RHOB 2412	NJ-12	
John Rutherford, FL-05	LHOB 1711	Norma Torres, CA-35	RHOB 2227
Tony Gonzales, TX-23	RHOB 2244	Pete Aguilar, CA-33	CHOB 108
David Valadao, CA-22	RHOB 2465	Adriano Espaillat, NY-13	RHOB 2332
Ben Cline, VA-06	RHOB 2443	Jennifer Wexton, VA-10	LHOB 1210
Ryan Zinke, MT-01	CHOB 512	Rosa DeLauro, CT-03	RHOB 2413
Juan Ciscomani, AZ-06	LHOB 1429		
Kay Granger, TX-12	RHOB 2308		

ARMED SERVICES

Room: RHOB 2216
Website: armedservices.house.gov
Phone: 202.225.4151
Ratio: 31 Republicans/27 Democrats
Subcommittees: 7

Majority:		Minority:	
C: Mike Rogers, AL-03	RHOB 2469	RM: Adam Smith, WA-09	RHOB 2264
Rob Wittman, VA-01	RHOB 2055	Patrick Ryan, NY-18	LHOB 1030
Joe Wilson, SC-02	LHOB 1436	Joe Courtney, CT-02	RHOB 2449
Mike Turner, OH-10	RHOB 2082	John Garamendi, CA-08	RHOB 2004
Doug Lamborn, CO-05	RHOB 2371	Donald Norcross, NJ-01	RHOB 2427
Austin Scott, GA-08	RHOB 2185	Ruben Gallego, AZ-03	LHOB 1114
Sam Graves, MO-06	LHOB 1135	Seth Moulton, MA-06	LHOB 1127
Elise Stefanik, NY-21	RHOB 2211	Salud Carbajal, CA-24	RHOB 2331
Scott DesJarlais, TN-04	RHOB 2304	Ro Khanna, CA-17	CHOB 306
Trent Kelly, MS-01	RHOB 2243	Bill Keating, MA-09	RHOB 2351

Mike Gallagher, WI-08	LHOB 1211	Andy Kim, NJ-03	RHOB 2444
Matt Gaetz, FL-01	RHOB 2021	Chrissy Houlahan, PA-06	LHOB 1727
Don Bacon, NE-02	RHOB 2104	Jason Crow, CO-06	LHOB 1323
Jim Banks, IN-03	RHOB 2418	Elissa Slotkin, MI-07	RHOB 2245
Jack Bergman, MI-01	CHOB 566	Mikie Sherrill, NJ-11	LHOB 1427
Mike Waltz, FL-06	CHOB 244	Veronica Escobar, TX-16	RHOB 2448
Mike Johnson, LA-04	CHOB 568	Jared Golden, ME-02	LHOB 1710
Lisa McClain, MI-09	CHOB 444	Sara Jacobs, CA-51	LHOB 1314
Ronny Jackson, TX-13	CHOB 118	Marilyn Strickland, WA-10	LHOB 1708
Pat Fallon, TX-04	RHOB 2416	Jeff Jackson, NC-14	LHOB 1318
Carlos Gimenez, FL-28	CHOB 448	Gabe Vasquez, NM-02	LHOB 1517
Nancy Mace, SC-01	LHOB 1728	Chris Deluzio, PA-17	LHOB 1222
Brad Finstad, MN-01	LHOB 1605	Jill Tokuda, HI-02	LHOB 1005
Dale Strong, AL-05	LHOB 1337	Don Davis, NC-01	LHOB 1123
Morgan Luttrell, TX-08	LHOB 1320	Terri Sewell, AL-07	LHOB 1035
Jen Kiggans, VA-02	LHOB 1037	Steven Horsford, NV-04	CHOB 406
Nicholas LaLota, NY-01	LHOB 1530	Jimmy Panetta, CA-19	CHOB 304
James Moylan, GU-01	LHOB 1628		
Mark Alford, MO-04	LHOB 1516		
Cory Mills, FL-07	LHOB 1237		
Richard McCormick, GA-06	LHOB 1213		

Majority CoS: Christopher Vieson   **Minority CoS:** Brian J. Garrett

————————————— Subcommittees —————————————

CYBER, INFORMATION TECHNOLOGY & INNOVATION
Room: RHOB 2216
Phone: 202.225.4151

Majority:		Minority:	
C: Mike Gallagher, WI-08	LHOB 1211	**RM: Ro Khanna, CA-17**	CHOB 306
Matt Gaetz, FL-01	RHOB 2021	Seth Moulton, MA-06	LHOB 1127
Lisa McClain, MI-09	CHOB 444	Bill Keating, MA-09	RHOB 2351
Pat Fallon, TX-04	RHOB 2416	Andy Kim, NJ-03	RHOB 2444
Dale Strong, AL-05	LHOB 1337	Elissa Slotkin, MI-07	RHOB 2245
Morgan Luttrell, TX-08	LHOB 1320	Jared Golden, ME-02	LHOB 1710
Jen Kiggans, VA-02	LHOB 1037	Patrick Ryan, NY-18	LHOB 1030
Nicholas LaLota, NY-01	LHOB 1530	Chris Deluzio, PA-17	LHOB 1222
Richard McCormick, GA-06	LHOB 1213		

INTELLIGENCE & SPECIAL OPERATIONS
Room: RHOB 2340
Phone: 202.225.4151

Majority:		Minority:	
C: Jack Bergman, MI-01	CHOB 566	**RM: Ruben Gallego, AZ-03**	LHOB 1114
Austin Scott, GA-08	RHOB 2185	Bill Keating, MA-09	RHOB 2351
Elise Stefanik, NY-21	RHOB 2211	Jason Crow, CO-06	LHOB 1323
Trent Kelly, MS-01	RHOB 2243	Elissa Slotkin, MI-07	RHOB 2245
Ronny Jackson, TX-13	CHOB 118	Sara Jacobs, CA-51	LHOB 1314
Nancy Mace, SC-01	LHOB 1728	Jeff Jackson, NC-14	LHOB 1318
Morgan Luttrell, TX-08	LHOB 1320	Jimmy Panetta, CA-19	CHOB 304
Cory Mills, FL-07	LHOB 1237		

MILITARY PERSONNEL
Room: RHOB 2340
Phone: 202.225.4151

Majority:		Minority:	
C: Jim Banks, IN-03	RHOB 2418	**RM: Andy Kim, NJ-03**	RHOB 2444
Elise Stefanik, NY-21	RHOB 2211	Chrissy Houlahan, PA-06	LHOB 1727
Matt Gaetz, FL-01	RHOB 2021	Veronica Escobar, TX-16	RHOB 2448
Jack Bergman, MI-01	CHOB 566	Marilyn Strickland, WA-10	LHOB 1708
Mike Waltz, FL-06	CHOB 244	Jill Tokuda, HI-02	LHOB 1005
Brad Finstad, MN-01	LHOB 1605	Don Davis, NC-01	LHOB 1123
James Moylan, GU-01	LHOB 1628	Terri Sewell, AL-07	LHOB 1035
Mark Alford, MO-04	LHOB 1516	Steven Horsford, NV-04	CHOB 406
Cory Mills, FL-07	LHOB 1237		

READINESS
Room: RHOB 2340
Phone: 202.225.4151

Majority:		Minority:	
C: Mike Waltz, FL-06	CHOB 244	**RM: John Garamendi, CA-08**	RHOB 2004
Joe Wilson, SC-02	LHOB 1436		
Austin Scott, GA-08	RHOB 2185	Jason Crow, CO-06	LHOB 1323
Mike Johnson, LA-04	CHOB 568	Mikie Sherrill, NJ-11	LHOB 1427
Carlos Gimenez, FL-28	CHOB 448	Veronica Escobar, TX-16	RHOB 2448
Brad Finstad, MN-01	LHOB 1605	Marilyn Strickland, WA-10	LHOB 1708
Dale Strong, AL-05	LHOB 1337	Gabe Vasquez, NM-02	LHOB 1517
Jen Kiggans, VA-02	LHOB 1037	Jill Tokuda, HI-02	LHOB 1005
James Moylan, GU-01	LHOB 1628	Don Davis, NC-01	LHOB 1123

SEAPOWER & PROJECTION FORCES
Room: RHOB 2340
Phone: 202.225.4151

Majority:		Minority:	
C: Trent Kelly, MS-01	RHOB 2243	RM: Joe Courtney, CT-02	RHOB 2449
Rob Wittman, VA-01	RHOB 2055	John Garamendi, CA-08	RHOB 2004
Scott DesJarlais, TN-04	RHOB 2304	Donald Norcross, NJ-01	RHOB 2427
Mike Gallagher, WI-08	LHOB 1211	Jared Golden, ME-02	LHOB 1710
Jack Bergman, MI-01	CHOB 566	Sara Jacobs, CA-51	LHOB 1314
Mike Johnson, LA-04	CHOB 568	Chris Deluzio, PA-17	LHOB 1222
Ronny Jackson, TX-13	CHOB 118	Jimmy Panetta, CA-19	CHOB 304
Nancy Mace, SC-01	LHOB 1728		
Jen Kiggans, VA-02	LHOB 1037		
Mark Alford, MO-04	LHOB 1516		

STRATEGIC FORCES
Room: RHOB 2340
Phone: 202.225.4151

Majority:		Minority:	
C: Doug Lamborn, CO-05	RHOB 2371	RM: Seth Moulton, MA-06	LHOB 1127
Joe Wilson, SC-02	LHOB 1436	John Garamendi, CA-08	RHOB 2004
Mike Turner, OH-10	RHOB 2082	Donald Norcross, NJ-01	RHOB 2427
Elise Stefanik, NY-21	RHOB 2211	Salud Carbajal, CA-24	RHOB 2331
Scott DesJarlais, TN-04	RHOB 2304	Ro Khanna, CA-17	CHOB 306
Don Bacon, NE-02	RHOB 2104	Chrissy Houlahan, PA-06	LHOB 1727
Jim Banks, IN-03	RHOB 2418	Gabe Vasquez, NM-02	LHOB 1517
Mike Waltz, FL-06	CHOB 244		
Dale Strong, AL-05	LHOB 1337		

TACTICAL AIR & LAND FORCES
Room: RHOB 2216
Phone: 202.225.4151

Majority:		Minority:	
C: Rob Wittman, VA-01	RHOB 2055	RM: Donald Norcross, NJ-01	RHOB 2427
Mike Turner, OH-10	RHOB 2082		
Doug Lamborn, CO-05	RHOB 2371	Joe Courtney, CT-02	RHOB 2449
Sam Graves, MO-06	LHOB 1135	Ruben Gallego, AZ-03	LHOB 1114
Don Bacon, NE-02	RHOB 2104	Salud Carbajal, CA-24	RHOB 2331
Lisa McClain, MI-09	CHOB 444	Mikie Sherrill, NJ-11	LHOB 1427
Pat Fallon, TX-04	RHOB 2416	Patrick Ryan, NY-18	LHOB 1030
Carlos Gimenez, FL-28	CHOB 448	Jeff Jackson, NC-14	LHOB 1318
Nicholas LaLota, NY-01	LHOB 1530	Steven Horsford, NV-04	CHOB 406
Richard McCormick, GA-06	LHOB 1213		

BUDGET

Room: CHOB 507
Website: budget.house.gov
Phone: 202.226.7270
Ratio: 21 Republicans/15 Democrats
Subcommittees: 0

Majority:		Minority:	
C: Jodey Arrington, TX-19	LHOB 1107	RM: Brendan Boyle, PA-02	LHOB 1502
Ralph Norman, SC-05	CHOB 569	Brian Higgins, NY-26	RHOB 2269
Tom McClintock, CA-05	RHOB 2256	Jan Schakowsky, IL-09	RHOB 2408
Glenn Grothman, WI-06	LHOB 1511	Earl Blumenauer, OR-03	LHOB 1111
Lloyd Smucker, PA-11	CHOB 302	Dan Kildee, MI-08	CHOB 200
Michael Burgess, TX-26	RHOB 2161	Scott Peters, CA-50	LHOB 1201
Buddy Carter, GA-01	RHOB 2432	Barbara Lee, CA-12	RHOB 2470
Ben Cline, VA-06	RHOB 2443	Lloyd Doggett, TX-37	RHOB 2307
Bob Good, VA-05	CHOB 461	Jennifer Wexton, VA-10	LHOB 1210
Jack Bergman, MI-01	CHOB 566	Sheila Jackson Lee, TX-18	RHOB 2426
Drew Ferguson, GA-03	RHOB 2239	Ilhan Omar, MN-05	LHOB 1730
Chip Roy, TX-21	LHOB 1005	David Trone, MD-06	RHOB 2404
Blake Moore, UT-01	LHOB 1131	Becca Balint, VT-01	LHOB 1408
David Valadao, CA-22	RHOB 2465	Bobby Scott, VA-03	RHOB 2328
Ron Estes, KS-04	RHOB 2234	Jimmy Panetta, CA-19	CHOB 304
Stephanie Bice, OK-05	RHOB 2437		
Lisa McClain, MI-09	CHOB 444		
Michelle Fischbach, MN-07	LHOB 1004		
Rudy Yakym, IN-02	CHOB 349		
Josh Brecheen, OK-02	LHOB 1208		
Chuck Edwards, NC-11	LHOB 1505		

Majority CoS: Gary J. Andres

Minority CoS: Diana Meredith
Minority Sched: Sheila A. McDowell

EDUCATION & WORKFORCE

Room: RHOB 2176
Website: edworkforce.house.gov
Phone: 202.225.4527
Ratio: 25 Republicans/20 Democrats
Subcommittees: 4

Majority:		Minority:	
C: Virginia Foxx, NC-05	RHOB 2462	RM: Bobby Scott, VA-03	RHOB 2328
Mary Miller, IL-15	LHOB 1740	Jahana Hayes, CT-05	RHOB 2458
Joe Wilson, SC-02	LHOB 1436	Raul Grijalva, AZ-07	LHOB 1203
Glenn Thompson, PA-15	CHOB 400	Joe Courtney, CT-02	RHOB 2449
Tim Walberg, MI-05	RHOB 2266	Gregorio Sablan, MP-01	RHOB 2267
Glenn Grothman, WI-06	LHOB 1511	Frederica Wilson, FL-24	RHOB 2080
Elise Stefanik, NY-21	RHOB 2211	Suzanne Bonamici, OR-01	RHOB 2231
Rick Allen, GA-12	CHOB 462	Mark Takano, CA-39	RHOB 2078
Jim Banks, IN-03	RHOB 2418	Alma Adams, NC-12	RHOB 2436
James Comer, KY-01	RHOB 2410	Mark DeSaulnier, CA-10	CHOB 503
Lloyd Smucker, PA-11	CHOB 302	Donald Norcross, NJ-01	RHOB 2427
Burgess Owens, UT-04	LHOB 1039	Pramila Jayapal, WA-07	RHOB 2346
Bob Good, VA-05	CHOB 461	Susan Wild, PA-07	LHOB 1027
Lisa McClain, MI-09	CHOB 444	Lucy McBath, GA-07	RHOB 2246
Michelle Steel, CA-45		Ilhan Omar, MN-05	LHOB 1730
Ron Estes, KS-04	RHOB 2234	Haley Stevens, MI-11	RHOB 2411
Julia Letlow, LA-05	CHOB 142	Teresa Leger Fernandez,	LHOB 1510
Kevin Kiley, CA-03	LHOB 1032	NM-03	
Aaron Bean, FL-04	LHOB 1239	Kathy Manning, NC-06	CHOB 307
Eric Burlison, MO-07	LHOB 1108	Frank Mrvan, IN-01	LHOB 1607
Nathaniel Moran, TX-01	LHOB 1541	Jamaal Bowman, NY-16	CHOB 345
John James, MI-10	LHOB 1015		
Lori Chavez-DeRemer, OR-05	LHOB 1722		
Brandon Williams, NY-22	LHOB 1022		
Erin Houchin, IN-09	LHOB 1632		

Majority CoS: Cyrus Artz   **Minority CoS:** Veronique F. Pluviose

——————— Subcommittees ———————

EARLY CHILDHOOD, ELEMENTARY & SECONDARY EDUCATION
Room: RHOB 2101
Phone: 202.225.4527

Majority:		Minority:	
C: Aaron Bean, FL-04	LHOB 1239	RM: Suzanne Bonamici,	RHOB 2231
Glenn Thompson, PA-15	CHOB 400	OR-01	
Burgess Owens, UT-04	LHOB 1039	Raul Grijalva, AZ-07	LHOB 1203
Lisa McClain, MI-09	CHOB 444	Gregorio Sablan, MP-01	RHOB 2267
Mary Miller, IL-15	LHOB 1740	Jahana Hayes, CT-05	RHOB 2458
Michelle Steel, CA-45		Jamaal Bowman, NY-16	CHOB 345
Kevin Kiley, CA-03	LHOB 1032	Frederica Wilson, FL-24	RHOB 2080
Nathaniel Moran, TX-01	LHOB 1541	Mark DeSaulnier, CA-10	CHOB 503
Brandon Williams, NY-22	LHOB 1022	Donald Norcross, NJ-01	RHOB 2427
Virginia Foxx, NC-05	RHOB 2462		

HEALTH, EMPLOYMENT, LABOR & PENSIONS
Room: RHOB 2101
Phone: 202.225.4527

Majority:		Minority:	
C: Bob Good, VA-05	CHOB 461	RM: Mark DeSaulnier,	CHOB 503
Joe Wilson, SC-02	LHOB 1436	CA-10	
Tim Walberg, MI-05	RHOB 2266	Joe Courtney, CT-02	RHOB 2449
Rick Allen, GA-12	CHOB 462	Donald Norcross, NJ-01	RHOB 2427
Jim Banks, IN-03	RHOB 2418	Susan Wild, PA-07	LHOB 1027
James Comer, KY-01	RHOB 2410	Frank Mrvan, IN-01	LHOB 1607
Lloyd Smucker, PA-11	CHOB 302	Pramila Jayapal, WA-07	RHOB 2346
Michelle Steel, CA-45		Lucy McBath, GA-07	RHOB 2246
Aaron Bean, FL-04	LHOB 1239	Jahana Hayes, CT-05	RHOB 2458
Eric Burlison, MO-07	LHOB 1108	Ilhan Omar, MN-05	LHOB 1730
Lori Chavez-DeRemer, OR-05	LHOB 1722	Kathy Manning, NC-06	CHOB 307
Erin Houchin, IN-09	LHOB 1632		

HIGHER EDUCATION & WORKFORCE INVESTMENT
Room: RHOB 2101
Phone: 202.225.4527

Majority:		Minority:	
C: Burgess Owens, UT-04	LHOB 1039	RM: Frederica Wilson,	RHOB 2080
Glenn Thompson, PA-15	CHOB 400	FL-24	
Glenn Grothman, WI-06	LHOB 1511	Mark Takano, CA-39	RHOB 2078
Elise Stefanik, NY-21	RHOB 2211	Pramila Jayapal, WA-07	RHOB 2346

Jim Banks, IN-03	RHOB 2418	Teresa Leger Fernandez, NM-03	LHOB 1510
Lloyd Smucker, PA-11	CHOB 302	Kathy Manning, NC-06	CHOB 307
Bob Good, VA-05	CHOB 461	Lucy McBath, GA-07	RHOB 2246
Nathaniel Moran, TX-01	LHOB 1541	Raul Grijalva, AZ-07	LHOB 1203
John James, MI-10	LHOB 1319	Joe Courtney, CT-02	RHOB 2449
Lori Chavez-DeRemer, OR-05	LHOB 1722	Gregorio Sablan, MP-01	RHOB 2267
Erin Houchin, IN-09	LHOB 1632	Suzanne Bonamici, OR-01	RHOB 2231
Brandon Williams, NY-22	LHOB 1022	Alma Adams, NC-12	RHOB 2436
Virginia Foxx, NC-05	RHOB 2462		

WORKFORCE PROTECTIONS
Room: RHOB 2101
Phone: 202.225.3725

Majority:		Minority:	
C: Kevin Kiley, CA-03	LHOB 1032	**RM: Alma Adams, NC-12**	RHOB 2436
Glenn Grothman, WI-06	LHOB 1511	Ilhan Omar, MN-05	LHOB 1730
Elise Stefanik, NY-21	RHOB 2211	Haley Stevens, MI-11	RHOB 2411
James Comer, KY-01	RHOB 2410	Mark Takano, CA-39	RHOB 2078
Mary Miller, IL-15	LHOB 1740		
Eric Burlison, MO-07	LHOB 1108		

ENERGY & COMMERCE
Room: RHOB 2125
Website: energycommerce.house.gov
Phone: 202.225.3641
Ratio: 29 Republicans/23 Democrats
Subcommittees: 6

Majority:		Minority:	
C: Cathy McMorris Rodgers, WA-05	RHOB 2188	**RM: Frank Pallone, NJ-06**	RHOB 2107
		Kim Schrier, WA-08	LHOB 1110
Kelly Armstrong, ND-01	RHOB 2267	Anna Eshoo, CA-16	CHOB 272
Michael Burgess, TX-26	RHOB 2161	Diana DeGette, CO-01	RHOB 2111
Bob Latta, OH-05	RHOB 2467	Jan Schakowsky, IL-09	RHOB 2408
Brett Guthrie, KY-02	RHOB 2434	Doris Matsui, CA-07	RHOB 2311
Morgan Griffith, VA-09	RHOB 2202	Kathy Castor, FL-14	RHOB 2052
Gus Bilirakis, FL-12	RHOB 2306	John Sarbanes, MD-03	RHOB 2370
Bill Johnson, OH-06	RHOB 2082	Paul Tonko, NY-20	RHOB 2369
Larry Bucshon, IN-08	RHOB 2313	Yvette Clarke, NY-09	RHOB 2058
Richard Hudson, NC-09	RHOB 2112	Tony Cardenas, CA-29	RHOB 2181
Tim Walberg, MI-05	RHOB 2266	Raul Ruiz, CA-25	RHOB 2342
Buddy Carter, GA-01	RHOB 2432	Scott Peters, CA-50	LHOB 1201
Jeff Duncan, SC-03	RHOB 2229	Debbie Dingell, MI-06	CHOB 102
Gary Palmer, AL-06	CHOB 170	Marc Veasey, TX-33	RHOB 2348
Neal Dunn, FL-02	CHOB 466	Ann Kuster, NH-02	RHOB 2201
John Curtis, UT-03	RHOB 2323	Robin Kelly, IL-02	RHOB 2329
Debbie Lesko, AZ-08	LHOB 1214	Nanette Barragan, CA-44	RHOB 2312
Greg Pence, IN-06	CHOB 404	Lisa Blunt Rochester, DE-01	LHOB 1724
Daniel Crenshaw, TX-02	CHOB 413	Darren Soto, FL-09	RHOB 2353
John Joyce, PA-13	CHOB 152	Angie Craig, MN-02	RHOB 2442
Randy Weber, TX-14	CHOB 107	Lori Trahan, MA-03	RHOB 2439
Rick Allen, GA-12	CHOB 462	Lizzie Fletcher, TX-07	CHOB 346
Troy Balderson, OH-12	RHOB 2429		
Russ Fulcher, ID-01	LHOB 1514		
August Pfluger, TX-11	LHOB 1124		
Diana Harshbarger, TN-01	CHOB 167		
Mariannette Miller-Meeks, IA-01	LHOB 1034		
Kat Cammack, FL-03	RHOB 2421		
Jay Obernolte, CA-23	LHOB 1029		

Majority CoS: Nate Hodson   **Minority CoS:** Tiffany Guarascio
———————————————— Subcommittees ————————————————

COMMUNICATIONS & TECHNOLOGY
Room: RHOB 2125
Phone: 202.225.3641

Majority:		Minority:	
C: Bob Latta, OH-05	RHOB 2467	**RM: Doris Matsui, CA-07**	RHOB 2311
Buddy Carter, GA-01	RHOB 2432	Yvette Clarke, NY-09	RHOB 2058
Gus Bilirakis, FL-12	RHOB 2306	Marc Veasey, TX-33	RHOB 2348
Tim Walberg, MI-05	RHOB 2266	Darren Soto, FL-09	RHOB 2353
Neal Dunn, FL-02	CHOB 466	Anna Eshoo, CA-16	CHOB 272
John Curtis, UT-03	RHOB 2323	Tony Cardenas, CA-29	RHOB 2181
John Joyce, PA-13	CHOB 152	Angie Craig, MN-02	RHOB 2442
Randy Weber, TX-14	CHOB 107	Lizzie Fletcher, TX-07	CHOB 346
Rick Allen, GA-12	CHOB 462	Debbie Dingell, MI-06	CHOB 102
Troy Balderson, OH-12	RHOB 2429	Ann Kuster, NH-02	RHOB 2201

Russ Fulcher, ID-01	LHOB 1514	Robin Kelly, IL-02	RHOB 2329
August Pfluger, TX-11	LHOB 1124	Frank Pallone, NJ-06	RHOB 2107
Diana Harshbarger, TN-01	CHOB 167		
Kat Cammack, FL-03	RHOB 2421		
Jay Obernolte, CA-23	LHOB 1029		
Cathy McMorris Rodgers, WA-05	RHOB 2188		

ENERGY, CLIMATE & GRID SECURITY
Room: RHOB 2125
Phone: 202.225.3641

Majority:		Minority:	
C: Jeff Duncan, SC-03	RHOB 2229	RM: Diana DeGette, CO-01	RHOB 2111
John Curtis, UT-03	RHOB 2323		
Michael Burgess, TX-26	RHOB 2161	Scott Peters, CA-50	LHOB 1201
Bob Latta, OH-05	RHOB 2467	Lizzie Fletcher, TX-07	CHOB 346
Brett Guthrie, KY-02	RHOB 2434	Doris Matsui, CA-07	RHOB 2311
Morgan Griffith, VA-09	RHOB 2202	Paul Tonko, NY-20	RHOB 2369
Bill Johnson, OH-06	RHOB 2082	Marc Veasey, TX-33	RHOB 2348
Larry Bucshon, IN-08	RHOB 2313	Ann Kuster, NH-02	RHOB 2201
Tim Walberg, MI-05	RHOB 2266	Kim Schrier, WA-08	LHOB 1110
Gary Palmer, AL-06	CHOB 170	Kathy Castor, FL-14	RHOB 2052
Debbie Lesko, AZ-08	LHOB 1214	John Sarbanes, MD-03	RHOB 2370
Greg Pence, IN-06	CHOB 404	Tony Cardenas, CA-29	RHOB 2181
Kelly Armstrong, ND-01	RHOB 2267	Lisa Blunt Rochester, DE-01	LHOB 1724
Randy Weber, TX-14	CHOB 107	Frank Pallone, NJ-06	RHOB 2107
Troy Balderson, OH-12	RHOB 2429		
August Pfluger, TX-11	LHOB 1124		
Cathy McMorris Rodgers, WA-05	RHOB 2188		

ENVIRONMENT, MANUFACTURING & CRITICAL MINERALS
Room: RHOB 2125
Phone: 202.225.3641

Majority:		Minority:	
C: Bill Johnson, OH-06	RHOB 2082	RM: Paul Tonko, NY-20	RHOB 2369
John Joyce, PA-13	CHOB 152	Diana DeGette, CO-01	RHOB 2111
Buddy Carter, GA-01	RHOB 2432	Jan Schakowsky, IL-09	RHOB 2408
Gary Palmer, AL-06	CHOB 170	John Sarbanes, MD-03	RHOB 2370
Daniel Crenshaw, TX-02	CHOB 413	Yvette Clarke, NY-09	RHOB 2058
Randy Weber, TX-14	CHOB 107	Raul Ruiz, CA-25	RHOB 2342
Rick Allen, GA-12	CHOB 462	Scott Peters, CA-50	LHOB 1201
Troy Balderson, OH-12	RHOB 2429	Nanette Barragan, CA-44	RHOB 2312
Russ Fulcher, ID-01	LHOB 1514	Frank Pallone, NJ-06	RHOB 2107
August Pfluger, TX-11	LHOB 1124		
Mariannette Miller-Meeks, IA-01	LHOB 1034		
Jay Obernolte, CA-23	LHOB 1029		
Cathy McMorris Rodgers, WA-05	RHOB 2188		

HEALTH
Room: RHOB 2125
Phone: 202.225.3641

Majority:		Minority:	
C: Brett Guthrie, KY-02	RHOB 2434	RM: Anna Eshoo, CA-16	CHOB 272
Larry Bucshon, IN-08	RHOB 2313	John Sarbanes, MD-03	RHOB 2370
Michael Burgess, TX-26	RHOB 2161	Tony Cardenas, CA-29	RHOB 2181
Bob Latta, OH-05	RHOB 2467	Raul Ruiz, CA-25	RHOB 2342
Morgan Griffith, VA-09	RHOB 2202	Debbie Dingell, MI-06	CHOB 102
Gus Bilirakis, FL-12	RHOB 2306	Ann Kuster, NH-02	RHOB 2201
Bill Johnson, OH-06	RHOB 2082	Robin Kelly, IL-02	RHOB 2329
Richard Hudson, NC-09	RHOB 2112	Nanette Barragan, CA-44	RHOB 2312
Buddy Carter, GA-01	RHOB 2432	Lisa Blunt Rochester, DE-01	LHOB 1724
Neal Dunn, FL-02	CHOB 466	Angie Craig, MN-02	RHOB 2442
Greg Pence, IN-06	CHOB 404	Kim Schrier, WA-08	LHOB 1110
Daniel Crenshaw, TX-02	CHOB 413	Lori Trahan, MA-03	RHOB 2439
John Joyce, PA-13	CHOB 152	Frank Pallone, NJ-06	RHOB 2107
Diana Harshbarger, TN-01	CHOB 167		
Mariannette Miller-Meeks, IA-01	LHOB 1034		
Jay Obernolte, CA-23	LHOB 1029		
Cathy McMorris Rodgers, WA-05	RHOB 2188		

INNOVATION, DATA & COMMERCE
Room: RHOB 2125
Phone: 202.225.3641

Majority:

C: Gus Bilirakis, FL-12	RHOB 2306
Tim Walberg, MI-05	RHOB 2266
Larry Bucshon, IN-08	RHOB 2313
Jeff Duncan, SC-03	RHOB 2229
Neal Dunn, FL-02	CHOB 466
Debbie Lesko, AZ-08	LHOB 1214
Greg Pence, IN-06	CHOB 404
Kelly Armstrong, ND-01	RHOB 2267
Rick Allen, GA-12	CHOB 462
Russ Fulcher, ID-01	LHOB 1514
Diana Harshbarger, TN-01	CHOB 167
Kat Cammack, FL-03	RHOB 2421
Cathy McMorris Rodgers, WA-05	RHOB 2188

Minority:

RM: Jan Schakowsky, IL-09	RHOB 2408
Kathy Castor, FL-14	RHOB 2052
Debbie Dingell, MI-06	CHOB 102
Robin Kelly, IL-02	RHOB 2329
Lisa Blunt Rochester, DE-01	LHOB 1724
Darren Soto, FL-09	RHOB 2353
Lori Trahan, MA-03	RHOB 2439
Yvette Clarke, NY-09	RHOB 2058
Frank Pallone, NJ-06	RHOB 2107

OVERSIGHT & INVESTIGATIONS

Room: RHOB 2125
Phone: 202.225.3641

Majority:

C: Morgan Griffith, VA-09	RHOB 2202
Debbie Lesko, AZ-08	LHOB 1214
Michael Burgess, TX-26	RHOB 2161
Brett Guthrie, KY-02	RHOB 2434
Jeff Duncan, SC-03	RHOB 2229
Gary Palmer, AL-06	CHOB 170
Daniel Crenshaw, TX-02	CHOB 413
Kelly Armstrong, ND-01	RHOB 2267
Kat Cammack, FL-03	RHOB 2421
Cathy McMorris Rodgers, WA-05	RHOB 2188

Minority:

RM: Kathy Castor, FL-14	RHOB 2052
Diana DeGette, CO-01	RHOB 2111
Jan Schakowsky, IL-09	RHOB 2408
Paul Tonko, NY-20	RHOB 2369
Raul Ruiz, CA-25	RHOB 2342
Scott Peters, CA-50	LHOB 1201
Frank Pallone, NJ-06	RHOB 2107

ETHICS

Room: LHOB 1015
Website: ethics.house.gov
Phone: 202.225.7103
Ratio: 5 Republicans/5 Democrats
Subcommittees: 0

Majority:

C: Michael Guest, MS-03	CHOB 450
Dave Joyce, OH-14	RHOB 2065
John Rutherford, FL-05	LHOB 1711
Andrew Garbarino, NY-02	RHOB 2344
Michelle Fischbach, MN-07	LHOB 1004

Minority:

RM: Susan Wild, PA-07	LHOB 1027
Veronica Escobar, TX-16	RHOB 2448
Mark DeSaulnier, CA-10	CHOB 503
Deborah Ross, NC-02	LHOB 1221
Glenn Ivey, MD-04	LHOB 1529

FINANCIAL SERVICES

Room: RHOB 2129
Website: financialservices.house.gov
Phone: 202.225.7502
Ratio: 30 Republicans/23 Democrats
Subcommittees: 6

Majority:

C: Patrick McHenry, NC-10	RHOB 2134
Frank Lucas, OK-03	RHOB 2405
Pete Sessions, TX-17	RHOB 2204
Bill Posey, FL-08	RHOB 2150
Blaine Luetkemeyer, MO-03	RHOB 2230
Bill Huizenga, MI-04	RHOB 2232
Ann Wagner, MO-02	RHOB 2350
Andy Barr, KY-06	RHOB 2430
Roger Williams, TX-25	RHOB 2336
French Hill, AR-02	LHOB 1533
Tom Emmer, MN-06	CHOB 464
Barry Loudermilk, GA-11	RHOB 2133
Alex Mooney, WV-02	RHOB 2228
Warren Davidson, OH-08	RHOB 2113
John Rose, TN-06	LHOB 2238
Bryan Steil, WI-01	LHOB 1526
Lance Gooden, TX-05	RHOB 2431
William Timmons, SC-04	CHOB 267
Ralph Norman, SC-05	CHOB 569
Dan Meuser, PA-09	CHOB 350
Young Kim, CA-40	LHOB 1306
Byron Donalds, FL-19	LHOB 1719

Minority:

RM: Maxine Waters, CA-43	RHOB 2221
Nydia Velazquez, NY-07	RHOB 2302
Brad Sherman, CA-32	RHOB 2365
Gregory Meeks, NY-05	RHOB 2310
David Scott, GA-13	CHOB 468
Stephen Lynch, MA-08	RHOB 2109
Al Green, TX-09	RHOB 2347
Emanuel Cleaver, MO-05	RHOB 2217
Jim Himes, CT-04	RHOB 2137
Bill Foster, IL-11	RHOB 2366
Joyce Beatty, OH-03	RHOB 2079
Juan Vargas, CA-52	RHOB 2334
Josh Gottheimer, NJ-05	CHOB 203
Vicente Gonzalez, TX-34	CHOB 154
Sean Casten, IL-06	RHOB 2440
Ayanna Pressley, MA-07	LHOB 1108
Ritchie Torres, NY-15	LHOB 1414
Steven Horsford, NV-04	CHOB 406
Rashida Tlaib, MI-12	RHOB 2438
Sylvia Garcia, TX-29	RHOB 2419
Nikema Williams, GA-05	LHOB 1406
Wiley Nickel, NC-13	LHOB 1133
Brittany Pettersen, CO-07	LHOB 1230

Andrew Garbarino, NY-02	RHOB 2344
Scott Fitzgerald, WI-05	LHOB 1507
Mike Flood, NE-01	CHOB 343
Michael Lawler, NY-17	LHOB 1013
Monica De La Cruz, TX-15	LHOB 1415
Andy Ogles, TN-05	CHOB 151
Erin Houchin, IN-09	LHOB 1632
Zach Nunn, IA-03	LHOB 1232

Majority CoS: Matthew P. Hoffmann   **Minority CoS:** Charla G. Ouertatani

———————————— Subcommittees ————————————

CAPITAL MARKETS
Room: RHOB 2129
Phone: 202.225.7502

Majority:		Minority:	
C: Ann Wagner, MO-02	RHOB 2350	RM: Brad Sherman, CA-32	RHOB 2365
Andrew Garbarino, NY-02	RHOB 2344	Gregory Meeks, NY-05	RHOB 2310
Frank Lucas, OK-03	RHOB 2405	David Scott, GA-13	CHOB 468
Pete Sessions, TX-17	RHOB 2204	Juan Vargas, CA-52	RHOB 2334
Bill Huizenga, MI-04	RHOB 2232	Josh Gottheimer, NJ-05	CHOB 203
French Hill, AR-02	LHOB 1533	Vicente Gonzalez, TX-34	CHOB 154
Tom Emmer, MN-06	CHOB 464	Sean Casten, IL-06	RHOB 2440
Alex Mooney, WV-02	RHOB 2228	Wiley Nickel, NC-13	LHOB 1133
Bryan Steil, WI-01	LHOB 1526	Stephen Lynch, MA-08	RHOB 2109
Dan Meuser, PA-09	CHOB 350	Emanuel Cleaver, MO-05	RHOB 2217
Michael Lawler, NY-17	LHOB 1013		
Zach Nunn, IA-03	LHOB 1232		
Erin Houchin, IN-09	LHOB 1632		

DIGITAL ASSETS, FINANCIAL TECHNOLOGY & INCLUSION
Room: RHOB 2129
Phone: 202.225.7502

Majority:		Minority:	
French Hill, AR-02	LHOB 1533	Stephen Lynch, MA-08	RHOB 2109
Warren Davidson, OH-08	RHOB 2113	Bill Foster, IL-11	RHOB 2366
Frank Lucas, OK-03	RHOB 2405	Josh Gottheimer, NJ-05	CHOB 203
Tom Emmer, MN-06	CHOB 464	Ritchie Torres, NY-15	LHOB 1414
John Rose, TN-06	LHOB 2238	Brad Sherman, CA-32	RHOB 2365
Bryan Steil, WI-01	LHOB 1526	Al Green, TX-09	RHOB 2347
William Timmons, SC-04	CHOB 267	Sean Casten, IL-06	RHOB 2440
Byron Donalds, FL-19	LHOB 1719	Wiley Nickel, NC-13	LHOB 1133
Mike Flood, NE-01	CHOB 343		
Erin Houchin, IN-09	LHOB 1632		

FINANCIAL INSTITUTIONS & MONETARY POLICY
Room: RHOB 2129
Phone: 202.225.7502

Majority:		Minority:	
C: Andy Barr, KY-06	RHOB 2430	RM: Bill Foster, IL-11	RHOB 2366
Barry Loudermilk, GA-11	RHOB 2133	Nydia Velazquez, NY-07	RHOB 2302
Bill Posey, FL-08	RHOB 2150	Brad Sherman, CA-32	RHOB 2365
Blaine Luetkemeyer, MO-03	RHOB 2230	Gregory Meeks, NY-05	RHOB 2310
		David Scott, GA-13	CHOB 468
Roger Williams, TX-25	RHOB 2336	Al Green, TX-09	RHOB 2347
John Rose, TN-06	LHOB 2238	Joyce Beatty, OH-03	RHOB 2079
William Timmons, SC-04	CHOB 267	Juan Vargas, CA-52	RHOB 2334
Ralph Norman, SC-05	CHOB 569	Sean Casten, IL-06	RHOB 2440
Scott Fitzgerald, WI-05	LHOB 1507	Ayanna Pressley, MA-07	LHOB 1108
Young Kim, CA-40	LHOB 1306		
Byron Donalds, FL-19	LHOB 1719		
Monica De La Cruz, TX-15	LHOB 1415		
Andy Ogles, TN-05	CHOB 151		

HOUSING & INSURANCE
Room: RHOB 2129
Phone: 202.225.7502

Majority:		Minority:	
C: Warren Davidson, OH-08	RHOB 2113	RM: Emanuel Cleaver, MO-05	RHOB 2217
Monica De La Cruz, TX-15	LHOB 1415	Nydia Velazquez, NY-07	RHOB 2302
Bill Posey, FL-08	RHOB 2150	Rashida Tlaib, MI-12	RHOB 2438
Blaine Luetkemeyer, MO-03	RHOB 2230	Ritchie Torres, NY-15	LHOB 1414
		Ayanna Pressley, MA-07	LHOB 1108
Ralph Norman, SC-05	CHOB 569	Sylvia Garcia, TX-29	RHOB 2419
Scott Fitzgerald, WI-05	LHOB 1507	Nikema Williams, GA-05	LHOB 1406
Andrew Garbarino, NY-02	RHOB 2344	Steven Horsford, NV-04	CHOB 406
Mike Flood, NE-01	CHOB 343	Brittany Pettersen, CO-07	LHOB 1230
Michael Lawler, NY-17	LHOB 1013		

Erin Houchin, IN-09   LHOB 1632

NAT'L SECURITY, ILLICIT FINANCE & INTERN'L FINANCIAL INSTITUTIONS

Room: RHOB 2129
Phone: 202.225.7502

Majority:		Minority:	
C: Blaine Luetkemeyer, MO-03	RHOB 2230	**RM: Joyce Beatty, OH-03**	RHOB 2079
		Vicente Gonzalez, TX-34	CHOB 154
Young Kim, CA-40	LHOB 1306	Wiley Nickel, NC-13	LHOB 1133
Andy Barr, KY-06	RHOB 2430	Brittany Pettersen, CO-07	LHOB 1230
Roger Williams, TX-25	RHOB 2336	Bill Foster, IL-11	RHOB 2366
Dan Meuser, PA-09	CHOB 350	Juan Vargas, CA-52	RHOB 2334
Zach Nunn, IA-03	LHOB 1232	Josh Gottheimer, NJ-05	CHOB 203
Monica De La Cruz, TX-15	LHOB 1415		
Andy Ogles, TN-05	CHOB 151		

OVERSIGHT & INVESTIGATIONS

Room: Thomas P. O'Neill Federal Bldg. 4340
Phone: 202.225.7502

Majority:		Minority:	
C: Bill Huizenga, MI-04	RHOB 2232	**RM: Al Green, TX-09**	RHOB 2347
John Rose, TN-06	LHOB 2238	Steven Horsford, NV-04	CHOB 406
Pete Sessions, TX-17	RHOB 2204	Rashida Tlaib, MI-12	RHOB 2438
Ann Wagner, MO-02	RHOB 2350	Sylvia Garcia, TX-29	RHOB 2419
Alex Mooney, WV-02	RHOB 2228	Nikema Williams, GA-05	LHOB 1406
Dan Meuser, PA-09	CHOB 350		
Andy Ogles, TN-05	CHOB 151		

FOREIGN AFFAIRS

Room: RHOB 2170
Website: foreignaffairs.house.gov
Phone: 202.226.8467
Ratio: 27 Republicans/23 Democrats
Subcommittees: 7

Majority:		Minority:	
C: Michael McCaul, TX-10	RHOB 2300	**RM: Gregory Meeks, NY-05**	RHOB 2310
Ann Wagner, MO-02	RHOB 2350		
Chris Smith, NJ-04	RHOB 2373	Kathy Manning, NC-06	CHOB 307
Joe Wilson, SC-02	LHOB 1436	Brad Sherman, CA-32	RHOB 2365
Scott Perry, PA-10	RHOB 2160	Gerry Connolly, VA-11	RHOB 2265
Darrell Issa, CA-48	RHOB 2108	Bill Keating, MA-09	RHOB 2351
Brian Mast, FL-21	RHOB 2182	David Cicilline, RI-01	RHOB 2233
Ken Buck, CO-04	RHOB 2455	Ami Bera, CA-06	CHOB 172
Tim Burchett, TN-02	LHOB 1122	Joaquin Castro, TX-20	RHOB 2241
Mark Green, TN-07	RHOB 2446	Dina Titus, NV-01	RHOB 2464
Andy Barr, KY-06	RHOB 2430	Ted Lieu, CA-36	RHOB 2454
Ronny Jackson, TX-13	CHOB 118	Susan Wild, PA-07	LHOB 1027
Young Kim, CA-40	LHOB 1306	Dean Phillips, MN-03	RHOB 2452
Maria Salazar, FL-27	RHOB 2162	Colin Allred, TX-32	CHOB 348
Bill Huizenga, MI-04	RHOB 2232	Andy Kim, NJ-03	RHOB 2444
Amata Radewagen, AS-01	RHOB 2001	Sara Jacobs, CA-51	LHOB 1314
French Hill, AR-02	LHOB 1533	Sheila Cherfilus-McCormick, FL-20	CHOB 242
Warren Davidson, OH-08	RHOB 2113		
Jim Baird, IN-04	RHOB 2303	Greg Stanton, AZ-04	CHOB 207
Mike Waltz, FL-06	CHOB 244	Madeleine Dean, PA-04	CHOB 120
Thomas Kean, NJ-07	CHOB 251	Jared Moskowitz, FL-23	LHOB 1130
Michael Lawler, NY-17	LHOB 1013	Jonathan Jackson, IL-01	LHOB 1641
Cory Mills, FL-07	LHOB 1237	Sydney Kamlager-Dove, CA-37	LHOB 1419
Richard McCormick, GA-06	LHOB 1213		
Nathaniel Moran, TX-01	LHOB 1541	Jim Costa, CA-21	RHOB 2081
John James, MI-10	LHOB 1319	Jason Crow, CO-06	LHOB 1323
Keith Self, TX-03	LHOB 1113		

Majority CoS: Brendan P. Shields   **Minority CoS:** Sophia Lafargue

———————————— Subcommittees ————————————

AFRICA

Room: RHOB 2170
Phone: 202.226.8467

Majority:		Minority:	
C: John James, MI-10	LHOB 1319	**RM: Sara Jacobs, CA-51**	LHOB 1314
Chris Smith, NJ-04	RHOB 2373	Sheila Cherfilus-McCormick, FL-20	CHOB 242
Young Kim, CA-40	LHOB 1306		
Jim Baird, IN-04	RHOB 2303	Colin Allred, TX-32	CHOB 348
Thomas Kean, NJ-07	CHOB 251	Jonathan Jackson, IL-01	LHOB 1641
Cory Mills, FL-07	LHOB 1237		

EUROPE
Room: RHOB 2170
Phone: 202.226.8467

Majority:		Minority:	
C: Thomas Kean, NJ-07	CHOB 251	**RM: Bill Keating, MA-09**	RHOB 2351
Joe Wilson, SC-02	LHOB 1436	Dina Titus, NV-01	RHOB 2464
Darrell Issa, CA-48	RHOB 2108	Madeleine Dean, PA-04	CHOB 120
Ann Wagner, MO-02	RHOB 2350	Jim Costa, CA-21	RHOB 2081
Bill Huizenga, MI-04	RHOB 2232	David Cicilline, RI-01	RHOB 2233
Michael Lawler, NY-17	LHOB 1013	Susan Wild, PA-07	LHOB 1027
Nathaniel Moran, TX-01	LHOB 1541		
Keith Self, TX-03	LHOB 1113		

GLOBAL HEALTH, GLOBAL HUMAN RIGHTS & INTERN'L ORGANIZATIONS
Room: RHOB 2170
Phone: 202.226.8467

Majority:		Minority:	
C: Chris Smith, NJ-04	RHOB 2373	**RM: Susan Wild, PA-07**	LHOB 1027
Maria Salazar, FL-27	RHOB 2162	Ami Bera, CA-06	CHOB 172
Amata Radewagen, AS-01	RHOB 2001	Sara Jacobs, CA-51	LHOB 1314
French Hill, AR-02	LHOB 1533	Kathy Manning, NC-06	CHOB 307
Richard McCormick, GA-06	LHOB 1213		
John James, MI-10	LHOB 1319		

INDO-PACIFIC
Room: RHOB 2170
Phone: 202.226.8467

Majority:		Minority:	
C: Young Kim, CA-40	LHOB 1306	**RM: Ami Bera, CA-06**	CHOB 172
Ann Wagner, MO-02	RHOB 2350	Andy Kim, NJ-03	RHOB 2444
Ken Buck, CO-04	RHOB 2455	Brad Sherman, CA-32	RHOB 2365
Mark Green, TN-07	RHOB 2446	Gerry Connolly, VA-11	RHOB 2265
Andy Barr, KY-06	RHOB 2430	Bill Keating, MA-09	RHOB 2351
Amata Radewagen, AS-01	RHOB 2001		
Warren Davidson, OH-08	RHOB 2113		
Mike Waltz, FL-06	CHOB 244		

MIDDLE EAST, NORTH AFRICA & CENTRAL ASIA
Room: RHOB 2170
Phone: 202.226.8467

Majority:		Minority:	
C: Joe Wilson, SC-02	LHOB 1436	**RM: Dean Phillips, MN-03**	RHOB 2452
Brian Mast, FL-21	RHOB 2182	Brad Sherman, CA-32	RHOB 2365
Tim Burchett, TN-02	LHOB 1122	Gerry Connolly, VA-11	RHOB 2265
Ronny Jackson, TX-13	CHOB 118	David Cicilline, RI-01	RHOB 2233
Jim Baird, IN-04	RHOB 2303	Kathy Manning, NC-06	CHOB 307
Michael Lawler, NY-17	LHOB 1013		
Richard McCormick, GA-06	LHOB 1213		

OVERSIGHT & ACCOUNTABILITY
Room: RHOB 2170
Phone: 202.226.8467

Majority:		Minority:	
C: Brian Mast, FL-21	RHOB 2182	**RM: Jason Crow, CO-06**	LHOB 1323
Scott Perry, PA-10	RHOB 2160	Dina Titus, NV-01	RHOB 2464
Darrell Issa, CA-48	RHOB 2108	Colin Allred, TX-32	CHOB 348
Tim Burchett, TN-02	LHOB 1122	Andy Kim, NJ-03	RHOB 2444
French Hill, AR-02	LHOB 1533	Sheila Cherfilus-	CHOB 242
Mike Waltz, FL-06	CHOB 244	McCormick, FL-20	
Cory Mills, FL-07	LHOB 1237	Madeleine Dean, PA-04	CHOB 120
Nathaniel Moran, TX-01	LHOB 1541		

WESTERN HEMISPHERE
Room: RHOB 2170
Phone: 202.226.8467

Majority:		Minority:	
C: Maria Salazar, FL-27	RHOB 2162	**RM: Joaquin Castro, TX-20**	RHOB 2241
Ken Buck, CO-04	RHOB 2455		
Mark Green, TN-07	RHOB 2446	Greg Stanton, AZ-04	CHOB 207
Bill Huizenga, MI-04	RHOB 2232	Jared Moskowitz, FL-23	LHOB 1130
Warren Davidson, OH-08	RHOB 2113	Sydney Kamlager-Dove,	LHOB 1419
Keith Self, TX-03	LHOB 1113	CA-37	

HOMELAND SECURITY

Room: FHOB H2-117
Website: homeland.house.gov
Phone: 202.226.8417
Ratio: 18 Republicans/15 Democrats
Subcommittees: 6

Majority:		Minority:	
C: Mark Green, TN-07	RHOB 2446	RM: Bennie Thompson, MS-02	RHOB 2466
Michael Guest, MS-03	CHOB 450	Delia Ramirez, IL-03	LHOB 1523
Michael McCaul, TX-10	RHOB 2300	Sheila Jackson Lee, TX-18	RHOB 2426
Clay Higgins, LA-03	CHOB 572	Donald Payne, NJ-10	CHOB 106
Dan Bishop, NC-08	RHOB 2459	Eric Swalwell, CA-14	CHOB 174
Carlos Gimenez, FL-28	CHOB 448	Lou Correa, CA-46	RHOB 2301
August Pfluger, TX-11	LHOB 1124	Troy Carter, LA-02	CHOB 442
Andrew Garbarino, NY-02	RHOB 2344	Shri Thanedar, MI-13	LHOB 1039
Marjorie Greene, GA-14	CHOB 403	Seth Magaziner, RI-02	LHOB 1218
Tony Gonzales, TX-23	RHOB 2244	Glenn Ivey, MD-04	LHOB 1529
Nicholas LaLota, NY-01	LHOB 1530	Daniel Goldman, NY-10	CHOB 245
Mike Ezell, MS-04	CHOB 443	Robert Garcia, CA-42	LHOB 1305
Anthony D'Esposito, NY-04	LHOB 1508	Robert Menendez, NJ-08	LHOB 1007
Laurel Lee, FL-15	LHOB 1118	Yvette Clarke, NY-09	RHOB 2058
Morgan Luttrell, TX-08	LHOB 1320	Dina Titus, NV-01	RHOB 2464
Dale Strong, AL-05	LHOB 1337		
Josh Brecheen, OK-02	LHOB 1208		
Eli Crane, AZ-02	LHOB 1229		

Majority CoS: Kyle D. Klein   **Minority CoS:** Hope E. Goins

--- Subcommittees ---

BORDER SECURITY & ENFORCEMENT
Room: FHOB H2-117
Phone: 202.226.8417

Majority:		Minority:	
C: Clay Higgins, LA-03	CHOB 572	RM: Lou Correa, CA-46	RHOB 2301
Morgan Luttrell, TX-08	LHOB 1320	Sheila Jackson Lee, TX-18	RHOB 2426
Michael Guest, MS-03	CHOB 450	Shri Thanedar, MI-13	LHOB 1039
Tony Gonzales, TX-23	RHOB 2244	Robert Garcia, CA-42	LHOB 1305
Marjorie Greene, GA-14	CHOB 403	Delia Ramirez, IL-03	LHOB 1523
Josh Brecheen, OK-02	LHOB 1208	Bennie Thompson, MS-02	RHOB 2466

COUNTERTERRORISM, LAW ENFORCEMENT & INTELLIGENCE
Room: FHOB H2-117
Phone: 202.226.8417

Majority:		Minority:	
C: August Pfluger, TX-11	LHOB 1124	RM: Seth Magaziner, RI-02	LHOB 1218
Tony Gonzales, TX-23	RHOB 2244		
Dan Bishop, NC-08	RHOB 2459	Lou Correa, CA-46	RHOB 2301
Anthony D'Esposito, NY-04	LHOB 1508	Daniel Goldman, NY-10	CHOB 245
Eli Crane, AZ-02	LHOB 1229	Dina Titus, NV-01	RHOB 2464
		Bennie Thompson, MS-02	RHOB 2466

CYBERSECURITY, INFRASTRUCTURE PROTECTION & INNOVATION
Room: FHOB H2-117
Phone: 202.226.8417

Majority:		Minority:	
C: Andrew Garbarino, NY-02	RHOB 2344	RM: Eric Swalwell, CA-14	CHOB 174
		Sheila Jackson Lee, TX-18	RHOB 2426
Laurel Lee, FL-15	LHOB 1118	Troy Carter, LA-02	CHOB 442
Carlos Gimenez, FL-28	CHOB 448	Robert Menendez, NJ-08	LHOB 1007
Morgan Luttrell, TX-08	LHOB 1320	Bennie Thompson, MS-02	RHOB 2466
Mike Ezell, MS-04	CHOB 443		

EMERGENCY MANAGEMENT & TECHNOLOGY
Room: FHOB H2-117
Phone: 202.226.8417

Majority:		Minority:	
C: Anthony D'Esposito, NY-04	LHOB 1508	RM: Troy Carter, LA-02	CHOB 442
		Donald Payne, NJ-10	CHOB 106
Dale Strong, AL-05	LHOB 1337	Daniel Goldman, NY-10	CHOB 245
Nicholas LaLota, NY-01	LHOB 1530	Bennie Thompson, MS-02	RHOB 2466
Josh Brecheen, OK-02	LHOB 1208		

OVERSIGHT, INVESTIGATIONS & ACCOUNTABILITY
Room: FHOB H2-117
Phone: 202.226.8417

Majority:		Minority:	
C: Dan Bishop, NC-08	RHOB 2459	RM: Glenn Ivey, MD-04	LHOB 1529
Mike Ezell, MS-04	CHOB 443	Shri Thanedar, MI-13	LHOB 1039
Marjorie Greene, GA-14	CHOB 403	Delia Ramirez, IL-03	LHOB 1523

Dale Strong, AL-05	LHOB 1337	Yvette Clarke, NY-09	RHOB 2058
Eli Crane, AZ-02	LHOB 1229	Bennie Thompson, MS-02	RHOB 2466

TRANSPORTATION & MARITIME SECURITY
Room: FHOB H2-117
Phone: 202.226.8417

Majority:		Minority:	
C: Carlos Gimenez, FL-28	CHOB 448	**RM: Shri Thanedar, MI-13**	LHOB 1039
Nicholas LaLota, NY-01	LHOB 1530	Donald Payne, NJ-10	CHOB 106
Clay Higgins, LA-03	CHOB 572	Robert Garcia, CA-42	LHOB 1305
Laurel Lee, FL-15	LHOB 1118	Bennie Thompson, MS-02	RHOB 2466

JUDICIARY

Room: RHOB 2138
Website: judiciary.house.gov
Phone: 202.225.6906
Ratio: 25 Republicans/19 Democrats
Subcommittees: 7

Majority:		Minority:	
C: Jim Jordan, OH-04	RHOB 2056	**RM: Jerry Nadler, NY-12**	RHOB 2132
Darrell Issa, CA-48	RHOB 2108	Zoe Lofgren, CA-18	LHOB 1401
Ken Buck, CO-04	RHOB 2455	Sheila Jackson Lee, TX-18	RHOB 2426
Matt Gaetz, FL-01	RHOB 2021	Steve Cohen, TN-09	RHOB 2268
Mike Johnson, LA-04	CHOB 568	Hank Johnson, GA-04	RHOB 2240
Andy Biggs, AZ-05	CHOB 252	Adam Schiff, CA-30	RHOB 2309
Tom McClintock, CA-05	RHOB 2256	David Cicilline, RI-01	RHOB 2233
Tom Tiffany, WI-07	CHOB 451	Eric Swalwell, CA-14	CHOB 174
Thomas Massie, KY-04	RHOB 2453	Ted Lieu, CA-36	RHOB 2454
Chip Roy, TX-21	LHOB 1005	Pramila Jayapal, WA-07	RHOB 2346
Dan Bishop, NC-08	RHOB 2459	Lou Correa, CA-46	RHOB 2301
Victoria Spartz, IN-05	LHOB 1609	Mary Scanlon, PA-05	LHOB 1227
Scott Fitzgerald, WI-05	LHOB 1507	Joe Neguse, CO-02	RHOB 2400
Cliff Bentz, OR-02	CHOB 409	Lucy McBath, GA-07	RHOB 2246
Ben Cline, VA-06	RHOB 2443	Madeleine Dean, PA-04	CHOB 120
Lance Gooden, TX-05	RHOB 2431	Veronica Escobar, TX-16	RHOB 2448
Jefferson Van Drew, NJ-02	RHOB 2447	Deborah Ross, NC-02	LHOB 1221
Troy Nehls, TX-22	LHOB 1104	Cori Bush, MO-01	RHOB 2463
Barry Moore, AL-02	LHOB 1504	Glenn Ivey, MD-04	LHOB 1529
Kevin Kiley, CA-03	LHOB 1032		
Harriet Hageman, WY-01	LHOB 1531		
Nathaniel Moran, TX-01	LHOB 1541		
Laurel Lee, FL-15	LHOB 1118		
Wesley Hunt, TX-38	LHOB 1520		
Russell Fry, SC-07	LHOB 1626		

Majority CoS: Christopher Hixon   **Minority CoS:** Aaron Hiller

———————————— Subcommittees ————————————

ADMINISTRATIVE STATE, REGULATORY REFORM & ANTITRUST
Room: RHOB 2138
Phone: 202.225.6906

Majority:		Minority:	
C: Thomas Massie, KY-04	RHOB 2453	**RM: David Cicilline, RI-01**	RHOB 2233
Darrell Issa, CA-48	RHOB 2108	Hank Johnson, GA-04	RHOB 2240
Ken Buck, CO-04	RHOB 2455	Eric Swalwell, CA-14	CHOB 174
Matt Gaetz, FL-01	RHOB 2021	Ted Lieu, CA-36	RHOB 2454
Mike Johnson, LA-04	CHOB 568	Pramila Jayapal, WA-07	RHOB 2346
Dan Bishop, NC-08	RHOB 2459	Lou Correa, CA-46	RHOB 2301
Victoria Spartz, IN-05	LHOB 1609	Mary Scanlon, PA-05	LHOB 1227
Scott Fitzgerald, WI-05	LHOB 1507	Joe Neguse, CO-02	RHOB 2400
Cliff Bentz, OR-02	CHOB 409	Lucy McBath, GA-07	RHOB 2246
Lance Gooden, TX-05	RHOB 2431	Zoe Lofgren, CA-18	LHOB 1401
Jefferson Van Drew, NJ-02	RHOB 2447	Steve Cohen, TN-09	RHOB 2268
Ben Cline, VA-06	RHOB 2443	Glenn Ivey, MD-04	LHOB 1529
Harriet Hageman, WY-01	LHOB 1531		
Nathaniel Moran, TX-01	LHOB 1541		

CONSTITUTION & LIMITED GOVERNMENT
Room: RHOB 2138
Phone: 202.225.6906

Majority:		Minority:	
C: Mike Johnson, LA-04	CHOB 568	**RM: Mary Scanlon, PA-05**	LHOB 1227
Tom McClintock, CA-05	RHOB 2256	Steve Cohen, TN-09	RHOB 2268
Chip Roy, TX-21	LHOB 1005	Veronica Escobar, TX-16	RHOB 2448
Dan Bishop, NC-08	RHOB 2459	Cori Bush, MO-01	RHOB 2463
Kevin Kiley, CA-03	LHOB 1032	Sheila Jackson Lee, TX-18	RHOB 2426
Harriet Hageman, WY-01	LHOB 1531	Hank Johnson, GA-04	RHOB 2240
Wesley Hunt, TX-38	LHOB 1520		

Russell Fry, SC-07   LHOB 1626

COURTS, INTELLECTUAL PROPERTY & INTERNET
Room: RHOB 2138
Phone: 202.225.6906

Majority:		Minority:	
C: Darrell Issa, CA-48	RHOB 2108	**RM: Hank Johnson, GA-04**	RHOB 2240
Thomas Massie, KY-04	RHOB 2453	Ted Lieu, CA-36	RHOB 2454
Scott Fitzgerald, WI-05	LHOB 1507	Joe Neguse, CO-02	RHOB 2400
Cliff Bentz, OR-02	CHOB 409	Deborah Ross, NC-02	LHOB 1221
Lance Gooden, TX-05	RHOB 2431	Adam Schiff, CA-30	RHOB 2309
Ben Cline, VA-06	RHOB 2443	Zoe Lofgren, CA-18	LHOB 1401
Kevin Kiley, CA-03	LHOB 1032	Madeleine Dean, PA-04	CHOB 120
Nathaniel Moran, TX-01	LHOB 1541	Glenn Ivey, MD-04	LHOB 1529
Laurel Lee, FL-15	LHOB 1118		
Russell Fry, SC-07	LHOB 1626		

CRIME & FEDERAL GOV'T SURVEILLANCE
Room: RHOB 2138
Phone: 202.225.6906

Majority:		Minority:	
C: Andy Biggs, AZ-05	CHOB 252	**RM: Sheila Jackson Lee, TX-18**	RHOB 2426
Matt Gaetz, FL-01	RHOB 2021		
Tom Tiffany, WI-07	CHOB 451	Lucy McBath, GA-07	RHOB 2246
Troy Nehls, TX-22	LHOB 1104	Madeleine Dean, PA-04	CHOB 120
Barry Moore, AL-02	LHOB 1504	Cori Bush, MO-01	RHOB 2463
Laurel Lee, FL-15	LHOB 1118	Steve Cohen, TN-09	RHOB 2268
Russell Fry, SC-07	LHOB 1626	David Cicilline, RI-01	RHOB 2233
Kevin Kiley, CA-03	LHOB 1032		

IMMIGRATION, INTEGRITY, SECURITY & ENFORCEMENT
Room: RHOB 2138
Phone: 202.225.6906

Majority:		Minority:	
C: Tom McClintock, CA-05	RHOB 2256	**RM: Pramila Jayapal, WA-07**	RHOB 2346
Ken Buck, CO-04	RHOB 2455		
Andy Biggs, AZ-05	CHOB 252	Zoe Lofgren, CA-18	LHOB 1401
Tom Tiffany, WI-07	CHOB 451	Lou Correa, CA-46	RHOB 2301
Chip Roy, TX-21	LHOB 1005	Veronica Escobar, TX-16	RHOB 2448
Jefferson Van Drew, NJ-02	RHOB 2447	Sheila Jackson Lee, TX-18	RHOB 2426
Troy Nehls, TX-22	LHOB 1104	Deborah Ross, NC-02	LHOB 1221
Barry Moore, AL-02	LHOB 1504	David Cicilline, RI-01	RHOB 2233
Wesley Hunt, TX-38	LHOB 1520	Eric Swalwell, CA-14	CHOB 174
Victoria Spartz, IN-05	LHOB 1609		

RESPONSIVENESS & ACCOUNTABILITY TO OVERSIGHT
Room: RHOB 2138
Phone: 202.225.6906

Majority:		Minority:	
C: Ben Cline, VA-06	RHOB 2443	**RM: Eric Swalwell, CA-14**	CHOB 174
Jefferson Van Drew, NJ-02	RHOB 2447	Glenn Ivey, MD-04	LHOB 1529
Laurel Lee, FL-15	LHOB 1118		
Nathaniel Moran, TX-01	LHOB 1541		

SELECT WEAPONIZATION OF THE FEDERAL GOVERNMENT
Room: RHOB 2142
Phone: 202.225.6906

Majority:		Minority:	
C: Jim Jordan, OH-04	RHOB 2056	**RM: Stacey Plaskett, VI-01**	RHOB 2059
Darrell Issa, CA-48	RHOB 2108	Stephen Lynch, MA-08	RHOB 2109
Thomas Massie, KY-04	RHOB 2453	Linda Sanchez, CA-38	RHOB 2428
Chris Stewart, UT-02	CHOB 166	Debbie Wasserman Schultz, FL-25	CHOB 270
Elise Stefanik, NY-21	RHOB 2211		
Mike Johnson, LA-04	CHOB 568	Gerry Connolly, VA-11	RHOB 2265
Matt Gaetz, FL-01	RHOB 2021	John Garamendi, CA-08	RHOB 2004
Kelly Armstrong, ND-01	RHOB 2267	Colin Allred, TX-32	CHOB 348
Greg Steube, FL-17	RHOB 2457	Sylvia Garcia, TX-29	RHOB 2419
Dan Bishop, NC-08	RHOB 2459	Daniel Goldman, NY-10	CHOB 245
Kat Cammack, FL-03	RHOB 2421	Jerry Nadler, NY-12	RHOB 2132
Harriet Hageman, WY-01	LHOB 1531		

NATURAL RESOURCES

Room: LHOB 1329
Website: naturalresources.house.gov
Phone: 202.225.2761
Ratio: 25 Republicans/29 Democrats
Subcommittees: 5
Majority: **Minority:**

C: Bruce Westerman, AR-04	CHOB 202	**RM: Raul Grijalva, AZ-07**	LHOB 1203
		Steve Cohen, TN-09	RHOB 2268
Doug Lamborn, CO-05	RHOB 2371	Diana DeGette, CO-01	RHOB 2111
Rob Wittman, VA-01	RHOB 2055	Paul Tonko, NY-20	RHOB 2369
Tom McClintock, CA-05	RHOB 2256	Betty McCollum, MN-04	RHOB 2426
Paul Gosar, AZ-09	RHOB 2057	Julia Brownley, CA-26	RHOB 2262
Garret Graves, LA-06	RHOB 2402	Jesús Garcia, IL-04	LHOB 1519
Amata Radewagen, AS-01	RHOB 2001	Lori Trahan, MA-03	RHOB 2439
Doug LaMalfa, CA-01	CHOB 408	Rashida Tlaib, MI-12	RHOB 2438
Daniel Webster, FL-11	RHOB 2184	Sydney Kamlager-Dove, CA-37	LHOB 1419
Jenniffer González-Colón, PR-01	RHOB 2338	Grace Napolitano, CA-31	LHOB 1610
Russ Fulcher, ID-01	LHOB 1514	Jim Costa, CA-21	RHOB 2081
Pete Stauber, MN-08	CHOB 145	Gregorio Sablan, MP-01	RHOB 2267
John Curtis, UT-03	RHOB 2323	Jared Huffman, CA-02	RHOB 2445
Tom Tiffany, WI-07	CHOB 451	Ruben Gallego, AZ-03	LHOB 1114
Jerry Carl, AL-01	LHOB 1330	Joe Neguse, CO-02	RHOB 2400
Matt Rosendale, MT-02	LHOB 1023	Mike Levin, CA-49	RHOB 2352
Lauren Boebert, CO-03	LHOB 1713	Katie Porter, CA-47	LHOB 1233
Cliff Bentz, OR-02	CHOB 409	Teresa Leger Fernandez, NM-03	LHOB 1510
Jen Kiggans, VA-02	LHOB 1037	Melanie Stansbury, NM-01	LHOB 1421
James Moylan, GU-01	LHOB 1628	Mary Peltola, AK-01	CHOB 153
Wesley Hunt, TX-38	LHOB 1520	Alexandria Ocasio-Cortez, NY-14	CHOB 250
Michael Collins, GA-10	LHOB 1223	Kevin Mullin, CA-15	LHOB 1404
Anna Luna, FL-13	LHOB 1017	Valerie Hoyle, OR-04	LHOB 1620
John Duarte, CA-13	LHOB 1535	Seth Magaziner, RI-02	LHOB 1218
Harriet Hageman, WY-01	LHOB 1531	Nydia Velazquez, NY-07	RHOB 2302
		Ed Case, HI-01	RHOB 2210
		Debbie Dingell, MI-06	CHOB 102

Majority CoS: Vivian Moeglein   **Minority CoS:** Lora Snyder

––––––––––––– Subcommittees –––––––––––––

ENERGY & MINERAL RESOURCES
Room: LHOB 1329
Phone: 202.225.2761

Majority:		Minority:	
C: Pete Stauber, MN-08	CHOB 145	**RM: Mike Levin, CA-49**	RHOB 2352
Wesley Hunt, TX-38	LHOB 1520	Diana DeGette, CO-01	RHOB 2111
Doug Lamborn, CO-05	RHOB 2371	Betty McCollum, MN-04	RHOB 2426
Rob Wittman, VA-01	RHOB 2055	Jared Huffman, CA-02	RHOB 2445
Paul Gosar, AZ-09	RHOB 2057	Debbie Dingell, MI-06	CHOB 102
Garret Graves, LA-06	RHOB 2402	Katie Porter, CA-47	LHOB 1233
Daniel Webster, FL-11	RHOB 2184		
Russ Fulcher, ID-01	LHOB 1514		
John Curtis, UT-03	RHOB 2323		
Tom Tiffany, WI-07	CHOB 451		
Matt Rosendale, MT-02	LHOB 1023		
Lauren Boebert, CO-03	LHOB 1713		
Michael Collins, GA-10	LHOB 1223		
John Duarte, CA-13	LHOB 1535		

INDIAN & INSULAR AFFAIRS
Room: LHOB 1329
Phone: 202.225.2761

Majority:		Minority:	
C: Harriet Hageman, WY-01	LHOB 1531	**RM: Teresa Leger Fernandez, NM-03**	LHOB 1510
Jenniffer González-Colón, PR-01	RHOB 2338	Betty McCollum, MN-04	RHOB 2426
		Melanie Stansbury, NM-01	LHOB 1421
Amata Radewagen, AS-01	RHOB 2001	Ruben Gallego, AZ-03	LHOB 1114
Doug LaMalfa, CA-01	CHOB 408	Darren Soto, FL-09	RHOB 2353
Jerry Carl, AL-01	LHOB 1330	Ed Case, HI-01	RHOB 2210
James Moylan, GU-01	LHOB 1628	Jesús Garcia, IL-04	LHOB 1519

NATIONAL PARKS, FORESTS & PUBLIC LANDS
Room: LHOB 1329
Phone: 202.225.2761

Majority:		Minority:	
C: Tom Tiffany, WI-07	CHOB 451	**RM: Joe Neguse, CO-02**	RHOB 2400
John Curtis, UT-03	RHOB 2323	Diana DeGette, CO-01	RHOB 2111
Doug Lamborn, CO-05	RHOB 2371	Paul Tonko, NY-20	RHOB 2369
Tom McClintock, CA-05	RHOB 2256	Gregorio Sablan, MP-01	RHOB 2267
Russ Fulcher, ID-01	LHOB 1514	Debbie Dingell, MI-06	CHOB 102
Pete Stauber, MN-08	CHOB 145	Ruben Gallego, AZ-03	LHOB 1114

Cliff Bentz, OR-02	CHOB 409	Katie Porter, CA-47	LHOB 1233
Jen Kiggans, VA-02	LHOB 1037	Ed Case, HI-01	RHOB 2210
James Moylan, GU-01	LHOB 1628	Lori Trahan, MA-03	RHOB 2439
		Rashida Tlaib, MI-12	RHOB 2438
		Teresa Leger Fernandez, NM-03	LHOB 1510

OVERSIGHT & INVESTIGATIONS
Room: LHOB 1329
Phone: 202.225.2761

Majority:		Minority:	
C: Paul Gosar, AZ-09	RHOB 2057	**RM: Katie Porter, CA-47**	LHOB 1233
Michael Collins, GA-10	LHOB 1223	Steve Cohen, TN-09	RHOB 2268
Matt Rosendale, MT-02	LHOB 1023	Nydia Velazquez, NY-07	RHOB 2302
Wesley Hunt, TX-38	LHOB 1520	Jared Huffman, CA-02	RHOB 2445
Anna Luna, FL-13	LHOB 1017	Jesús Garcia, IL-04	LHOB 1519

WATER, WILDLIFE & FISHERIES
Room: LHOB 1329
Phone: 202.225.2761

Majority:		Minority:	
C: Cliff Bentz, OR-02	CHOB 409	**RM: Jared Huffman, CA-02**	RHOB 2445
Jen Kiggans, VA-02	LHOB 1037	Steve Cohen, TN-09	RHOB 2268
Rob Wittman, VA-01	RHOB 2055	Nydia Velazquez, NY-07	RHOB 2302
Tom McClintock, CA-05	RHOB 2256	Jim Costa, CA-21	RHOB 2081
Garret Graves, LA-06	RHOB 2402	Grace Napolitano, CA-31	LHOB 1610
Amata Radewagen, AS-01	RHOB 2001	Raul Grijalva, AZ-07	LHOB 1203
Doug LaMalfa, CA-01	CHOB 408	Julia Brownley, CA-26	RHOB 2262
Daniel Webster, FL-11	RHOB 2184	Melanie Stansbury, NM-01	LHOB 1421
Jenniffer González-Colón, PR-01	RHOB 2338	Debbie Dingell, MI-06	CHOB 102
Jerry Carl, AL-01	LHOB 1330	Darren Soto, FL-09	RHOB 2353
Lauren Boebert, CO-03	LHOB 1713	Ed Case, HI-01	RHOB 2210
Anna Luna, FL-13	LHOB 1017	Mike Levin, CA-49	RHOB 2352
John Duarte, CA-13	LHOB 1535		
Harriet Hageman, WY-01	LHOB 1531		

OVERSIGHT & ACCOUNTABILITY

Room: RHOB 2157
Website: oversight.house.gov
Phone: 202.225.5074
Ratio: 26 Republicans/21 Democrats
Subcommittees: 6

Majority:		Minority:	
C: James Comer, KY-01	RHOB 2410	**RM: Jamie Raskin, MD-08**	RHOB 2242
Jim Jordan, OH-04	RHOB 2056	Eleanor Norton, DC-01	RHOB 2136
Mike Turner, OH-10	RHOB 2082	Stephen Lynch, MA-08	RHOB 2109
Paul Gosar, AZ-09	RHOB 2057	Gerry Connolly, VA-11	RHOB 2265
Virginia Foxx, NC-05	RHOB 2462	Raja Krishnamoorthi, IL-08	RHOB 2367
Glenn Grothman, WI-06	LHOB 1511	Ro Khanna, CA-17	CHOB 306
Gary Palmer, AL-06	CHOB 170	Kweisi Mfume, MD-07	RHOB 2263
Clay Higgins, LA-03	CHOB 572	Alexandria Ocasio-Cortez, NY-14	CHOB 250
Andy Biggs, AZ-05	CHOB 252		
Nancy Mace, SC-01	LHOB 1728	Katie Porter, CA-47	LHOB 1233
Jake LaTurner, KS-02	RHOB 2441	Cori Bush, MO-01	RHOB 2463
Pat Fallon, TX-04	RHOB 2416	Shontel Brown, OH-11	CHOB 449
Byron Donalds, FL-19	LHOB 1719	Jimmy Gomez, CA-34	CHOB 506
Pete Sessions, TX-17	RHOB 2204	Melanie Stansbury, NM-01	LHOB 1421
Kelly Armstrong, ND-01	RHOB 2267	Robert Garcia, CA-42	LHOB 1305
Scott Perry, PA-10	RHOB 2160	Maxwell Frost, FL-10	LHOB 1224
William Timmons, SC-04	CHOB 267	Becca Balint, VT-01	LHOB 1408
Tim Burchett, TN-02	LHOB 1122	Summer Lee, PA-12	CHOB 243
Marjorie Greene, GA-14	CHOB 403	Gregorio Casar, TX-35	LHOB 1339
Lisa McClain, MI-09	CHOB 444	Jasmine Crockett, TX-30	LHOB 1616
Lauren Boebert, CO-03	LHOB 1713	Daniel Goldman, NY-10	CHOB 245
Russell Fry, SC-07	LHOB 1626	Jared Moskowitz, FL-23	LHOB 1130
Anna Luna, FL-13	LHOB 1017		
Chuck Edwards, NC-11	LHOB 1505		
Nicholas Langworthy, NY-23	LHOB 1630		
Eric Burlison, MO-07	LHOB 1108		

Majority CoS: Mark D. Marin   **Minority CoS:** Julie Tagen
——————————— Subcommittees ———————————

CYBERSECURITY, INFORMATION TECHNOLOGY & GOV'T INNOVATION
Room: RHOB 2157
Phone: 202.225.5074

Majority:		Minority:	
C: Nancy Mace, SC-01	LHOB 1728	Gerry Connolly, VA-11	RHOB 2265
William Timmons, SC-04	CHOB 267	Ro Khanna, CA-17	CHOB 306
Marjorie Greene, GA-14	CHOB 403	Stephen Lynch, MA-08	RHOB 2109
Tim Burchett, TN-02	LHOB 1122	Kweisi Mfume, MD-07	RHOB 2263
Anna Luna, FL-13	LHOB 1017	Jimmy Gomez, CA-34	CHOB 506
Chuck Edwards, NC-11	LHOB 1505	Daniel Goldman, NY-10	CHOB 245
Nicholas Langworthy, NY-23	LHOB 1630	Jared Moskowitz, FL-23	LHOB 1130
Eric Burlison, MO-07	LHOB 1108		

ECONOMIC GROWTH, ENERGY POLICY & REGULATORY AFFAIRS
Room: RHOB 2157
Phone: 202.225.5074

Majority:		Minority:	
C: Pat Fallon, TX-04	RHOB 2416	Cori Bush, MO-01	RHOB 2463
Byron Donalds, FL-19	LHOB 1719	Shontel Brown, OH-11	CHOB 449
Lauren Boebert, CO-03	LHOB 1713	Melanie Stansbury, NM-01	LHOB 1421
Nicholas Langworthy, NY-23	LHOB 1630	Eleanor Norton, DC-01	RHOB 2136
Anna Luna, FL-13	LHOB 1017	Ro Khanna, CA-17	CHOB 306
Chuck Edwards, NC-11	LHOB 1505	Jamie Raskin, MD-08	RHOB 2242
Scott Perry, PA-10	RHOB 2160		
Lisa McClain, MI-09	CHOB 444		
Russell Fry, SC-07	LHOB 1626		

GOVERNMENT OPERATIONS & FEDERAL WORKFORCE
Room: RHOB 2157
Phone: 202.225.5074

Majority:		Minority:	
C: Pete Sessions, TX-17	RHOB 2204	Kweisi Mfume, MD-07	RHOB 2263
Gary Palmer, AL-06	CHOB 170	Eleanor Norton, DC-01	RHOB 2136
Andy Biggs, AZ-05	CHOB 252	Maxwell Frost, FL-10	LHOB 1224
Marjorie Greene, GA-14	CHOB 403	Gregorio Casar, TX-35	LHOB 1339
Clay Higgins, LA-03	CHOB 572	Gerry Connolly, VA-11	RHOB 2265
Byron Donalds, FL-19	LHOB 1719	Shontel Brown, OH-11	CHOB 449
Lauren Boebert, CO-03	LHOB 1713	Melanie Stansbury, NM-01	LHOB 1421
Russell Fry, SC-07	LHOB 1626	Robert Garcia, CA-42	LHOB 1305
Eric Burlison, MO-07	LHOB 1108	Becca Balint, VT-01	LHOB 1408
Chuck Edwards, NC-11	LHOB 1505	Summer Lee, PA-12	CHOB 243
Tim Burchett, TN-02	LHOB 1122		
William Timmons, SC-04	CHOB 267		

HEALTH CARE & FINANCIAL SERVICES
Room: RHOB 2157
Phone: 202.225.5074

Majority:		Minority:	
C: Lisa McClain, MI-09	CHOB 444	Raja Krishnamoorthi, IL-08	RHOB 2367
Paul Gosar, AZ-09	RHOB 2057	Alexandria Ocasio-Cortez, NY-14	CHOB 250
Virginia Foxx, NC-05	RHOB 2462		
Glenn Grothman, WI-06	LHOB 1511	Jimmy Gomez, CA-34	CHOB 506
Russell Fry, SC-07	LHOB 1626	Robert Garcia, CA-42	LHOB 1305
Anna Luna, FL-13	LHOB 1017	Becca Balint, VT-01	LHOB 1408
Nicholas Langworthy, NY-23	LHOB 1630	Summer Lee, PA-12	CHOB 243
Eric Burlison, MO-07	LHOB 1108	Jasmine Crockett, TX-30	LHOB 1616

NATIONAL SECURITY, THE BORDER & FOREIGN AFFAIRS
Room: RHOB 2157
Phone: 202.225.5074

Majority:		Minority:	
C: Glenn Grothman, WI-06	LHOB 1511	Katie Porter, CA-47	LHOB 1233
		Stephen Lynch, MA-08	RHOB 2109
Virginia Foxx, NC-05	RHOB 2462	Daniel Goldman, NY-10	CHOB 245
Clay Higgins, LA-03	CHOB 572	Jared Moskowitz, FL-23	LHOB 1130
Pete Sessions, TX-17	RHOB 2204	Alexandria Ocasio-Cortez, NY-14	CHOB 250
Andy Biggs, AZ-05	CHOB 252		
Jake LaTurner, KS-02	RHOB 2441	Cori Bush, MO-01	RHOB 2463
Kelly Armstrong, ND-01	RHOB 2267	Maxwell Frost, FL-10	LHOB 1224
Scott Perry, PA-10	RHOB 2160	Jasmine Crockett, TX-30	LHOB 1616
Nancy Mace, SC-01	LHOB 1728	Robert Garcia, CA-42	LHOB 1305
Pat Fallon, TX-04	RHOB 2416		

SELECT SUBCOMMITTEE ON THE CORONAVIRUS PANDEMIC
Room: RHOB 2157
Phone: 202.225.5074

Majority:		Minority:	
C: Brad Wenstrup, OH-02	RHOB 2335	**RM: Raul Ruiz, CA-25**	RHOB 2342
Nicole Malliotakis, NY-11	CHOB 351	Debbie Dingell, MI-06	CHOB 102
Mariannette Miller-Meeks, IA-01	LHOB 1034	Kweisi Mfume, MD-07	RHOB 2263
		Deborah Ross, NC-02	LHOB 1221
Debbie Lesko, AZ-08	LHOB 1214	Robert Garcia, CA-42	LHOB 1305
Michael Cloud, TX-27	CHOB 171	Jamie Raskin, MD-08	RHOB 2242
John Joyce, PA-13	CHOB 152		
Marjorie Greene, GA-14	CHOB 403		
Ronny Jackson, TX-13	CHOB 118		
Richard McCormick, GA-06	LHOB 1213		

RULES
Room: The Capitol H-152
Website: rules.house.gov
Phone: 202.225.9191
Ratio: 9 Republicans/4 Democrats
Subcommittees: 2

Majority:		Minority:	
C: Tom Cole, OK-04	RHOB 2207	**RM: Jim McGovern, MA-02**	CHOB 370
Michael Burgess, TX-26	RHOB 2161	Mary Scanlon, PA-05	LHOB 1227
Guy Reschenthaler, PA-14	CHOB 409	Joe Neguse, CO-02	RHOB 2400
Michelle Fischbach, MN-07	LHOB 1004	Teresa Leger Fernandez, NM-03	LHOB 1510
Thomas Massie, KY-04	RHOB 2453		
Ralph Norman, SC-05	CHOB 569		
Chip Roy, TX-21	LHOB 1005		
Erin Houchin, IN-09	LHOB 1632		
Nicholas Langworthy, NY-23	LHOB 1630		

Majority CoS: Kelly A. Dixon Chambers   **Minority CoS:** Donald C. Sisson

--------- Subcommittees ---------

LEGISLATIVE & BUDGET PROCESS
Room: The Capitol H-152
Phone: 202.225.9191

Majority:		Minority:	
C: Michael Burgess, TX-26	RHOB 2161	**RM: Mary Scanlon, PA-05**	LHOB 1227
Tom Cole, OK-04	RHOB 2207	Jim McGovern, MA-02	CHOB 370
		Joe Neguse, CO-02	RHOB 2400

RULES & ORGANIZATION OF THE HOUSE
Room: The Capitol H-152
Phone: 202.225.9191

Majority:		Minority:	
C: Guy Reschenthaler, PA-14	CHOB 409	**RM: Jim McGovern, MA-02**	CHOB 370
		Mary Scanlon, PA-05	LHOB 1227
Tom Cole, OK-04	RHOB 2207	Joe Neguse, CO-02	RHOB 2400

SCIENCE, SPACE & TECHNOLOGY
Room: RHOB 2319
Website: science.house.gov
Phone: 202.225.6371
Ratio: 19 Republicans/16 Democrats
Subcommittees: 5

Majority:		Minority:	
C: Frank Lucas, OK-03	RHOB 2405	**RM: Zoe Lofgren, CA-18**	LHOB 1401
Bill Posey, FL-08	RHOB 2150	Suzanne Bonamici, OR-01	RHOB 2231
Randy Weber, TX-14	CHOB 107	Haley Stevens, MI-11	RHOB 2411
Brian Babin, TX-36	RHOB 2236	Jamaal Bowman, NY-16	CHOB 345
Jim Baird, IN-04	RHOB 2303	Deborah Ross, NC-02	LHOB 1221
Daniel Webster, FL-11	RHOB 2184	Eric Sorensen, IL-17	LHOB 1205
Mike Garcia, CA-27	CHOB 144	Andrea Salinas, OR-06	CHOB 109
Stephanie Bice, OK-05	RHOB 2437	Valerie Foushee, NC-04	LHOB 1716
Jay Obernolte, CA-23	LHOB 1029	Kevin Mullin, CA-15	LHOB 1404
Darrell Issa, CA-48	RHOB 2108	Jeff Jackson, NC-14	LHOB 1318
Rick Crawford, AR-01	RHOB 2422	Emilia Sykes, OH-13	LHOB 1217
Claudia Tenney, NY-24	RHOB 2349	Maxwell Frost, FL-10	LHOB 1224
Scott Franklin, FL-18	CHOB 249	Yadira Caraveo, CO-08	LHOB 1024
Dale Strong, AL-05	LHOB 1337	Summer Lee, PA-12	CHOB 243
Max Miller, OH-07	CHOB 143	Ted Lieu, CA-36	RHOB 2454
Richard McCormick, GA-06	LHOB 1213	Sean Casten, IL-06	RHOB 2440
Michael Collins, GA-10	LHOB 1223		

| Brandon Williams, NY-22 | LHOB 1022 |
| Thomas Kean, NJ-07 | CHOB 251 |

Majority CoS: Josh Mathis **Minority CoS:** Richard Obermann
———————————— Subcommittees ————————————

ENERGY
Room: RHOB 2319
Phone: 202.225.6371

Majority:		Minority:	
C: Brandon Williams, NY-22	LHOB 1022	RM: Jamaal Bowman, NY-16	CHOB 345
Randy Weber, TX-14	CHOB 107	Summer Lee, PA-12	CHOB 243
Claudia Tenney, NY-24	RHOB 2349	Deborah Ross, NC-02	LHOB 1221
Jim Baird, IN-04	RHOB 2303	Eric Sorensen, IL-17	LHOB 1205
Stephanie Bice, OK-05	RHOB 2437	Andrea Salinas, OR-06	CHOB 109
Max Miller, OH-07	CHOB 143	Valerie Foushee, NC-04	LHOB 1716
Thomas Kean, NJ-07	CHOB 251		

ENVIRONMENT
Room: RHOB 2319
Phone: 202.225.6371

Majority:		Minority:	
C: Max Miller, OH-07	CHOB 143	RM: Deborah Ross, NC-02	LHOB 1221
Bill Posey, FL-08	RHOB 2150	Suzanne Bonamici, OR-01	RHOB 2231
Rick Crawford, AR-01	RHOB 2422	Maxwell Frost, FL-10	LHOB 1224
Michael Collins, GA-10	LHOB 1223		

INVESTIGATIONS & OVERSIGHT
Room: RHOB 2319
Phone: 202.225.6371

Majority:		Minority:	
C: Jay Obernolte, CA-23	LHOB 1029	RM: Valerie Foushee, NC-04	LHOB 1716
Brian Babin, TX-36	RHOB 2236		
Richard McCormick, GA-06	LHOB 1213	Kevin Mullin, CA-15	LHOB 1404
Max Miller, OH-07	CHOB 143	Jeff Jackson, NC-14	LHOB 1318

RESEARCH & TECHNOLOGY
Room: RHOB 2319
Phone: 202.225.6371

Majority:		Minority:	
C: Michael Collins, GA-10	LHOB 1223	RM: Haley Stevens, MI-11	RHOB 2411
Darrell Issa, CA-48	RHOB 2108	Andrea Salinas, OR-06	CHOB 109
Rick Crawford, AR-01	RHOB 2422	Kevin Mullin, CA-15	LHOB 1404
Jim Baird, IN-04	RHOB 2303	Emilia Sykes, OH-13	LHOB 1217
Scott Franklin, FL-18	CHOB 249	Suzanne Bonamici, OR-01	RHOB 2231
Brandon Williams, NY-22	LHOB 1022		
Thomas Kean, NJ-07	CHOB 251		

SPACE & AERONAUTICS
Room: RHOB 2319
Phone: 202.225.6371

Majority:		Minority:	
C: Brian Babin, TX-36	RHOB 2236	RM: Eric Sorensen, IL-17	LHOB 1205
Darrell Issa, CA-48	RHOB 2108	Mike Garcia, CA-27	CHOB 144
Bill Posey, FL-08	RHOB 2150	Jeff Jackson, NC-14	LHOB 1318
Daniel Webster, FL-11	RHOB 2184	Yadira Caraveo, CO-08	LHOB 1024
Dale Strong, AL-05	LHOB 1337	Jamaal Bowman, NY-16	CHOB 345
Richard McCormick, GA-06	LHOB 1213		

SMALL BUSINESS

Room: RHOB 2069
Website: smallbusiness.house.gov
Phone: 202.225.5821
Ratio: 14 Republicans/12 Democrats
Subcommittees: 5

Majority:		Minority:	
C: Roger Williams, TX-25	RHOB 2336	RM: Nydia Velazquez, NY-07	RHOB 2302
Blaine Luetkemeyer, MO-03	RHOB 2230	Jared Golden, ME-02	LHOB 1710
Pete Stauber, MN-08	CHOB 145	Kweisi Mfume, MD-07	RHOB 2263
Dan Meuser, PA-09	CHOB 350	Dean Phillips, MN-03	RHOB 2452
Beth Van Duyne, TX-24	LHOB 1725	Greg Landsman, OH-01	LHOB 1432
Maria Salazar, FL-27	RHOB 2162	Marie Gluesenkamp Perez, WA-03	LHOB 1431
Tracey Mann, KS-01	CHOB 344		
Jake Ellzey, TX-06	LHOB 1721	Shri Thanedar, MI-13	LHOB 1039
Marcus Molinaro, NY-19	LHOB 1207	Morgan McGarvey, KY-03	LHOB 1527
Mark Alford, MO-04	LHOB 1516	Hillary Scholten, MI-03	LHOB 1317
Eli Crane, AZ-02	LHOB 1229	Judy Chu, CA-28	RHOB 2423

HOUSE COMMITTEES

Aaron Bean, FL-04	LHOB 1239	Sharice Davids, KS-03	RHOB 2435
Wesley Hunt, TX-38	LHOB 1520	Chris Pappas, NH-01	CHOB 452
Nicholas LaLota, NY-01	LHOB 1530		

Majority CoS: David M. Planning

Minority CoS: Melissa Jung
Minority Sched: Mory Garcia

———————————— Subcommittees ————————————

CONTRACTING & INFRASTRUCTURE
Room: RHOB 2069
Phone: 202.225.5821

Majority:		Minority:	
C: Nicholas LaLota, NY-01	LHOB 1530	**RM: Hillary Scholten,**	LHOB 1317
Maria Salazar, FL-27	RHOB 2162	**MI-03**	
Jake Ellzey, TX-06	LHOB 1721	Kweisi Mfume, MD-07	RHOB 2263
Marcus Molinaro, NY-19	LHOB 1207	Morgan McGarvey, KY-03	LHOB 1527
Aaron Bean, FL-04	LHOB 1239	Judy Chu, CA-28	RHOB 2423
		Shri Thanedar, MI-13	LHOB 1039

ECONOMIC GROWTH, TAX & CAPITAL ACCESS
Room: RHOB 2069
Phone: 202.225.5821

Majority:		Minority:	
C: Dan Meuser, PA-09	CHOB 350	**RM: Greg Landsman,**	LHOB 1432
Blaine Luetkemeyer,	RHOB 2230	**OH-01**	
MO-03		Dean Phillips, MN-03	RHOB 2452
Beth Van Duyne, TX-24	LHOB 1725	Judy Chu, CA-28	RHOB 2423
Mark Alford, MO-04	LHOB 1516	Sharice Davids, KS-03	RHOB 2435
Nicholas LaLota, NY-01	LHOB 1530	Jared Golden, ME-02	LHOB 1710

INNOVATION, ENTREPRENEURSHIP & WORKFORCE DEVELOPMENT
Room: RHOB 2069
Phone: 202.225.5821

Majority:		Minority:	
C: Marcus Molinaro,	LHOB 1207	**RM: Morgan McGarvey,**	LHOB 1527
NY-19		**KY-03**	
Tracey Mann, KS-01	CHOB 344	Shri Thanedar, MI-13	LHOB 1039
Maria Salazar, FL-27	RHOB 2162	Chris Pappas, NH-01	CHOB 452
Jake Ellzey, TX-06	LHOB 1721	Dean Phillips, MN-03	RHOB 2452
Eli Crane, AZ-02	LHOB 1229	Judy Chu, CA-28	RHOB 2423

OVERSIGHT, INVESTIGATIONS & REGULATIONS
Room: RHOB 2069
Phone: 202.225.5821

Majority:		Minority:	
C: Beth Van Duyne, TX-24	LHOB 1725	**RM: Kweisi Mfume, MD-07**	RHOB 2263
Mark Alford, MO-04	LHOB 1516	Marie Gluesenkamp Perez,	LHOB 1431
Eli Crane, AZ-02	LHOB 1229	WA-03	
Aaron Bean, FL-04	LHOB 1239	Jared Golden, ME-02	LHOB 1710
Wesley Hunt, TX-38	LHOB 1520		

RURAL DEVELOPMENT, ENERGY & SUPPLY CHAINS
Room: RHOB 2069
Phone: 202.225.5821

Majority:		Minority:	
C: Wesley Hunt, TX-38	LHOB 1520	**RM: Marie Gluesenkamp**	LHOB 1431
Blaine Luetkemeyer,	RHOB 2230	**Perez, WA-03**	
MO-03		Jared Golden, ME-02	LHOB 1710
Pete Stauber, MN-08	CHOB 145	Hillary Scholten, MI-03	LHOB 1317
Dan Meuser, PA-09	CHOB 350	Greg Landsman, OH-01	LHOB 1432
Tracey Mann, KS-01	CHOB 344		

TRANSPORTATION & INFRASTRUCTURE

Room: RHOB 2165
Website: transportation.house.gov
Phone: 202.225.9446
Ratio: 35 Republicans/30 Democrats
Subcommittees: 6

Majority:		Minority:	
C: Sam Graves, MO-06	LHOB 1135	**RM: Rick Larsen, WA-02**	RHOB 2163
Jefferson Van Drew, NJ-02	RHOB 2447	Eleanor Norton, DC-01	RHOB 2136
Rick Crawford, AR-01	RHOB 2422	Grace Napolitano, CA-31	LHOB 1610
Daniel Webster, FL-11	RHOB 2184	Steve Cohen, TN-09	RHOB 2268
Thomas Massie, KY-04	RHOB 2453	John Garamendi, CA-08	RHOB 2004
Scott Perry, PA-10	RHOB 2160	Hank Johnson, GA-04	RHOB 2240
Brian Babin, TX-36	RHOB 2236	Andre Carson, IN-07	RHOB 2135
Garret Graves, LA-06	RHOB 2402	Dina Titus, NV-01	RHOB 2464
David Rouzer, NC-07	RHOB 2333	Jared Huffman, CA-02	RHOB 2445

Mike Bost, IL-12	CHOB 352	Julia Brownley, CA-26	RHOB 2262
Doug LaMalfa, CA-01	CHOB 408	Frederica Wilson, FL-24	RHOB 2080
Bruce Westerman, AR-04	CHOB 202	Donald Payne, NJ-10	CHOB 106
Brian Mast, FL-21	RHOB 2182	Mark DeSaulnier, CA-10	CHOB 503
Jenniffer González-Colón, PR-01	RHOB 2338	Salud Carbajal, CA-24	RHOB 2331
		Greg Stanton, AZ-04	CHOB 207
Pete Stauber, MN-08	CHOB 145	Colin Allred, TX-32	CHOB 348
Tim Burchett, TN-02	LHOB 1122	Sharice Davids, KS-03	RHOB 2435
Dusty Johnson, SD-01	LHOB 1714	Jesús Garcia, IL-04	LHOB 1519
Troy Nehls, TX-22	LHOB 1104	Chris Pappas, NH-01	CHOB 452
Lance Gooden, TX-05	RHOB 2431	Seth Moulton, MA-06	LHOB 1127
Tracey Mann, KS-01	CHOB 344	Jake Auchincloss, MA-04	LHOB 1524
Burgess Owens, UT-04	LHOB 1039	Marilyn Strickland, WA-10	LHOB 1708
Rudy Yakym, IN-02	CHOB 349	Troy Carter, LA-02	CHOB 442
Lori Chavez-DeRemer, OR-05	LHOB 1722	Patrick Ryan, NY-18	LHOB 1030
		Mary Peltola, AK-01	CHOB 153
Chuck Edwards, NC-11	LHOB 1505	Robert Menendez, NJ-08	LHOB 1007
Thomas Kean, NJ-07	CHOB 251	Valerie Hoyle, OR-04	LHOB 1620
Anthony D'Esposito, NY-04	LHOB 1508	Emilia Sykes, OH-13	LHOB 1217
Eric Burlison, MO-07	LHOB 1108	Hillary Scholten, MI-03	LHOB 1317
John James, MI-10	LHOB 1319	Valerie Foushee, NC-04	LHOB 1716
Derrick Van Orden, WI-03	LHOB 1513		
Brandon Williams, NY-22	LHOB 1022		
Marcus Molinaro, NY-19	LHOB 1207		
Michael Collins, GA-10	LHOB 1223		
Mike Ezell, MS-04	CHOB 443		
John Duarte, CA-13	LHOB 1535		
Aaron Bean, FL-04	LHOB 1239		

Majority CoS: Jack Ruddy   **Minority CoS:** Kathy Dedrich

— Subcommittees —

AVIATION
Room: FHOB 592
Phone: 202.226.3220

Majority:		Minority:	
C: Garret Graves, LA-06	RHOB 2402	**RM: Steve Cohen, TN-09**	RHOB 2268
Rudy Yakym, IN-02	CHOB 349	Hank Johnson, GA-04	RHOB 2240
Rick Crawford, AR-01	RHOB 2422	Andre Carson, IN-07	RHOB 2135
Thomas Massie, KY-04	RHOB 2453	Julia Brownley, CA-26	RHOB 2262
Scott Perry, PA-10	RHOB 2160	Mark DeSaulnier, CA-10	CHOB 503
Bruce Westerman, AR-04	CHOB 202	Greg Stanton, AZ-04	CHOB 207
Brian Mast, FL-21	RHOB 2182	Colin Allred, TX-32	CHOB 348
Pete Stauber, MN-08	CHOB 145	Sharice Davids, KS-03	RHOB 2435
Tim Burchett, TN-02	LHOB 1122	Jesús Garcia, IL-04	LHOB 1519
Dusty Johnson, SD-01	LHOB 1714	Jake Auchincloss, MA-04	LHOB 1524
Jefferson Van Drew, NJ-02	RHOB 2447	Mary Peltola, AK-01	CHOB 153
Lance Gooden, TX-05	RHOB 2431	Hillary Scholten, MI-03	LHOB 1317
Tracey Mann, KS-01	CHOB 344	Dina Titus, NV-01	RHOB 2464
Burgess Owens, UT-04	LHOB 1039	Donald Payne, NJ-10	CHOB 106
Lori Chavez-DeRemer, OR-05	LHOB 1722	Salud Carbajal, CA-24	RHOB 2331
		Robert Menendez, NJ-08	LHOB 1007
Thomas Kean, NJ-07	CHOB 251	Eleanor Norton, DC-01	RHOB 2136
Anthony D'Esposito, NY-04	LHOB 1508	Frederica Wilson, FL-24	RHOB 2080
John James, MI-10	LHOB 1319	Rick Larsen, WA-02	RHOB 2163
Marcus Molinaro, NY-19	LHOB 1207		
Michael Collins, GA-10	LHOB 1223		
Aaron Bean, FL-04	LHOB 1239		
Sam Graves, MO-06	LHOB 1135		

COAST GUARD & MARITIME TRANSPORTATION
Room: FHOB 505
Phone: 202.226.3552

Majority:		Minority:	
C: Daniel Webster, FL-11	RHOB 2184	**RM: Salud Carbajal, CA-24**	RHOB 2331
Mike Ezell, MS-04	CHOB 443	John Garamendi, CA-08	RHOB 2004
Brian Babin, TX-36	RHOB 2236	Chris Pappas, NH-01	CHOB 452
Brian Mast, FL-21	RHOB 2182	Jake Auchincloss, MA-04	LHOB 1524
Jenniffer González-Colón, PR-01	RHOB 2338	Mary Peltola, AK-01	CHOB 153
Jefferson Van Drew, NJ-02	RHOB 2447	Hillary Scholten, MI-03	LHOB 1317
Aaron Bean, FL-04	LHOB 1239	Rick Larsen, WA-02	RHOB 2163
Sam Graves, MO-06	LHOB 1135		

ECONOMIC DEV'T, PUBLIC BUILDINGS & EMERGENCY MANAGEMENT
Room: FHOB 505
Phone: 202.225.3014

Majority:		Minority:	
C: Scott Perry, PA-10	RHOB 2160	**RM: Dina Titus, NV-01**	RHOB 2464
Lori Chavez-DeRemer, OR-05	LHOB 1722	Eleanor Norton, DC-01	RHOB 2136
		Sharice Davids, KS-03	RHOB 2435
Garret Graves, LA-06	RHOB 2402	Troy Carter, LA-02	CHOB 442
Jenniffer González-Colón, PR-01	RHOB 2338	Grace Napolitano, CA-31	LHOB 1610
		John Garamendi, CA-08	RHOB 2004
Chuck Edwards, NC-11	LHOB 1505	Jared Huffman, CA-02	RHOB 2445
Anthony D'Esposito, NY-04	LHOB 1508	Rick Larsen, WA-02	RHOB 2163
Derrick Van Orden, WI-03	LHOB 1513		
Mike Ezell, MS-04	CHOB 443		
Sam Graves, MO-06	LHOB 1135		

HIGHWAYS & TRANSIT
Room: FHOB 590
Phone: 202.225.6715

Majority:		Minority:	
C: Rick Crawford, AR-01	RHOB 2422	**RM: Eleanor Norton, DC-01**	RHOB 2136
John Duarte, CA-13	LHOB 1535		
Daniel Webster, FL-11	RHOB 2184	Jared Huffman, CA-02	RHOB 2445
Thomas Massie, KY-04	RHOB 2453	Chris Pappas, NH-01	CHOB 452
Mike Bost, IL-12	CHOB 352	Marilyn Strickland, WA-10	LHOB 1708
Doug LaMalfa, CA-01	CHOB 408	Patrick Ryan, NY-18	LHOB 1030
Pete Stauber, MN-08	CHOB 145	Robert Menendez, NJ-08	LHOB 1007
Tim Burchett, TN-02	LHOB 1122	Valerie Hoyle, OR-04	LHOB 1620
Dusty Johnson, SD-01	LHOB 1714	Valerie Foushee, NC-04	LHOB 1716
Jefferson Van Drew, NJ-02	RHOB 2447	Grace Napolitano, CA-31	LHOB 1610
Troy Nehls, TX-22	LHOB 1104	Steve Cohen, TN-09	RHOB 2268
Lance Gooden, TX-05	RHOB 2431	Hank Johnson, GA-04	RHOB 2240
Tracey Mann, KS-01	CHOB 344	Julia Brownley, CA-26	RHOB 2262
Burgess Owens, UT-04	LHOB 1039	Greg Stanton, AZ-04	CHOB 207
Rudy Yakym, IN-02	CHOB 349	Colin Allred, TX-32	CHOB 348
Lori Chavez-DeRemer, OR-05	LHOB 1722	Jesús Garcia, IL-04	LHOB 1519
		Seth Moulton, MA-06	LHOB 1127
Chuck Edwards, NC-11	LHOB 1505	Emilia Sykes, OH-13	LHOB 1217
Thomas Kean, NJ-07	CHOB 251	John Garamendi, CA-08	RHOB 2004
Anthony D'Esposito, NY-04	LHOB 1508	Dina Titus, NV-01	RHOB 2464
Eric Burlison, MO-07	LHOB 1108	Salud Carbajal, CA-24	RHOB 2331
Derrick Van Orden, WI-03	LHOB 1513	Jake Auchincloss, MA-04	LHOB 1524
Brandon Williams, NY-22	LHOB 1022	Mark DeSaulnier, CA-10	CHOB 503
Marcus Molinaro, NY-19	LHOB 1207	Rick Larsen, WA-02	RHOB 2163
Michael Collins, GA-10	LHOB 1223		
Aaron Bean, FL-04	LHOB 1239		
Sam Graves, MO-06	LHOB 1135		

RAILROADS, PIPELINES & HAZARDOUS MATERIALS
Room: FHOB 590
Phone: 202.226.0727

Majority:		Minority:	
C: Troy Nehls, TX-22	LHOB 1104	**RM: Donald Payne, NJ-10**	CHOB 106
Brandon Williams, NY-22	LHOB 1022	Frederica Wilson, FL-24	RHOB 2080
Brian Babin, TX-36	RHOB 2236	Seth Moulton, MA-06	LHOB 1127
David Rouzer, NC-07	RHOB 2333	Troy Carter, LA-02	CHOB 442
Mike Bost, IL-12	CHOB 352	Andre Carson, IN-07	RHOB 2135
Doug LaMalfa, CA-01	CHOB 408	Mark DeSaulnier, CA-10	CHOB 503
Bruce Westerman, AR-04	CHOB 202	Marilyn Strickland, WA-10	LHOB 1708
Pete Stauber, MN-08	CHOB 145	Valerie Foushee, NC-04	LHOB 1716
Tim Burchett, TN-02	LHOB 1122	Grace Napolitano, CA-31	LHOB 1610
Dusty Johnson, SD-01	LHOB 1714	Steve Cohen, TN-09	RHOB 2268
Lance Gooden, TX-05	RHOB 2431	Hank Johnson, GA-04	RHOB 2240
Tracey Mann, KS-01	CHOB 344	Jared Huffman, CA-02	RHOB 2445
Rudy Yakym, IN-02	CHOB 349	Jesús Garcia, IL-04	LHOB 1519
Thomas Kean, NJ-07	CHOB 251	Robert Menendez, NJ-08	LHOB 1007
Eric Burlison, MO-07	LHOB 1108	Rick Larsen, WA-02	RHOB 2163
Marcus Molinaro, NY-19	LHOB 1207		
John Duarte, CA-13	LHOB 1535		
Sam Graves, MO-06	LHOB 1135		

WATER RESOURCES & ENVIRONMENT
Room: FHOB 592
Phone: 202.225.4360

Majority:		Minority:	
C: David Rouzer, NC-07	RHOB 2333	**RM: Grace Napolitano, CA-31**	LHOB 1610
John James, MI-10	LHOB 1319		
Daniel Webster, FL-11	RHOB 2184	John Garamendi, CA-08	RHOB 2004
Thomas Massie, KY-04	RHOB 2453	Emilia Sykes, OH-13	LHOB 1217
Brian Babin, TX-36	RHOB 2236	Jared Huffman, CA-02	RHOB 2445
Mike Bost, IL-12	CHOB 352	Frederica Wilson, FL-24	RHOB 2080

Doug LaMalfa, CA-01	CHOB 408	Patrick Ryan, NY-18	LHOB 1030
Bruce Westerman, AR-04	CHOB 202	Valerie Hoyle, OR-04	LHOB 1620
Brian Mast, FL-21	RHOB 2182	Hillary Scholten, MI-03	LHOB 1317
Jenniffer González-Colón, PR-01	RHOB 2338	Julia Brownley, CA-26	RHOB 2262
		Mark DeSaulnier, CA-10	CHOB 503
Burgess Owens, UT-04	LHOB 1039	Greg Stanton, AZ-04	CHOB 207
Chuck Edwards, NC-11	LHOB 1505	Chris Pappas, NH-01	CHOB 452
Eric Burlison, MO-07	LHOB 1108	Seth Moulton, MA-06	LHOB 1127
Derrick Van Orden, WI-03	LHOB 1513	Troy Carter, LA-02	CHOB 442
Brandon Williams, NY-22	LHOB 1022	Eleanor Norton, DC-01	RHOB 2136
Michael Collins, GA-10	LHOB 1223	Rick Larsen, WA-02	RHOB 2163
Mike Ezell, MS-04	CHOB 443		
John Duarte, CA-13	LHOB 1535		
Sam Graves, MO-06	LHOB 1135		

VETERANS' AFFAIRS

Room: Thomas P. O'Neill Federal Bldg. 3460
Website: veterans.house.gov
Phone: 202.225.3527
Ratio: 14 Republicans/12 Democrats
Subcommittees: 5

Majority:		Minority:	
C: Mike Bost, IL-12	CHOB 352	RM: Mark Takano, CA-39	RHOB 2078
Amata Radewagen, AS-01	RHOB 2001	Julia Brownley, CA-26	RHOB 2262
Jack Bergman, MI-01	CHOB 566	Mike Levin, CA-49	RHOB 2352
Nancy Mace, SC-01	LHOB 1728	Chris Pappas, NH-01	CHOB 452
Matt Rosendale, MT-02	LHOB 1023	Frank Mrvan, IN-01	LHOB 1607
Mariannette Miller-Meeks, IA-01	LHOB 1034	Sheila Cherfilus-McCormick, FL-20	CHOB 242
Gregory Murphy, NC-03	CHOB 407	Morgan McGarvey, KY-03	LHOB 1527
Scott Franklin, FL-18	CHOB 249	Chris Deluzio, PA-17	LHOB 1222
Derrick Van Orden, WI-03	LHOB 1513	Delia Ramirez, IL-03	LHOB 1523
Morgan Luttrell, TX-08	LHOB 1320	Greg Landsman, OH-01	LHOB 1432
Juan Ciscomani, AZ-06	LHOB 1429	Nicole Budzinski, IL-13	LHOB 1009
Eli Crane, AZ-02	LHOB 1229	Ted Lieu, CA-36	RHOB 2454
Keith Self, TX-03	LHOB 1113		
Jen Kiggans, VA-02	LHOB 1037		

Majority CoS: Jon Clark

Minority CoS: Matthew N. Reel
Minority Sched: Carol Murray

─────────── Subcommittees ───────────

DISABILITY ASSISTANCE & MEMORIAL AFFAIRS
Room: Thomas P. O'Neill Federal Bldg. 3460
Phone: 202.225.3527

Majority:		Minority:	
C: Morgan Luttrell, TX-08	LHOB 1320	RM: Chris Pappas, NH-01	CHOB 452
Scott Franklin, FL-18	CHOB 249	Chris Deluzio, PA-17	LHOB 1222
Juan Ciscomani, AZ-06	LHOB 1429	Morgan McGarvey, KY-03	LHOB 1527
Eli Crane, AZ-02	LHOB 1229	Delia Ramirez, IL-03	LHOB 1523
Keith Self, TX-03	LHOB 1113		

ECONOMIC OPPORTUNITY
Room: Thomas P. O'Neill Federal Bldg. 3460
Phone: 202.225.3527

Majority:		Minority:	
C: Derrick Van Orden, WI-03	LHOB 1513	RM: Mike Levin, CA-49	RHOB 2352
		Frank Mrvan, IN-01	LHOB 1607
Nancy Mace, SC-01	LHOB 1728	Morgan McGarvey, KY-03	LHOB 1527
Scott Franklin, FL-18	CHOB 249	Delia Ramirez, IL-03	LHOB 1523
Juan Ciscomani, AZ-06	LHOB 1429		
Eli Crane, AZ-02	LHOB 1229		

HEALTH
Room: Thomas P. O'Neill Federal Bldg. 3460
Phone: 202.225.3527

Majority:		Minority:	
C: Mariannette Miller-Meeks, IA-01	LHOB 1034	RM: Julia Brownley, CA-26	RHOB 2262
		Mike Levin, CA-49	RHOB 2352
Amata Radewagen, AS-01	RHOB 2001	Chris Deluzio, PA-17	LHOB 1222
Jack Bergman, MI-01	CHOB 566	Nicole Budzinski, IL-13	LHOB 1009
Gregory Murphy, NC-03	CHOB 407	Greg Landsman, OH-01	LHOB 1432
Derrick Van Orden, WI-03	LHOB 1513		
Morgan Luttrell, TX-08	LHOB 1320		
Jen Kiggans, VA-02	LHOB 1037		

OVERSIGHT & INVESTIGATIONS

Room: Thomas P. O'Neill Federal Bldg. 3460
Phone: 202.225.3527

Majority:		Minority:	
C: Jen Kiggans, VA-02	LHOB 1037	**RM: Frank Mrvan, IN-01**	LHOB 1607
Amata Radewagen, AS-01	RHOB 2001	Chris Pappas, NH-01	CHOB 452
Jack Bergman, MI-01	CHOB 566	Sheila Cherfilus-	CHOB 242
Matt Rosendale, MT-02	LHOB 1023	McCormick, FL-20	

TECHNOLOGY MODERNIZATION

Room: Thomas P. O'Neill Federal Bldg. 3460
Phone: 202.225.3527

Majority:		Minority:	
C: Matt Rosendale, MT-02	LHOB 1023	**RM: Sheila Cherfilus-**	CHOB 242
Nancy Mace, SC-01	LHOB 1728	**McCormick, FL-20**	
Keith Self, TX-03	LHOB 1113	Greg Landsman, OH-01	LHOB 1432

WAYS & MEANS

Room: LHOB 1139
Website: waysandmeans.house.gov
Phone: 202.225.4021
Ratio: 25 Republicans/18 Democrats
Subcommittees: 6

Majority:		Minority:	
C: Jason Smith, MO-08	LHOB 1011	**RM: Richard Neal, MA-01**	CHOB 372
Vern Buchanan, FL-16	RHOB 2110	Judy Chu, CA-28	RHOB 2423
Adrian Smith, NE-03	CHOB 502	Lloyd Doggett, TX-37	RHOB 2307
Mike Kelly, PA-16	LHOB 1707	Mike Thompson, CA-04	CHOB 268
David Schweikert, AZ-01	CHOB 460	John Larson, CT-01	LHOB 1501
Darin LaHood, IL-16	LHOB 1424	Earl Blumenauer, OR-03	LHOB 1111
Brad Wenstrup, OH-02	RHOB 2335	Bill Pascrell, NJ-09	RHOB 2409
Jodey Arrington, TX-19	LHOB 1107	Danny Davis, IL-07	RHOB 2159
Drew Ferguson, GA-03	RHOB 2239	Linda Sanchez, CA-38	RHOB 2428
Ron Estes, KS-04	RHOB 2234	Brian Higgins, NY-26	RHOB 2269
Lloyd Smucker, PA-11	CHOB 302	Terri Sewell, AL-07	LHOB 1035
Kevin Hern, OK-01	LHOB 1019	Suzan DelBene, WA-01	RHOB 2330
Carol Miller, WV-01	CHOB 465	Gwen Moore, WI-04	RHOB 2252
Gregory Murphy, NC-03	CHOB 407	Dan Kildee, MI-08	CHOB 200
David Kustoff, TN-08	CHOB 560	Don Beyer, VA-08	LHOB 1119
Brian Fitzpatrick, PA-01	CHOB 271	Dwight Evans, PA-03	LHOB 1105
Greg Steube, FL-17	RHOB 2457	Brad Schneider, IL-10	CHOB 300
Claudia Tenney, NY-24	RHOB 2349	Jimmy Panetta, CA-19	CHOB 304
Michelle Fischbach, MN-07	LHOB 1004		
Blake Moore, UT-01	LHOB 1131		
Michelle Steel, CA-45			
Beth Van Duyne, TX-24	LHOB 1725		
Randy Feenstra, IA-04	LHOB 1440		
Nicole Malliotakis, NY-11	CHOB 351		
Mike Carey, OH-15	LHOB 1433		

Majority CoS: Mark Roman   **Minority CoS:** Brandon Casey

———— Subcommittees ————

HEALTH

Room: LHOB 1139
Phone: 202.225.4021

Majority:		Minority:	
C: Vern Buchanan, FL-16	RHOB 2110	**RM: Lloyd Doggett, TX-37**	RHOB 2307
Adrian Smith, NE-03	CHOB 502	Mike Thompson, CA-04	CHOB 268
Mike Kelly, PA-16	LHOB 1707	Earl Blumenauer, OR-03	LHOB 1111
Brad Wenstrup, OH-02	RHOB 2335	Brian Higgins, NY-26	RHOB 2269
Gregory Murphy, NC-03	CHOB 407	Terri Sewell, AL-07	LHOB 1035
Kevin Hern, OK-01	LHOB 1019	Judy Chu, CA-28	RHOB 2423
Carol Miller, WV-01	CHOB 465	Dwight Evans, PA-03	LHOB 1105
Brian Fitzpatrick, PA-01	CHOB 271	Danny Davis, IL-07	RHOB 2159
Claudia Tenney, NY-24	RHOB 2349		
Blake Moore, UT-01	LHOB 1131		
Michelle Steel, CA-45			

OVERSIGHT

Room: LHOB 1139
Phone: 202.225.4021

Majority:		Minority:	
C: David Schweikert,	CHOB 460	**RM: Bill Pascrell, NJ-09**	RHOB 2409
AZ-01		Judy Chu, CA-28	RHOB 2423
Brian Fitzpatrick, PA-01	CHOB 271	Brad Schneider, IL-10	CHOB 300
Greg Steube, FL-17	RHOB 2457	Suzan DelBene, WA-01	RHOB 2330
Claudia Tenney, NY-24	RHOB 2349	Gwen Moore, WI-04	RHOB 2252

Michelle Fischbach, MN-07   LHOB 1004
Beth Van Duyne, TX-24   LHOB 1725
Randy Feenstra, IA-04   LHOB 1440
Nicole Malliotakis, NY-11   CHOB 351

SOCIAL SECURITY
Room: LHOB 1139
Phone: 202.225.4021

Majority:		Minority:	
C: Drew Ferguson, GA-03	RHOB 2239	**RM: John Larson, CT-01**	LHOB 1501
Mike Carey, OH-15	LHOB 1433	Bill Pascrell, NJ-09	RHOB 2409
David Schweikert, AZ-01	CHOB 460	Linda Sanchez, CA-38	RHOB 2428
Ron Estes, KS-04	RHOB 2234	Brian Higgins, NY-26	RHOB 2269
Blake Moore, UT-01	LHOB 1131	Dan Kildee, MI-08	CHOB 200
Randy Feenstra, IA-04	LHOB 1440		
Greg Steube, FL-17	RHOB 2457		
David Kustoff, TN-08	CHOB 560		

TAX
Room: LHOB 1139
Phone: 202.225.4021

Majority:		Minority:	
C: Mike Kelly, PA-16	LHOB 1707	**RM: Mike Thompson,**	CHOB 268
David Schweikert, AZ-01	CHOB 460	**CA-04**	
Jodey Arrington, TX-19	LHOB 1107	Lloyd Doggett, TX-37	RHOB 2307
Drew Ferguson, GA-03	RHOB 2239	John Larson, CT-01	LHOB 1501
Kevin Hern, OK-01	LHOB 1019	Linda Sanchez, CA-38	RHOB 2428
Ron Estes, KS-04	RHOB 2234	Suzan DelBene, WA-01	RHOB 2330
Lloyd Smucker, PA-11	CHOB 302	Gwen Moore, WI-04	RHOB 2252
David Kustoff, TN-08	CHOB 560	Don Beyer, VA-08	LHOB 1119
Beth Van Duyne, TX-24	LHOB 1725	Brad Schneider, IL-10	CHOB 300
Randy Feenstra, IA-04	LHOB 1440		
Nicole Malliotakis, NY-11	CHOB 351		

TRADE
Room: LHOB 1139
Phone: 202.225.4021

Majority:		Minority:	
C: Adrian Smith, NE-03	CHOB 502	**RM: Earl Blumenauer,**	LHOB 1111
Vern Buchanan, FL-16	RHOB 2110	**OR-03**	
Darin LaHood, IL-16	LHOB 1424	Brian Higgins, NY-26	RHOB 2269
Jodey Arrington, TX-19	LHOB 1107	Dan Kildee, MI-08	CHOB 200
Ron Estes, KS-04	RHOB 2234	Jimmy Panetta, CA-19	CHOB 304
Carol Miller, WV-01	CHOB 465	Suzan DelBene, WA-01	RHOB 2330
Lloyd Smucker, PA-11	CHOB 302	Don Beyer, VA-08	LHOB 1119
Gregory Murphy, NC-03	CHOB 407	Linda Sanchez, CA-38	RHOB 2428
Greg Steube, FL-17	RHOB 2457	Terri Sewell, AL-07	LHOB 1035
Michelle Fischbach, MN-07	LHOB 1004		
David Kustoff, TN-08	CHOB 560		

WORK & WELFARE
Room: LHOB 1139
Phone: 202.225.4021

Majority:		Minority:	
C: Darin LaHood, IL-16	LHOB 1424	**RM: Danny Davis, IL-07**	RHOB 2159
Brad Wenstrup, OH-02	RHOB 2335	Judy Chu, CA-28	RHOB 2423
Mike Carey, OH-15	LHOB 1433	Gwen Moore, WI-04	RHOB 2252
Blake Moore, UT-01	LHOB 1131	Dwight Evans, PA-03	LHOB 1105
Michelle Steel, CA-45		Terri Sewell, AL-07	LHOB 1035
Lloyd Smucker, PA-11	CHOB 302		
Adrian Smith, NE-03	CHOB 502		
Claudia Tenney, NY-24	RHOB 2349		

SELECT AND SPECIAL COMMITTEES

PERMANENT SELECT ON INTELLIGENCE

Room: The Capitol Visitors Center HVC-304
Website: intelligence.house.gov
Phone: 202.225.4121
Ratio: 14 Republicans/13 Democrats
Subcommittees: 5

Majority:		Minority:	
C: Mike Turner, OH-10	RHOB 2082	RM: Jim Himes, CT-04	RHOB 2137
Brad Wenstrup, OH-02	RHOB 2335	Andre Carson, IN-07	RHOB 2135
Chris Stewart, UT-02	CHOB 166	Robert Garcia, CA-42	LHOB 1305
Rick Crawford, AR-01	RHOB 2422	Joaquin Castro, TX-20	RHOB 2241
Elise Stefanik, NY-21	RHOB 2211	Raja Krishnamoorthi, IL-08	RHOB 2367
Trent Kelly, MS-01	RHOB 2243	Jason Crow, CO-06	LHOB 1323
Darin LaHood, IL-16	LHOB 1424	Ami Bera, CA-06	CHOB 172
Brian Fitzpatrick, PA-01	CHOB 271	Stacey Plaskett, VI-01	RHOB 2059
Mike Gallagher, WI-08	LHOB 1211	Josh Gottheimer, NJ-05	CHOB 203
Austin Scott, GA-08	RHOB 2185	Jimmy Gomez, CA-34	CHOB 506
French Hill, AR-02	LHOB 1533	Chrissy Houlahan, PA-06	LHOB 1727
Daniel Crenshaw, TX-02	CHOB 413	Abigail Spanberger, VA-07	CHOB 562
Mike Waltz, FL-06	CHOB 244	Betty McCollum, MN-04	RHOB 2426
Mike Garcia, CA-27	CHOB 144		

Majority CoS: Adam Howard

Minority CoS: Jeff Lowenstein

Subcommittees

CENTRAL INTELLIGENCE AGENCY
Room: The Capitol Visitors Center HVC-304
Phone: 202.225.4121

Majority:		Minority:	
C: Rick Crawford, AR-01	RHOB 2422	RM: Andre Carson, IN-07	RHOB 2135
Austin Scott, GA-08	RHOB 2185	Joaquin Castro, TX-20	RHOB 2241
Elise Stefanik, NY-21	RHOB 2211	Raja Krishnamoorthi, IL-08	RHOB 2367
Mike Gallagher, WI-08	LHOB 1211	Jason Crow, CO-06	LHOB 1323
Mike Waltz, FL-06	CHOB 244		
Daniel Crenshaw, TX-02	CHOB 413		

DEFENSE INTELLIGENCE & OVERHEAD ARCHITECTURE
Room: The Capitol Visitors Center HVC-304
Phone: 202.225.4121

Majority:		Minority:	
C: Trent Kelly, MS-01	RHOB 2243	RM: Chrissy Houlahan, PA-06	LHOB 1727
Brad Wenstrup, OH-02	RHOB 2335		
Chris Stewart, UT-02	CHOB 166	Stacey Plaskett, VI-01	RHOB 2059
Rick Crawford, AR-01	RHOB 2422	Jason Crow, CO-06	LHOB 1323
Brian Fitzpatrick, PA-01	CHOB 271	Abigail Spanberger, VA-07	CHOB 562
		Mike Garcia, CA-27	CHOB 144

NATIONAL INTELLIGENCE ENTERPRISE
Room: The Capitol Visitors Center HVC-304
Phone: 202.225.4121

Majority:		Minority:	
C: Brian Fitzpatrick, PA-01	CHOB 271	RM: Stacey Plaskett, VI-01	RHOB 2059
Brad Wenstrup, OH-02	RHOB 2335	Ami Bera, CA-06	CHOB 172
French Hill, AR-02	LHOB 1533	Josh Gottheimer, NJ-05	CHOB 203
Trent Kelly, MS-01	RHOB 2243	Abigail Spanberger, VA-07	CHOB 562
Darin LaHood, IL-16	LHOB 1424		
Daniel Crenshaw, TX-02	CHOB 413		

NATIONAL SECURITY AGENCY & CYBER
Room: The Capitol Visitors Center HVC-304
Phone: 202.225.4121

Majority:		Minority:	
C: Darin LaHood, IL-16	LHOB 1424	RM: Josh Gottheimer, NJ-05	CHOB 203
Austin Scott, GA-08	RHOB 2185		
French Hill, AR-02	LHOB 1533	Ami Bera, CA-06	CHOB 172
Mike Gallagher, WI-08	LHOB 1211	Joaquin Castro, TX-20	RHOB 2241
Mike Waltz, FL-06	CHOB 244	Jimmy Gomez, CA-34	CHOB 506
		Mike Garcia, CA-27	CHOB 144

OVERSIGHT
Room: The Capitol Visitors Center HVC-304
Phone: 202.225.4121

Majority:		Minority:
C: Chris Stewart, UT-02	CHOB 166	Information not available as of press time.

SELECT CHINA COMMITTEE

Room: LHOB 1230
Website:
Phone: 202.225.5665
Ratio: 13 Republicans/11 Democrats

Subcommittees: 0

Majority:		Minority:	
C: Mike Gallagher, WI-08	LHOB 1211	**RM: Raja Krishnamoorthi, IL-08**	RHOB 2367
Rob Wittman, VA-01	RHOB 2055		
Blaine Luetkemeyer, MO-03	RHOB 2230	Kathy Castor, FL-14	RHOB 2052
Andy Barr, KY-06	RHOB 2430	Andre Carson, IN-07	RHOB 2135
Dan Newhouse, WA-04	CHOB 504	Seth Moulton, MA-06	LHOB 1127
John Moolenaar, MI-02	CHOB 246	Ro Khanna, CA-17	CHOB 306
Darin LaHood, IL-16	LHOB 1424	Andy Kim, NJ-03	RHOB 2444
Neal Dunn, FL-02	CHOB 466	Mikie Sherrill, NJ-11	LHOB 1427
Jim Banks, IN-03	RHOB 2418	Haley Stevens, MI-11	RHOB 2411
Dusty Johnson, SD-01	LHOB 1714	Jake Auchincloss, MA-04	LHOB 1524
Michelle Steel, CA-45		Ritchie Torres, NY-15	LHOB 1414
Ashley Hinson, IA-02	LHOB 1717	Shontel Brown, OH-11	CHOB 449
Carlos Gimenez, FL-28	CHOB 448		

Majority CoS: Dave Hanke

EXECUTIVE BRANCH

The Executive Branch of the U.S. government was formed through Article II of the U.S. Constitution. The Executive Branch is primarily composed of the President (who is also the Commander-in-Chief of the armed services), the White House staff, the Executive Office of the President, the Vice President, as well as the 14 Federal departments, the heads of which form the President's Cabinet.

Also included under the purview of the Executive Branch are the various subordinate divisions of the Federal departments, independent Federal agencies, the independent Federal reserve system, and several permanent and ad hoc agencies, boards, commissions and committees. The Executive Branch is responsible for carrying out and enforcing the federal laws and protecting the people of the United States.

President of the United States **Joseph R. Biden Jr. (D)**   p **202.456.1111**

1600 Pennsylvania Ave. NW
Washington, DC 20500
Bio. 11/20/1942 • Scranton, PA • The University of Delaware, B.A., 1965; The University of Delaware, B.A., 1965; Syracuse University - College of Law (NY), J.D., 1968 • Catholic • M. Jill Biden, 4 ch (2 deceased); 5 gr-ch
Salary $400,000

Vice President **Kamala D. Harris (D)**   p **202.456.1111**

1600 Pennsylvania Ave. NW
Washington, DC 20500
Bio. 10/20/1964 • Oakland, CA • Howard University, B.A.; University of California, Hastings, J.D. • Baptist • M. Douglas Emhoff, 2 stepch
Salary $235,100

THE OFFICE OF THE PRESIDENT

                                          www.whitehouse.gov

President
Joseph R. Biden Jr.   202.456.0373

Chief of Staff
Ron Klain

Counselor to the President
Steve Ricchetti   202.456.0373

Deputy Chief of Staff
Bruce Reed

Deputy Chief of Staff
Jen O'Malley Dillon

Director of Communications
Kate Bedingfield   202.456.0373

National Security Advisor
Jake Sullivan   202.456.2744

Press Secretary
Karine Jean-Pierre

Senior Advisor
Gene Sperling

Senior Advisor
John Podesta

Senior Advisor
Julie Rodriguez

Senior Advisor
Keisha Lance Bottoms

Senior Advisor
Michael C. Donilon

Senior Advisor
Mitch Landrieu

Senior Advisor
Neera Tanden

THE OFFICE OF THE VICE PRESIDENT

                              www.whitehouse.gov/vicepresident

Vice President
Kamala D. Harris

Chief of Staff
Lorraine Voles

Second Gentleman
Douglas Emhoff

THE OFFICE OF THE FIRST LADY

www.whitehouse.gov/firstlady

First Lady
Jill Biden

202.456.7458

Chief of Staff
Julissa Reynoso Pantaleón

EXECUTIVE OFFICE OF THE PRESIDENT

www.whitehouse.gov

Through the U.S. Code's Reorganization Act of 1939, authority over a variety of Federal agencies was transferred to the Executive Branch, which has since formed the Executive Office of the President. The composition of the Executive Office customarily changes with each administration to reflect the policy goals of the President.

The President, through the Office of Management and Budget (OMB), manages the Executive Office of the President. It is through the OMB that the Executive Branch's departments, agency programs, policies and expenditures are shaped. In addition to OMB, the following agencies comprise the Executive Office of the President.

Council on Environmental Quality
1600 Pennsylvania Ave. NW
Washington, DC 20500

202.456.1111

Council on Environmental Quality (CEQ)
Eisenhower Executive Office Bldg. (EEOB)
1600 Pennsylvania Ave. NW
Washington, WV 20500
Chairman: Brenda Mallory

202.456.1111

Domestic Policy Council (DPC)
1600 Pennsylvania Ave. NW
Washington, WA 20500
Director: Susan Rice

202.456.1111

National Economic Council (NEC)
Eisenhower Executive Office Bldg. (EEOB)
1600 Pennsylvania Ave. NW
Washington, WA 20500
Director: Brian Deese

202.456.1111

National Security Council (NSC)
1600 Pennsylvania Ave. NW
Washington, WA 20500
Jake Sullivan

202.456.1111

Office of Administration
1600 Pennsylvania Ave. NW
Washington, DC 20500

202.456.1111

Office of Faith-Based and Neighborhood Partnerships
1600 Pennsylvania Ave. NW
Washington, DC 20500

202.456.1111

Office of Intergovernmental Affairs
1600 Pennsylvania Ave. NW
Washington, DC 20500
Director: Julie Chavez Rodriguez

202.456.1111

Office of Management and Budget (OMB)
725 17th St. NW
Washington, DC 20503

202.395.3080

Office of National AIDS Policy
The White House
1600 Pennsylvania Ave. NW
Washington, DC 20500

202.456.4533

Office of National Drug Control Policy
1600 Pennsylvania Ave. NW
Washington, WA 20500
Acting Director: Regina LaBelle

202.456.1111

Office of Public Engagement
1600 Pennsylvania Ave. NW
Washington, DC 20500
Director: Rep. Cedric Richmond

202.456.1111

Office of Science and Technology Policy
Eisenhower Executive Office Building
1600 Pennsylvania Ave. NW
Washington, DC 20504

202.456.4444

Office of Social Innovation and Civic Participation
1600 Pennsylvania Ave. NW
Washington, DC 20500

202.456.1111

Office of the U.S. Trade Representative
600 17th St. NW
Washington, DC 20508

202.395.2870

President's Intelligence Advisory Board
1600 Pennsylvania Ave. NW
Washington, DC 20500

202.456.1111

White House Military Office
1600 Pennsylvania Ave. NW
Washington, DC 20500

202.456.1111

THE CABINET

The Executive Branch's 14 department Secretaries form the President's Cabinet. The President appoints each Secretary, who must be confirmed by the Senate. The Cabinet advises the President on various aspects of the Executive Branch and then proceed as the president directs. The annual salary for Department Secretaries is $203,700.

The President also has the authority to appoint members of the Executive Office of the President and other officials to Cabinet-level rank, The Vice President and the President's chief of staff are considered members of the Cabinet. Under the Biden administration, the following administrators also are considered members of the Cabinet.

Director, Office of Management and Budget
Shalanda Young
Chief of Staff
Ron Klain
Trade Representative
Katherine C. Tai
Director, National Intelligence
Avril Haines
Director, Office of Science and Technology Policy
Arati Prabhakar
Chairman, Council of Economic Advisors
Cecilia Elena Rouse
Ambassador to the United Nations
Linda Thomas Greenfield
Administrator, Environmental Protection Agency
Michael S. Regan
Administrator, Small Business Administration
Isabel Guzman

Department of Agriculture (USDA)
Secretary Thomas J. Vilsack (VIL-sak)　　　　　　　　p 202.720.2791

1400 Independence Ave., S.W.
Washington, DC 20250
Website usda.gov
Bio. 12/12/1950 • Pittsburgh, PA • Governor (Iowa); State Senator; Mayor • Hamilton College (NY), B.A., 1972; Albany Law School, J.D., 1975 • Catholic • M. Christie Bell, 2 ch; 2 gr-ch

Department of Commerce (DOC)
Gov. Gina Raimondo (ruh-MON-doh)　　　　　　　　p 202.482.2000

1401 Constitution Ave NW
Washington, DC 20230
Website commerce.gov
Bio. 05/17/1971 • Smithfield, RI • General Treasurer (RI); Chair of Democratic Governors Association; Governor (RI) • Harvard University, B.A., 1993; Yale University (CT), J.D., 1998; University of Oxford (UK), M.A., 2002; University of Oxford (UK), Ph.D., 2002 • Catholic • M. Andrew Moffit, 2 ch

Department of Defense (DOD)
Lloyd Austin (AW-stuhn)　　　　　　　　p 703.571.3343

1400 Defense Pentagon
Washington, DC 20301
Website defense.gov
Bio. 08/08/1953 • Mobile, AL • Vice Chief of Staff of the U.S. Army; Commander of the U.S. Central Command • U.S. Military Academy - West Point (NY), B.S., 1975; Auburn University, M.A., 1986; Webster University (MO), M.B.A., 1989 • Catholic • M. Charlene Banner, 2 stepch

Department of Education (ED)
Dr. Miguel Cardona (KAR-dohn-ah)   p **202.401.2000**

400 Maryland Avenue, SW
Washington, DC 20202
Website ed.gov
Bio. 07/11/1975 • Meriden, CT • Education Commissioner
(CT) • Central Connecticut State University (CT), B.S.,
1997; University of Connecticut, M.S., 2001; University of
Connecticut, Ed.D., 2011 • M. Marissa Peréz, 2 ch

Department of Energy (DOE)
Jennifer M. Granholm (GRAHN-"home")   p **202.586.5000**

1000 Independence Ave., SW
Washington, DC 20585
Website energy.gov
Bio. 02/05/1959 • VancouverCorporation Counsel, Wayne
County ; Michigan Attorney General; Mbr., Natl. Governors
Assn. • University of California, Berkeley, B.A., 1984; Harvard
University, J.D., 1987 • Catholic • M. Daniel Mulhern, 3 ch

Department of Health and Human Services (HHS)
Xavier Becerra (beh-SEH-rah)   p **202.690.7000**

200 Independence Avenue, S.W.
Washington, DC 20201
Website hhs.gov
Bio. 01/26/1958 • Sacramento, CA • State Deputy Attorney;
Attorney; State Legislator • Stanford University (CA), B.A.,
1980; Stanford University Law School (CA), J.D., 1984 •
Roman Catholic • M. Dr. Carolina Reyes, 3 ch

Department of Homeland Security (DHS)
Alejandro Mayorkas (mai-YOR-kus)   p **202.282.8000**

245 Murray Lane, SW
Washington, DC 20528
Website dhs.gov
Bio. 11/24/1959 • HavanaU.S. Attorney (Central District of
CA); Director, U.S. Citizenship and Immigration Services;
Deputy Secretary of Homeland Security • University of
California, Berkeley, B.A., 1981; Loyola Marymount University,
J.D., 1985 • M. , 2 ch

Department of Housing and Urban Development (HUD)
Rep. Marcia L. Fudge (fuhj)   p **202.708.1112**

451 7th St., SW
Washington, DC 20410
Website hud.gov
Bio. 10/29/1952 • Cleveland, OH • Mayor (Warrensville
Heights); Congressional Staffer; Attorney • Ohio State
University, B.S., 1975; Cleveland State University Marshall
College of Law (OH), J.D., 1983 • Baptist • S.

Department of Justice (DOJ)
Merrick Garland (GAR-lend)   p **202.514.2000**

950 Pennsylvania Ave. NW
Washington, DC 20530
Website justice.gov
Bio. 11/13/1952 • Chicago, IL • Judge, U.S. Court of Appeals;
Chief Judge, U.S. Court of Appeals • Harvard University,
B.A., 1974; Harvard University, J.D., 1977 • Jewish • M. Lynn
Rosenman, 2 ch

Department of Labor (DOL)
Marty Walsh (walsh) p **866.487.2365**

200 Constitution Ave NW
Washington, DC 20210
Bio. 04/10/1967 • Boston, MA • Member, House of
Representatives (MA); Mayor of Boston • Boston College
(MA), B.A., 2009 • Roman Catholic • S.

Department of State (DOS)
Anthony Blinken p **202.647.4000**

2201 C St., NW
Washington, DC 20520
Bio. 04/16/1962 • Yonkers, NY • National Security Advisor to
the Vice President; U.S. Deputy National Security Advisor; U.S.
Deputy Secretary of State • Harvard University, B.A., 1984;
Columbia University (NY), J.D., 1988 • Jewish • M. Evan Ryan,
2 ch

Department of the Interior (DOI)
Deb A. Haaland (HAH-lund) p **202.208.3100**

1849 C St., NW
Washington, DC 20240
Website doi.gov
Bio. 12/02/1960 • Winslow, AZ • Chair, New Mexico
Democratic Party; Member, U.S. House of Representatives
(NM) • University of New Mexico, B.A., 1994; University of
New Mexico Law School, J.D., 2006 • Catholic • S. , 1 ch

Department of Transportation (DOT)
Pete Buttigieg (BOO-tuh-jej) p **202.366.4000**

1200 New Jersey Ave, SE
Washington, DC 20590
Website transportation.gov
Bio. 01/19/1982 • South Bend, IN • U.S. Navy Lieutenant;
Mayor of South Bend (IN) • Harvard University, B.A., 2004;
Pembroke College at Oxford University, England, B.A., 2007 •
M. Chasten Glezman

Department of Treasury
Janet L. Yellen (YEHL-len) p **202.622.2000**

1500 Pennsylvania Avenue, NW
Washington, DC 20220
Website home.treasury.gov
Bio. 08/13/1946 • Brooklyn, NY • Chair, Council of Economic
Advisors, President, Federal Reserve Bank of San Francisco;
Member, Federal Reserve Board of Governors; Vice Chair,
Federal Reserve; Chair, Federal Reserve • Brown University
(RI), B.A., 1967; Yale University (CT), Ph.D., 1971 • Jewish • M.
George Akerlof, 1 ch

Department of Veterans Affairs (VA)

Denis R. McDonough (mik-DUH-nuh)   p **202.724.5454**

441 4th Street, NW
Washington, DE 20001
Website va.gov
Bio. 12/02/1969 • Stillwater, MN • U.S. Deputy National
Security Advisor; White House Chief of Staff • St. John's
University (MN), B.A., 1992; Georgetown University (DC), M.S.,
1996 • Catholic • M. Karin Hillstrom, 3 ch

SELECTED FEDERAL AGENCIES

American Battle Monuments Commission   abmc.gov
2300 Clarendon Blvd.   **703.584.1501**
Courthouse Plaza II., Suite 500
Arlington, VA 22201

AMTRAK - Natl Railroad Passenger Corporation   amtrak.com
60 Massachusetts Ave. NE   **202.906.3000**
Washington, DC 20002

Bureau of Alcohol, Tobacco, Firearms and   atf.gov
Explosives (ATF)   **202.648.8500**
Department of Justice (DOJ)
99 New York Ave. NE
Washington, DC 20226

Bureau of Indian Affairs (BIA)   bia.gov
Department of the Interior (DOI)   **202.208.5116**
1849 C St. NW
MS-4606
Washington, DC 20240

Bureau of Land Management (BLM)   blm.gov
Department of the Interior (DOI)   **202.208.3801**
1849 C St. NW
Room 5665
Washington, DC 20240

Bureau of Ocean Energy Management   boem.gov
Department of the Interior (DOI)   **202.208.6474**
1849 C St. NW
Office of Public Affairs
Washington, DC 20240

Central Intelligence Agency (CIA)   cia.gov
Office of Public Affairs   **703.482.0623**
Washington, DC 20505

Commodity Futures Trading Commission (CFTC)   cftc.gov
1155 21st St. NW   **202.418.5000**
Three Lafayette Centre
Washington, DC 20581

Congressional Budget Office (CBO)   cbo.gov
Second & D Streets, SW   **202.226.2602**
Fourth Floor
Washington, DC 20515-6925

Corporation for National & Community Service   nationalservice.gov
250 E St. SW   **202.606.9390**
Suite 4100
Washington, DC 20525

Director of National Intelligence (ODNI)   dni.gov
Office of the Director of National Intelligence   **703.733.8600**
Washington, DC 20511

Election Assistance Commission (EAC)   eac.gov
633 Third St. NW   **301.563.3919**
Suite 200
Washington, DC 20001

Export-Import Bank of the United States   exim.gov
811 Vermont Ave. NW   **202.565.3946**
Washington, DC 20571

Farm Credit Administration   fca.gov
1501 Farm Credit Dr.   **703.883.4056**
McLean, VA 22102-5090

Federal Accounting Standards Advisory Board   fasab.gov
(FASAB)   **202.512.7350**
441 G St. NW
Suite 1155
Washington, DC 20548

Federal Aviation Administration (FAA)
800 Independence Ave. SW
Washington, DC 20591

faa.gov
866.835.5322

Federal Bureau of Investigation (FBI)
Department of Justice (DOJ)
935 Pennsylvania Ave. NW
Washington, DC 20535-0001

fbi.gov
202.324.3000

Federal Communications Commission
45 L St. NE
Washington, DC 20554

fcc.gov
202.418.1122

Federal Deposit Insurance Corporation
550 17th St. NW
Washington, DC 20429-9990

fdic.gov
877.275.3342

Federal Election Commission (FEC)
1050 First St. NE
Washington, DC 20463

fec.gov
202.694.1000

Federal Emergency Management Agency (FEMA)
Department of Homeland Security (DHS)
500 C St. SW
Washington, DC 20472

fema.gov
202.646.2500

Federal Energy Regulatory Commission
888 First St. NE
Washington, DC 20426

ferc.gov
202.502.6088

Federal Highway Administration (FHA)
1200 New Jersey Ave. SE
Washington, DC 20590

fhwa.dot.gov
202.366.4000

Federal Housing Finance Agency
400 Seventh St. SW
Constitution Center
Washington, DC 20019

fhfa.gov
202.649.3800

Federal Labor Relations Authority (FLRA)
1400 K St. NW
Washington, DC 20424

flra.gov
202.218.7770

Federal Maritime Commission
800 N. Capitol St. NW
Washington, DC 20573

fmc.gov
202.523.5725

Federal Mediation & Conciliation Service
2100 K St. NW
Washington, DC 20427

fmcs.gov
202.606.8100

Federal Railroad Administration
1200 New Jersey Ave. SE
Washington, DC 20590

fra.dot.gov
202.493.6014

Federal Reserve System
20th St. & Constitution Ave. NW
Washington, DC 20551

federalreserve.gov
202.452.3000

Federal Trade Commission (FTC)
600 Pennsylvania Ave. NW
Washington, DC 20580

ftc.gov
202.326.2222

Federal Transit Administration
1200 New Jersey Ave. SE
Washington, DC 20590

fta.dot.gov
202.366.4043

Forest Service
1400 Independence Ave. SW
Washington, DC 20250

fs.fed.us
800.832.1355

Government Accountability Office
441 G St. NW
Washington, DC 20548

gao.gov
202.512.3000

Government National Mortgage Association
451 Seventh St. SW
Room B-133
Washington, DC 20410

ginniemae.gov
202.475.4930

Government Printing Office (GPO)
732 N. Capitol St. NW
Washington, DC 20401

gpo.gov
202.512.1800

Institute of Museum and Library Services (IMLS)
955 L'Enfant Plaza North SW
Suite 4000
Washington, DC 20024-2135

imls.gov
202.653.4657

Inter-American Foundation
1331 Pennsylvania Ave. NW
Suite 1200 North
Washington, DC 20004

iaf.gov
202.360.4530

Internal Revenue Service (IRS)
1750 Forest Dr.
Suite 110
Annapolis, MD 21401

irs.gov
410.224.5000

Legal Services Corporation
3333 K St. NW
Washington, DC 20007

lsc.gov
202.295.1500

Library of Congress (LOC)
101 Independence Ave. SE
Washington, DC 20540

loc.gov
202.707.5000

**Medicare Payment Advisory Commission
(MedPAC)**
425 I St. NW
Suite 701
Washington, DC 20001

medpac.gov
202.220.3700

Merit Systems Protection Board
1615 M St. NW
Washington, DC 20419

mspb.gov
202.653.7200

National Aeronautics and Space Administration
300 E St. SW
Suite 5R30
Washington, DC 20546

nasa.gov
202.358.0001

National Archives and Records Administration
8601 Adelphi Rd.
College Park, MD 20740-6001

archives.gov
866.272.6272

National Council on Disability
1331 F St. NW
Suite 850
Washington, DC 20004

ncd.gov
202.272.2004

National Credit Union Administration
1775 Duke St.
Alexandria, VA 22314-3428

ncua.gov
703.518.6300

National Endowment For the Arts
400 Seventh St. SW
Washington, DC 20506-0001

arts.gov
202.682.5400

**National Highway Traffic Safety Administration
(NHTSA)**
1200 New Jersey Ave. SE
Washington, DC 20590

nhtsa.gov
888.327.4236

National Indian Gaming Commission
Department of the Interior (DOI)
90 K St. NE
Suite 200
Washington, DC 20002

nigc.gov
202.632.7003

National Labor Relations Board
1015 Half St. SE
Washington, DC 20570-0001

nlrb.gov
202.273.1000

National Mediation Board
1301 K St. NW
Suite 250 East
Washington, DC 20005-7011

nmb.gov
202.692.5000

National Park Service (NPS)
Department of the Interior (DOI)
1849 C St. NW
Washington, DC 20240

nps.gov
202.208.6843

National Science Foundation
2415 Eisenhower Ave.
Alexandria, VA 22314

nsf.gov
703.292.5111

National Transportation Safety Board
490 L'Enfant Plaza SW
Washington, DC 20594

ntsb.gov
202.314.6000

Occupational Safety and Health Administration
200 Constitution Ave. NW
Room Number N3626
Washington, DC 20210

osha.gov
800.321.6742

Office of Government Ethics (OGE)
1201 New York Ave. NW
Suite 500
Washington, DC 20005

oge.gov
202.482.9300

Office of Housing
Department of Housing and Urban Development
(HUD)
451 7th St SW
Washington, DC 20410

202.708.1112

Office of Housing and Urban Development
451 Seventh St. SW
Washington, DC 20410

hud.gov
202.708.1112

Office of Special Counsel
1730 M St. NW
Suite 218
Washington, DC 20036-4505

osc.gov
202.254.3600

Office of the Comptroller of the Currency
400 Seventh St. SW
Washington, DC 20219
occ.gov
202.649.6800

Overseas Private Investment Corp (OPIC)
1100 New York Ave. NW
Washington, DC 20527
opic.gov
202.336.8400

Peace Corps
1275 First St. NE
Washington, DC 20526
peacecorps.gov
855.855.1961

Pension Benefit Guaranty Corporation
P.O. Box 151750
Alexandria, VA 22315-1750
pbgc.gov
202.326.4000

Postal Regulatory Commission
901 New York Ave. NW
Suite 200
Washington, DC 20268-0001
prc.gov
202.789.6800

Selective Service System
P.O. Box 94638
Palatine, IL 60094-4638
sss.gov
847.688.6888

Smithsonian Institution
P.O. Box 37012
Room 153, MRC 010
Washington, DC 20013-7012
si.edu
202.633.1000

Social Security Administration
6401 Security Blvd.
1100 West High Rise
Baltimore, MD 21235
ssa.gov
800.772.1213

Trade & Development Agency (TDA)
1101 Wilson Blvd.
Suite 1100
Arlington, VA 22209
ustda.gov
703.875.4357

U.S. Agency for International Development
1300 Pennsylvania Ave. NW
Washington, DC 20523
usaid.gov
202.712.1150

U.S. Census Bureau
Department of Commerce (DOC)
4600 Silver Hill Road
Washington, DC 20233
301.763.4636

U.S. Chemical Safety & Hazard Investigation Board
1750 Pennsylvania Ave. NW
Suite 910
Washington, DC 20006
csb.gov
202.261.7600

U.S. Citizenship and Immigration Services
Department of Homeland Security (DHS)
5900 Capital Gateway Dr.
Suite 1S100, First Floor
Suitland, MD 20746
uscis.gov
800.375.5283

U.S. Commission of Fine Arts
401 F St. NW
Suite 312
Washington, DC 20001-2728
cfa.gov
202.504.2200

U.S. Commission on Civil Rights
1331 Pennsylvania Ave. NW
Suite 1150
Washington, DC 20425
usccr.gov
202.376.7700

U.S. Consumer Product Safety Commission
4330 East West Hwy.
Bethesda, MD 20814
cpsc.gov
800.638.2772

U.S. Copyright Office
101 Independence Ave. SE
Washington, DC 20559-6000
copyright.gov
202.707.3000

U.S. Customs & Border Protection
Department of Homeland Security (DHS)
1300 Pennsylvania Ave. NW
Washington, DC 20229
cbp.gov
202.325.8000

U.S. Drug Enforcement Administration
Department of Justice (DOJ)
800 K St. NW
Suite 500
Washington, DC 20001
dea.gov
202.305.8500

U.S. Environmental Protection Agency
1200 Pennsylvania Ave. NW
Washington, DC 20460
epa.gov
202.564.4700

U.S. Equal Employment Opportunity Commission
131 M St. NE
Washington, DC 20507
eeoc.gov
202.663.4900

U.S. Fish and Wildlife Service fws.gov
Department of the Interior (DOI) 202.208.6541
1849 C St. NW
Washington, DC 20240

U.S. General Services Administration gsa.gov
1800 F St. NW 202.208.4949
Washington, DC 20405

U.S. Institute of Peace usip.org
2301 Constitution Ave. NW 202.457.1700
Washington, DC 20037

U.S. International Trade Commission usitc.gov
500 E St. SW 202.205.2000
Washington, DC 20436

U.S. Marshals Service usmarshals.gov
Department of Justice (DOJ) 202.353.0600
Third & Constitution Ave. NW
Room 1103
Washington, DC 20001

U.S. Mint usmint.gov
801 Ninth St. NW 800.872.6468
Washington, DC 20220-0012

U.S. Nuclear Regulatory Commission nrc.gov
11555 Rockville Pike 301.415.7000
One White Flint North
Rockville, MD 20852-2738

U.S. Office of Personnel Management opm.gov
1900 E St. NW 202.606.1800
Washington, DC 20415-1000

U.S. Postal Service usps.gov
475 L'Enfant Plaza SW 202.268.2608
Room 1P830
Washington, DC 20260-1101

U.S. Secret Service secretservice.gov
Department of Homeland Security (DHS) 202.406.5708
245 Murray Ln. SW
Bldg. T-Five
Washington, DC 20223

U.S. Securities and Exchange Commission sec.gov
100 F St. NE 202.942.8088
Washington, DC 20549

U.S. Small Business Administration sba.gov
409 Third St. SW 800.827.5722
Washington, DC 20416

Veterans Employment & Training Service dol.gov
200 Constitution Ave. NW 866.487.2365
Room S-1325
Washington, DC 20210

Violence Against Women Program ovw.usdoj.gov
Department of Justice (DOJ) 202.307.6026
145 N St. NE
Suite 10W.121
Washington, DC 20530

THE SUPREME COURT OF THE UNITED STATES

One First St. NE
Washington, DC 20543
202.479.3000
www.supremecourt.gov

Court Officers

Administrative assistant of the Chief Justice	Jeffrey P. Minear
Budget Director	George Everly
Clerk	Scott Harris
Counselor to the Chief Justice	Hon. Robert M. Dow Jr.
Court Counsel	Ethan Torrey
Curator	Catherine Fitts
Director of Information Technology	Charles W. Gerald
Director, Human Resources	Tonia J. Powell
Marshal	Gail Curley
Public Information Officer	Patricia McCabe
Public Information Officer	Patricia McCabe
Reporter of Decisions	Rebecca A. Womeldorf

U.S. Supreme Court and Federal Court Resources

Federal Judicial Center	**fjc.gov**
Federal Judiciary	**uscourts.gov**
Supreme Court Historical Society	**supremecourthistory.org**
U.S. Court of Appeals for the Federal Circuit	**cafc.uscourts.gov**
U.S. Supreme Court Opinion Announcements	**202.479.3360**
U.S. Supreme Court Public Information Office	**202.479.3211**
U.S. Supreme Court Visitor Information Line	**202.479.3030**

2022 UNITED STATES SUPREME COURT

Chief Justice John G. Roberts (RAH bertz)

Nominated by George W. Bush, 2005
Bio. 01/27/1955 • Buffalo, NY • United States Court of Appeals for the District of Columbia Circuit; Private Practicing Attorney; U.S. Department of Justice; Office of the White House Counsel • Harvard College (MA), A.B, 1976; Harvard University Law School (MA), J.D., 1979 • Catholic • M. Jane Marie Sullivan Roberts, 2 ch
Law Clerks Samuel Adkission • Christina Gay • Maxwell Gottschall • Dennis Howe
Salary $263,300
Jurisdiction United States Court of Appeals for the District of Columbia, Fourth and Federal Circuits

Associate Justice Clarence Thomas (TOM as)

Nominated by George H.W. Bush, 1991
Bio. 06/23/1948 • Pin Point, GA • Judge, U.S. Court of Appeals for the DC Circuit; Chair, U.S. Equal Opportunity Employment Commission; Assistant Secretary, U.S. Department of Education; Assistant Attorney General of Missouri • College of The Holy Cross (MA), A.B; Yale University Law School (CT), J.D., 1974 • Catholic • M. Virginia 'Ginni' Lamp Thomas, 1 ch
Law Clerks Christopher Goodnow • Steven Lindsay • Michael Proctor • Jose Valle
Salary $251,800
Jurisdiction U.S. Court of Appeals for the Eleventh Circuit

Associate Justice Samuel A. Alito (Ah LEE tow)

Nominated by George W. Bush, 2006
Bio. 04/01/1950 • Trenton, NJ • Judge, U.S. Court of Appeals for the Third District; Law Professor; U.S. Attorney; Deputy Assistant Attorney General; Assistant to the Solicitor General; Assistant U.S. Attorney; Law Clerk • Princeton University (NJ), A.B; Yale University Law School (CT), J.D. • Catholic • M. Martha-Ann Bomgardner Alito, 2 ch
Law Clerks Shelby Baird • Thomas Gaiser • Eric Palmer • Edward West Jr.
Salary $251,800
Jurisdiction U.S. Court of Appeals for the Third and Fifth Circuits

Associate Justice Sonia M. Sotomayor (so-"toe"-my-YOR)

Nominated by Barack H. Obama, 2009
Bio. 06/25/1954 • The Bronx, NY • Judge, U.S. District Court of Appeals for the Second District; Judge, U.S. District Court for the Southern District of New York • Princeton University (NJ), A.B, 1976; Yale University Law School (CT), J.D., 1979 • Catholic • D.
Law Clerks Whitney Brown • Amit Jain • Katherine Munyan • Kelley Schiffman
Salary $251,800
Jurisdiction U.S. Court of Appeals for the Second Circuit

Associate Justice Elena Kagan (KAY-guhn)

Nominated by Barack H. Obama, 2010
Bio. 04/28/1960 • New York, NY • Law Professor and Dean, Harvard Law School; US Solicitor General • Princeton Universtiy, A.B, 1981; Oxford University (England), M.Phil, 1983; Harvard University Law School (MA), J.D., 1986 • Jewish • S.
Law Clerks Jennifer Fischell • Alexandra Lim • Christine Smith • Andrew Waks
Salary $251,800
Jurisdiction U.S. Court of Appeals for the Ninth Circuit

Associate Justice Neil M. Gorsuch (GOR-such)

Nominated by Donald J. Trump, 2017
Bio. 08/29/1967 • Denver, CO • United States Court of Appeals for the Tenth Circuit; Judicial Clerk (1991-1994); Attorney • Oxford University (England), DPhil; Columbia University (NY), B.A., 1988; Harvard University Law School (MA), J.D, 1991 • Episcopalian • M. Louise Gorsuch, 2 ch
Law Clerks Stephanie Barclay • Louis Capozzi • Mark Storslee • John Thompson
Salary $251,800
Jurisdiction U.S. Court of Appeals for the Tenth Circuit

Associate Justice Brett M. Kavanaugh (cah vuh NAW)

Nominated by Donald J. Trump, 2018
Bio. 02/12/1965 • Washington, DC • Yale University (CT), B.A.; Yale University (CT), J.D • Catholic • M. Ashley Estes Kavanaugh, 2 ch
Law Clerks Alexa Baltes • Athanasia Livas • Jennifer Pavelec • Sarah Welch
Salary $251,800
Jurisdiction U.S. Court of Appeals for the Sixth and Eighth Circuit

Associate Justice Amy Coney Barrett (kow-nee beh-ruht)

Nominated by Donald J. Trump, 2020
Bio. 01/28/1972 • New Orleans, LA • Judge, U.S. Court of Appeals; Law Professor • Rhodes College, B.A.; University of Notre Dame (IN), J.D • Catholic • M. , 7 ch
Law Clerks Libby Baird • Mike Heckmann • Max Schulman • Zachary Tyree
Salary $251,800
Jurisdiction U.S. Court of Appeals for the Seventh Circuits

Associate Justice Ketanji Brown Jackson (ke-TAHN-jee)

Nominated by Joseph R. Biden, 2022
Bio. 09/14/1970 • Washington, DC • Associate Justice of the Supreme Court of the United States • Radcliffe University, A.B; Harvard Law School (MA), J.D • M. Patrick Graves Jackson, 2 Children
Law Clerks Claire Madill • Kerrel Murray • Michael Qian • Natalie Salmanowitz
Salary $
Jurisdiction U.S. Court of Appeals for the First Circuit

The Electoral College was established in Article II of the U.S. Constitution. The Electoral College requires that the President and Vice President be elected through a group of electors based on state population rather than by popular vote. This ensures that less populated states, such as Vermont and North Dakota, will have a bearing on the results of the national election, rather than the election being determined primarily by the more populated states such as California and New York.

For example, the Electoral College ensures that candidates must visit all of the states, as an election cannot be won based on winning only the most populated states. A candidate must therefore make an effort to visit and win a majority of states in order to win an election.

Each state has an amount of electors equal to the number of their Members in Congress. Therefore, each state has at least three electors (the District of Columbia also receives three electors for a national total of 538 electors). Though laws vary from state to state, the state parties typically choose electors. Electors in some states cast their ballot based on the popular vote of the state and others cast their vote based on the party candidate. However, rarely will an elector vote opposite of the vote of the people.

Electors in each state meet in their respective state capitals in December to cast their votes for President and Vice President. Once these ballots have been cast, they are sent to Congress, where they are counted by the President of the Senate on January 6 (or the following day if January 6 falls on a Sunday). The candidate with an absolute majority prevails. If no candidate receives an absolute majority of electoral votes, the House of Representatives selects the next President and the Senate selects the next Vice President.

For more information on the Electoral College, contact the National Archives and Records Administration at **www.archives.gov**.

The Electoral College

Total: 538
Majority Needed to Elect: 270

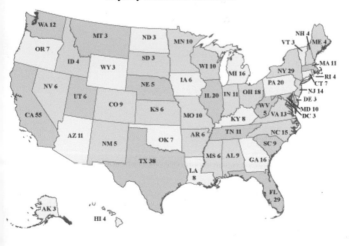

NOTES